GOLD
MINES
of california

D1602057

Headframe of the Argonaut mine, near Jackson,
as it appeared to artist Marjolaine O'Neill in 1969.

GOLD MINES
of california

An illustrated history of the most productive
mines with descriptions of the
interesting people who owned
and operated them, by

Jack R. Wagner

BERKELEY · Howell -North Books · CALIFORNIA

GOLD MINES OF CALIFORNIA

Printed and bound in the United States of America

Library of Congress Catalog Card No. 79-115852

ISBN 0-8310-7002-1

Published by Howell-North Books

1050 Parker Street, Berkeley, California 94710

PREFACE

As a native Californian I was brought up to think of California as the "Golden State", not only because of its heritage, but because gold mining was still a fairly important industry. Today this is no longer the case and I now realize that much of the California I knew is slipping away. Even the physical evidence is rapidly eroding due to the ravages of time, neglect and the constant rearranging of the landscape.

In its own way I hope his book will capture the dramatic life and sad ending of what was once a major California industry producing between 1848 and 1967 nearly $2.5 billion in gold. It was an industry that influenced the placement and development of many California towns and contributed enormously to the prosperity of our state.

I do not propose to deal with the Gold Rush and the Days of Forty-nine, but with the last era of California gold mining, the era of deep mines and heavy equipment that came later, when the technology of gold recovery was raised to the point where California-designed machines and systems were in use all over the world.

From the discovery of gold-bearing quartz on Gold Hill near Grass Valley in 1850 until December 31, 1965 when the Sixteen to One mine at Alleghany shut down, California was world renowned as one of the most important gold fields. Fortunately, in 1850, about the time when most of the easily-mined placer claims were worked out, miners were able to turn to deep or hard-rock mining. This period, which lasted 115 years, was aided by the newly discovered dynamite and the perfection of the air drill, both of which carried gold production to great heights and the mines to great depths.

Actually, it was the Sixteen to One mine that led to my undertaking this project in the first place. It all began when I read a short article hidden away on the financial page of a San Francisco newspaper, reporting the demise of California's last producing gold mine. While I had known for years that profitable gold mines were few and far between I had no idea of how many or how few still existed in California. It became apparent to me that this was truly the end of an era in our time and I determined to set some of it down on paper before it became lost entirely. Since the Sixteen to One was the "last operating quartz mine", it also seemed appropriate that it should be the final chapter in the book, which means that I wrote the last first.

The first two chapters deal with hydraulic mining and dredges, telling the history and application of this type of mining, and providing a natural transition from placer to hard-rock mining. This is not intended to be a technical book on mining or a guide to the gold country, but rather a profile of the more famous of the California gold mines selected for their interest, varied geographical location and their importance in terms of production (the least amount produced by any of them was $7,500,000).

The story of California's deep quartz mines then actually begins with Chapter 3 and the Eagle-Shawmut mine which is located near Jacksonville in Tuolumne County. From there on each chapter deals with a separate mine as we proceed up the state in a northerly direction, covering an area from Tuolumne to Sierra County. This section contains the heart of the gold country and encompasses both the Mother Lode and the Northern Mines. I think most authorities will agree that the most important gold mining in California over the years has occurred within these boundaries.

As a valued addition to my writing I am pleased to have the fourteen excellent water colors which precede each chapter and set the mood and location. These paintings were painstakingly done at the mines by professional artist Marjolaine O'Neill and constitute one of the most complete collections I have seen covering California mining. Where my descriptions are necessarily involved or technical the reader has the alternative of gazing at her warm and colorful depictions of the actual scenes.

Throughout the more than three years spent in gathering material for this book I have traveled many hundreds of miles and talked with dozens of people. Unfortunately it was already too late for many interviews with actual eyewitnesses and participants. Many of the mine employees had scattered and most of the engineers, superintendents, managers and owners were either too old to be of much help or had permanently left this world. The short overlapping of the generations had been stretched to the breaking point and the slender golden thread connecting us with the past had parted.

I did manage to make some valuable contacts with mining men who had been connected with some of the more recent operations and also with mining families who still remembered the work of their fathers and grandfathers; to them I am grateful for the personal touch their recollections and cherished personal accounts lend to this work. I have used this material whenever it was available. Many of these generous people contributed photographs, firsthand knowledge and general encouragement. I acknowledge my debt to them one and all. Their names are listed in this volume, and I sincerely hope none have been omitted.

My final word of appreciation goes to my mother, who at age 85, read every page of the manuscript and corrected my atrocious spelling. God bless her.

JACK RUSSELL WAGNER

May, 1969

Sausalito, California

ACKNOWLEDGMENTS

The author gratefully acknowledges the assistance and encouragement given by numerous people interested in telling the story of the heyday of California gold mining:

Stanley D. Anderson, Pacific Coast Stock Exchange

Mrs. Sybil Arata, owner Kennedy mine, Jackson

Joe Azevedo, Tuttletown

C. A. Bennett, former superintendent Sixteen to One mine, Alleghany

Lyman Booth, Yuba Industries, Inc., Benicia

Oliver Bowen, geologist, California Division of Mines and Geology

Philip R. Bradley, chairman, California Division of Mines and Geology

Richard Brooks, Sixteen to One mine, Alleghany

Lee Burtis, head, Iconography Dept., California Historical Society, San Francisco

Carl Beyer, resident manager, Empire mine, Grass Valley

Suzanne Caster, librarian, San Francisco *Chronicle*

Richard C. Clark, administrative assistant, Golden Gate Bridge, San Francisco

William B. Clark, geologist, California Division of Mines and Geology

George W. Clemson, co-owner Eagle-Shawmut mine, Jacksonville

John Coll, librarian, Rare Books and Special Collections, San Francisco Public Library

Michael E. Conway, Yuba Industries, Inc., San Francisco

Mrs. Ray Conway, daughter of the late A. B. Foote, superintendent of the North Star mine, Grass Valley

Charles C. Crespi, Angels Camp

Frank Crespi, Angels Camp

C. M. De Ferrari, county clerk, Tuolumne County

Richard H. Dillon, head librarian, Sutro Library, San Francisco

Earle Edmiston, Hillcrest Studio, Angels Camp

Elisabeth L. Egenhoff, editor, California Division of Mines and Geology

John Finn, consulting chemist, San Francisco

Doris Foley, historian and co-author of the book "Gold Cities"

G. L. Fox, vice president, Parr Industrial Corp., San Francisco

A. "Babe" Garbarini, editor and publisher of the Amador *Ledger* and nephew of the late V. S. Garbarini, superintendent of the Argonaut mine at the time of the fire

Mrs. Emmet H. Garbarini, daughter-in-law of the late V. S. Garbarini and past president of the Amador County Historical Society, Jackson

Malcolm E. Hammill, Nevada County District Fair, Grass Valley

Mary R. Hill, information officer, California Division of Mines and Geology

R. Peter Ingram, publisher Grass Valley-Nevada City *Union*

Norman Jarrett, vice president, Eldorado Insurance Company, San Francisco and former safety engineer at the Central Eureka mine, Sutter Creek

George A. "Jerry" Jarrett, journalist and friend of the late Errol MacBoyle of the Idaho-Maryland

Mrs. Eileen Kennedy, daughter of the late Fred G. Stevenot of the Carson Hill mine

Robert A. Lapachet, Murphys

Erick H. Leffingwell, supervisor, Malakoff Diggings State Historic Park

Harvey C. McGee, publisher of the *Daily Union Democrat*, Sonora

Harry L. McMasters, editorial supervisor, Pacific Gas & Electric Company, San Francisco

Harold Merklen, resident librarian, the New York Public Library

Irene Simpson Neasham, director, History Room, Wells Fargo Bank, San Francisco

James H. Nickley, Sr., Eagle-Shawmut mine, Jacksonville

Kenneth A. Nobs, California State Dept. of Industrial Relations and son of the late F. W. Nobs, former superintendent Empire mine, Grass Valley

Arthur Norman, former superintendent Central Eureka mine, Sutter Creek

Mrs. Martha Seffer O'Bryon, assistant curator Stuart Library, California Historical Foundation, University of the Pacific, Stockton

James P. Oliver, manager Tuolumne County Chamber of Commerce, Sonora

Allan R. Ottley, head California Section, California State Library, Sacramento

Gordon Pates, managing editor, San Francisco *Chronicle*

Hazel Pollock, curator, Siskiyou County Museum, Yreka

William Ramariz, librarian, History Dept., San Francisco Public Library

A. S. Ryland, formerly associated with D. C. Demarest's Angels Iron Works, pioneer Mother Lode builder of mining machinery

William A. Sansburn, librarian, California Division of Mines and Geology

Don Segerstrom, son of the late Charles H. Segerstrom, Carson Hill mine and others, Sonora

Irvil P. Shultz, librarian, U.S. Geological Survey, Denver, Colorado

Miriam E. Skeahan, secretary Grass Valley Area Chamber of Commerce (California's oldest Chamber of Commerce)

T. Calvert Slater, former superintendent Central Eureka mine, Sutter Creek

Donald D. Smith, president, Pacific Industries, San Francisco, former president Central Eureka mine, Sutter Creek

R. G. Smith, 55 year veteran of the Natomas Company and its president from 1947 to 1966

Sid Smith, manager, Amador County Chamber of Commerce, Jackson

Louis A. Spinetti, Jackson

Mrs. Erma L. Stephens, great niece of the late Archie D. Stevenot

Archie D. Stevenot, "Mr. Mother Lode," Sonora

John A. Thorne, executive secretary, Folsom Chamber of Commerce, Folsom

John Barr Tompkins, head public services, Bancroft Library, University of California, Berkeley

J. C. Twissleman, former employee of the Utica Mining Company, Angels Camp

Mrs. John Vierra, Angels Camp

. . . and the staffs of:

Bancroft Library, University of California, Berkeley

California Historical Society, San Francisco

California State Library, Sacramento

Grass Valley Public Library, Grass Valley

Mechanics Institute, San Francisco

Sausalito Public Library, Sausalito

Society of California Pioneers, San Francisco

Tuolumne County Library, Sonora

TABLE OF CONTENTS

The collar of a typical Mother Lode double compartment incline shaft is pictured here. The men rode inside the steel skips as well as on the bail or crosshead, doing well to "watch the head" at all times. The white line at the right of the shaft is the signal cord from below. It rang a bell in the hoist house so that the engineer could know when and where to move the skips. *(Stuart Library of Western Americana)*

INTRODUCTION

Gold is a metal of intrinsic value, not only as a store of wealth wherever people are free to hold it, but because of its unique properties which are in great demand for industrial and artistic uses. The yellow metal was known and highly valued by the earliest of civilizations, the Egyptian, Minoan, Assyrian and the Etruscan, and from all of these periods ornaments of great value and beauty have survived. No less than 1400 years before the dawn of the Christian era, the Greeks were using gold for objects of ornamentation. But even they were not the originators, having borrowed the practice from the Egyptians, who had been enticing their women with gold jewelry for more than 1000 years before the Greeks had thought of it. In fact it has been advanced by no less an authority than the Encyclopedia Americana that it was this use of gold as a means of buying favors of the opposite sex that first suggested its use as a symbol of exchange and finally led to the standard upon which the coinage of the world was based.[*]

The original Argonauts are supposed to have made their quest in the direction of the famous gold deposits of Colchis, west of the Caucasus, and their determined search for the Golden Fleece has been explained by the fact that fleeces have been used effectively to catch fine gold in ditches and sluices just as woolen blankets were used in the early mines of California.

---

[*]Although many nations throughout history were wealthy in terms of gold, discoveries of large amounts of gold were actually made during the middle and last half of the 19th century, i.e. California 1848, Australia 1851, British Columbia 1858, South Africa 1886, Klondike, 1897.

It has been said by some historians that it was the curtailment of gold and silver that led to the eventual downfall of Rome. While this may or may not have been the case it is certainly true that Persia, Egypt, Greece and Italy all prospered in proportion to the gold mines they owned or controlled.

The premise that gold is power drove the alchemists of the middle ages to search for the secret of manufacturing gold from base metals by means of the "philosopher's stone" and while all of their experiments ended in failure many of the first advances made by chemistry were the direct result of this research. Most of the early land and sea explorations were undertaken in the search for gold and as many times as not they found it already being mined by natives who had somehow instinctively sensed its value and usefulness.

In later years the prospector, using milder methods than the soldier-explorers, opened the isolated regions of the world to be followed by mining enterprise which in turn brought transportation and civilization; these were followed in their turn by agriculture, industry, commerce and eventually a cultural and economic system that continued to flourish long after the mines had faded from the scene.

Volumes have been written about the lure and legends of gold, but this book will confine itself to gold mining in this country and particularly in California. If the reader is conversant with California history some of it will be familiar. If he is new to the state or new to the subject it may be well to review a few facts.

In the first place, gold was *not* first discovered at Coloma on January 19, 1848 by James Marshall, though the event triggered the great Gold Rush. Gold was not only known to exist but was actually mined in California much earlier. Even Sir Francis Drake, who touched the coast of California in 1579, reported gold as "occurring in abundance", although that may have been wishful thinking on his part. At any rate, it is known that the Mexicans discovered placer deposits in southeastern California in 1775 and in 1812 near the Spanish mission of San Fernando. Other reports speak of gold being found during the governorship of José Argüello, in office 1814 to 1815, under the Spanish regime, but nothing was done at the time because of Indian hostility. By 1824 placer gold was being taken by Spanish soldiers who used it for barter, but it was not until 1842 that it caused any great public stir. It was then that one Francisco Lopez, head of the great San Fernando Rancho, and one of his men were riding after some stray cattle in the mountains near the ranch. Alighting to rest, Lopez was using his knife to dig out some wild onions when he noticed particles attached to the roots that appeared to be gold. Continuing with his knife he found additional deposits and there followed what might be called the first gold rush in California history.

At first the argonauts came only from the pueblo of Los Angeles, a mere thirty-five miles distant, although within a year men with greater mining experience began to arrive from Sonora, Mexico. The production of those early placers in what is today suburban Los Angeles was not insignificant and has been estimated to have been as much as $80,000 to $100,000 during the first two years.

It is further a matter of record that a packet of California gold dust was sent to the United States Mint by Don Abel Stearns, a resident of Los Angeles. Transported around the Horn it was received at the mint in Philadelphia on July 8, 1843, and was purchased at the rate of $19.00 an ounce. Nor was it any great secret, for Thomas O. Larkin, the vice consul at Monterey, notified Secretary of State James Buchanan of the existence of gold in an official communication in March of 1846.

So it has been pretty well established and documented that gold was mined in California prior

to 1848, but as so often happens it took just the proper combination of time and events to catapult James Marshall's "discovery" into the pages of history beginning the westward migration that hasn't stopped yet.

✓   ✓   ✓

People now often refer to the past in such general terms as "in the early days", "during the gold rush" or some other vague phrase which relieves the speaker of the responsibility of pinpointing places and dates. Actually the term "Mother Lode" is often misused by people to indicate a vacationland somewhere up in the mountains where men used to mine for gold, not realizing that the Mother Lode was a precise geological and geographical area which covered (and still does) a five county strip of the Sierra Nevada foothills beginning at Mariposa on the south and extending along Highway 49 to Georgetown on the north. The mining districts north of Highway 80, including Grass Valley and Nevada City, were called the "Northern Mines". There were, of course, other rich mining districts in Butte, Sierra, Trinity and Siskiyou Counties, but I will not attempt to cover them in this book.

The heart of the California gold country is dotted with picturesque little hamlets with their iron-shuttered buildings. Not all are ghost towns, mind you, but lively villages with interesting shops and some good restaurants. One can still see some of the signs of gold mining in the form of an occasional headframe and deserted mine buildings, although time is taking its toll and many of the physical signs of mining are rapidly dwindling. Most of the steel headframes have fallen to the cutting torch while the wooden ones have rotted and machinery worth salvaging has been removed. Even the mine dumps, great piles of rock laboriously brought to the surface from deep within the earth, and considered eyesores by many people, are rapidly being used up as aggregate which is already a scarcity in today's highly populous California.*

---

*This is also true in the flatlands where good use has been found for the huge piles of rock left by the dredgers. At the new Oroville Dam, for instance, many thousands of tons of these tailings were transported to the dam site for use as fill.

Should the reader develop a similar interest in California's mining past and wish to visit the area there are still relics to see, but I would offer a friendly word of caution when it comes to exploring individual mines. They are on private property, usually fenced and posted, and unless permission is secured it would be best not to trespass. There is always some hazard around decaying buildings, open pits and old machinery, and the owners are reluctant to assume responsibility for your safety. Also, unfortunate but true, a succession of vandals before you has made all trespassers suspect.

There are only two mines that I know of that have been made into state parks. One is the Plumas-Eureka at Johnstown in Plumas County and the other is the famous hydraulic pit of the Malakoff mine in Nevada County. There are several very good mining museums maintained by counties and their historical societies. Two of the best are at Jackson and Grass Valley and, of course, the State of California has now rebuilt the site of Marshall's discovery of gold at Coloma into quite a nice replica. The entire town of Columbia in Tuolumne County has been preserved by the State and it admirably presents a full-sized model of that "Gem of the Southern Mines" as it appeared in the 1850s. On the other side of the Sierra, in Mono County, the once wild and woolly ghost town of Bodie has been made into a State Park and is being preserved in a state of "arrested deterioration".

Perhaps the first real attempt to preserve the relics of this period has been made by the Nevada County Historical Society in Grass Valley. Here they are establishing a museum of the actual heavy machines salvaged from the deep mines of that area. These are being assembled at the old North Star powerhouse on Mill Street, itself an interesting historical site.

✦   ✦   ✦

The close of World War I saw many mines suffering from high costs brought about by an inflated postwar economy and a fixed price of gold then pegged at $20.67 an ounce.

In October of 1933 President Franklin D. Roosevelt, as part of his New Deal reorganization, appointed a committee consisting of Jesse Jones, Dean Acheson and Henry Morgenthau, Jr., to fix the price of gold. The new price was set on October 25 at $31.36 per fine ounce, increased the next day to $34.01 and finally stabilized on January 31, 1934, when, by presidential proclamation the weight of the gold dollar was officially established. This caused the price of gold to go to $35.00 an ounce, where it has been rigidly kept for over 35 years.

It was this increase in the price of gold in the 1930s, combined with the lower wages and material costs prevailing during the Depression, that made gold mining such an attractive proposition at that time, causing many old mines to reopen and active ones to become still more active. Nor was it only the big operators who benefited in those days, for many unemployed Californians took to the hills where they could squeeze out a few dollars a day by panning and sluicing the streams and working one-man mines. As of 1936 there were 3200 gold mines of all sizes operating in California employing 11,000 men. This is not to say that all of these were profitable operations, although gold mining was considered a major industry in the United States at that time, putting millions of dollars in circulation. However, the avant-garde economists and presidential advisers of the New Deal did not view gold or hard money as entirely necessary. The wealth of our country lay in our ability to produce and not in the amount of gold stored in Fort Knox, they argued. A responsible government could print money and set its value without such backing. The old theory that paper money must be represented by valuable metal was outmoded.

During World War II the United States Government thought so little of gold mining that all of the country's gold mines were ordered closed by the War Production Board's Order No. L 208. The mines were considered nonessential to the war effort, although many more frivolous industries were permitted to operate and use manpower. The War Production Board claimed that their action was taken in the hope that the labor force in the gold mines would be redirected to copper and other mines then producing metals more urgently needed by the war effort. Gold mining men, however, felt that this was just another expression

13

of the administration's attitude toward gold and certainly they couldn't understand the new economics which proposed to fight a war entirely on credit and paper money.

In 1945 gold mining was permitted to resume, but it was not to be that easy. During the three years of inactivity many of the deep mines had flooded, caved in and otherwise deteriorated to the point where the cost of reopening was prohibitive. Some of the mines did try to come back and operated for a time but others didn't even attempt it. A few of the mines brought suit against the government for indemnification for damages caused by this enforced closure, but none of them were ever able to collect payment.

Today we find ourselves in a managed economy with a government that apparently still feels that gold as a measure of wealth is outmoded. It is true that everything is relative and perhaps this premise could be made to stick if all nations played by the same rules. But other countries, many unfriendly, are still stacking up gold reserves as fast as they can get their hands on them. Much of the gold, of course, is ours which they obtain through foreign aid, military spending abroad, imbalance of payments and so on. Thus with gold leaving our shores at the rate of about $779,000,000 a year, making our gold reserves now around $10,000,000,000, we have reached a point of some concern. An increase in the price of gold would probably not encourage production of much more gold and at the same time would in effect devaluate our dollar and give an immediate and unearned raise to every nation that has been accumulating gold, among them Russia, France, Egypt, the Middle East and Red China.

That the general public also regards gold as the safest form of investment when all else fails is repeatedly shown in the rush to acquire gold in the countries where it is legal to own and gold stocks where it is not. Economists, like it or not, have to admit that when people lose faith in printing press money it is still gold that is regarded throughout the world as the basic measure of wealth.

Even if we were to discount the importance of gold as a standard of value the fact remains that in today's highly complex and sophisticated technology it is becoming more and more in demand for its medical and scientific applications. Since it is a rare metal no matter how you look at it, it is quite obvious that it will always have considerable worth.

⚹ ⚹ ⚹

With gold mining on the decline, not only in the United States, and with many of the "mature" mines of Canada, South Africa and elsewhere beginning to show signs that they are past their prime, we might well ask from where the gold of the future is to come.

First, some of the gold will continue to be produced as a by-product from copper, and other ores containing small quantities of gold. Then we must not completely overlook the possibilities of new discoveries, although most of the mining areas of the world have been pretty well picked over. As a case in point we would cite the recently discovered Carlin mine in the Tuscarora Mountains of northern Nevada where science perfected refining methods that enabled the recovery of gold in particles so small that an electron microscope was required to see them. It also took the ability to handle efficiently large quantities of earth, for at Carlin four tons of overburden are removed to get one ton of ore and it takes three *tons* of ore to produce an *ounce* of gold. This high-volume open-pit operation of the Newmont Mining Corporation is today the second largest gold mine in the United States. The number one is still the Homestake, the famous deep mine at Lead, South Dakota. These two are the only important gold mines operating in the United States today.

We must also look to completely new ideas such as space mining and oceanography. Both of these areas hold exciting promise for the explorers of the future. Surprisingly enough, even modern science is still intrigued by the possibilities of producing "artificial" gold by alchemy although they don't call it by that name anymore. More aptly it is the transmutation of metals by atomic bombardment. It has actually been done as a laboratory experiment although it is horrendously expensive, both as a process and from the standpoint that the scale of atomic weight is not necessarily in accord with our established scale of values. For example, gold, atomic weight 197, has been successfully transmuted into mercury, atomic weight 198; a highly significant laboratory experiment, but hardly a good investment.

But what is the future for California gold mining? It all hinges, of course, on the price of gold and this is still discussed and argued from the bars and crossroad stores of the mountain communities to the board rooms of New York.

The more optimistic tell us that a jump in the price of gold to some point beyond today's high operating costs would signal a general revival of gold mining in California. The truth of the matter is that the exhaustion of the profitable ore deposits and the new era of higher costs were coincidental. Even in 1940 only a few of the mines were profitable and in all probability would have closed in a few years at best.

There are a small handful of mines which did have some ore left at the time of closing, but to reopen any of these mines today or in the future would incur costs not evident to the layman. In most instances mining was taking place at a depth of a mile or more on the vein. The access shafts or tunnels, whichever was the case, required constant maintenance and retimbering to keep them open and safe. Now after so many years of neglect it is reasonable to assume that the majority of these openings are hopelessly caved. Since it is much cheaper to make new openings than to attempt to rehabilitate the old it would virtually mean starting the mine all over again. New hoisting works and mills are fantastically expensive to erect and in many cases real estate would have to be reacquired. Add to this the item of pumping out a mile of water and you will often arrive at a cost in excess of the possible production of the mine.

When most of the mines closed during World War II, the wages of the miners were approximately $6 a day and the price of gold was $35 an ounce. Today the same men would get $30 a day and the price of gold would have to be $175 an ounce. Since our creeping inflation goes on steadily creeping it would be necessary to plan for higher future wages and higher gold prices to compensate.

A further problem to be encountered is the sad fact that there are only a few people left today with successful gold mining experience behind them and these will not be around too much longer. (Today's miners tend to be truck drivers and shovel operators). This means that if the deep mines were to be reopened many would be operated by men of no real experience or knowledge and the percentage of costly failures would be high.

It is true that new machines have been put to use in mining, but these are expensive to buy and costly to maintain, so the cost of mining today is in much the same relation to the economy as it was thirty years ago.

The same is true of gold dredging when you consider that the first successful gold dredge in California was built at a cost of $25,000, this cost increasing with size and engineering improvements to around $750,000 during the peak of the dredging era. Today a suitable floating plant could not be duplicated for under four million dollars.

There is, however, one slight hope in that today newly mined gold can be sold on the world market at a price slightly higher than the official price of $35 an ounce. Undoubtedly the world price will go higher, but it will take time; then if the price ever goes high enough some activity in the California mines may be seen. A few of the better properties may be economically successful for a time, but their yield in ounces will be but a fraction of their former production.

One thing is certain, any resumption of gold mining, if it does come, will bring forth a new generation of promoters with dreams of riches and stock to sell. But new discoveries will be rare, and, as we have seen, only a few of the major properties will warrant reopening and they will be expensive operations. Devoid of romantic stories of rags to riches and swashbuckling adventures, mining will be for the cost accountants, the engineers and the metallurgists.

ϟ   ϟ   ϟ

Quite frankly, the size of my topic was larger than anticipated and in recording the stories and histories of the various mines it just was not possible to use all of the material I would have liked to have included. For instance ghost stories, a whole book could be written on this subject, ranging from the Tommyknockers, those legendary gnome-like creatures of the deep mines, who, according to the Cornish miners, made the mine safe by making repairs between shifts, to the well-dressed spectre who solemnly walked the drifts of the Sixteen to One with his head tucked underneath his arm.

The ancient and dishonorable practice of high-grading would also provide much story material. This term applied to the pilfering of high-grade ore from a mine and many an otherwise honest miner yielded to this temptation. While the mine owners kept thinking up ways to stamp out this practice the ingenious miners thought up as many ways to continue it. In a day when gold was easy to own and dispose of, many an underground laboratory must have served to refine the gold in this illicit trade. There are even stories of wholesale theft involving, of course, the cooperation of the mine foreman, and on many a night shift the good ore has been trammed to the dump to be picked up the next morning by a passing teamster who, as he could use the rock for fill, would volunteer to haul the material away free of charge. Even an honest miner had best join the group or else be trusted to keep his mouth shut, otherwise an "accident" in the form of a loose boulder or a runaway ore car would surely remove him from the scene once and for all.

Speaking of accidents . . . I have never enjoyed writing about violent death or bloodshed, but the mines had their share of that. Underground mining has always been a hazardous occupation and the miners have accepted it at that. One thing to be said for the quartz mines of California was that they were in controllable ground. Some were wet and hot, but at least they were without the black damp and other lethal gases of the coal mines. They did, of course, have the dangers of moving machinery, explosives and underground timber fires. Because of the complexity of hazards, both natural and mechanical, the accidents recorded were masterpieces of gruesomeness. Such as the unhappy fate of the trammer in the Sixteen to One, who while speeding along the rails was suddenly run through by a jutting piece of steel, or the miner, also in the Sixteen to One, who panicked . . . frightened by a ghost they say . . . and ran out of the drift and into the shaft, where he dropped to his death in the blackness below.

In the Utica, while hoisting, some pipe came loose from a bundle and fell to the bottom. On the way down one of the pipes hit a man standing at a station, taking a core out of his center from top to bottom as it went.

Many families who have picnicked in the grassy park in the center of Angels Camp, benignly watched over by a statue of Mark Twain, have never dreamed that far below are the bodies of nineteen men so isolated by a cave-in back in the '90s that they were never recovered. "Buried as good there as anyplace", they said at the time.

While up at the Central Eureka at Sutter Creek there was the shift boss who, upon coming up out of the mine, violated his own safety rule, stuck his head out of the skip and was immediately decapitated. Then at the same mine and for no apparent reason, a skip tender suddenly obsessed with the desire to commit suicide, wrapped a heavy chain around his middle and jumped into the shaft.

At the Empire mine in Grass Valley in 1888 a surface explosion caused death and injury to a number of workers, including a young lad who was killed on his first day on the job. Even gold dredges had their hazards and on at least one known occasion (this one near Yreka in 1936) an oiler was ground to death by the machinery.

But enough of this topic of accidents. Miners are traditionally the very essence of optimism, and although there are many aspects of mining that categorize it as an engineering science, there is much room for luck, opinion and tenacity. In the chapters to follow, you will see examples of miners whose luck deserted them and miners whose hunches to "sink a shaft another foot" paid off handsomely.

Today, many high-ranking officials of both government and finance are becoming convinced that our dwindling gold supply represents a serious problem. Exemplifying this new attitude, teams of government geologists have recently been combing the country and voluminous technical reports have been prepared on where our nation's gold reserves exist.

As a further stimulation several bills in recent years have been presented to both the House and Senate which, if enacted, would have granted a subsidy to the gold mine operators to make up the difference between the official but unprofitable $35 an ounce and a price to be determined which would justify resumption of mining.

Another approach was the establishment in 1968 of a two-tier pricing system for gold which maintained the old $35 price as a monetary base, but allowed the operation of a second so-called "free" commercial market. The use of the word "free" is somewhat incorrect, since the transactions must be handled by licensed gold dealers and are subject to some restrictions. Nevertheless this system released a sizable quantity of gold and allowed it to seek its own price level.

Whether this is the complete answer or whether future gold mining falls into the category of wishful thinking and is some nostalgic attempt to hold on to our colorful past only time will tell. The following case histories of the great gold producing mines of California should clearly illustrate the problem and help the reader form his own opinion.

Yes, there's still gold in the California hills, but today's miner is more apt to be a weekend hobbyist than an entrepreneur. Skin diving and homemade suction dredges are employed on the Stanislaus and other rivers of the Sierra foothills.

Devastation, destruction and scenes of great beauty all resulted from the era of hydraulic mining when huge streams of water under tremendous pressure thundered against the mountains with spectacular effect. This miniature Bryce Canyon is the famous Malakoff hydraulic pit at North Bloomfield where banks 550 feet high cut by the water attest to its power.

CHAPTER 1

LITTLE DROPS OF WATER

HYDRAULIC MINING 1852 to 1884

Total estimated production by this method $270,000,000

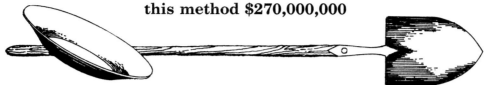

Water and the gold miner have gone hand in hand throughout the long history of mining. Whether it is the small amount necessary to pan a showing of gold or the millions of gallons that once raced through hundreds of miles of flumes, ditches and pipelines to that ingenious California invention the Monitor; it was water that was the tool, and because of the high specific gravity of gold, water has always been, and still is, one of the basic factors in the recovery process.

In the later days of lode mining when men pierced the earth to depths of a mile or more, it was also water that poured into the shafts and drifts, making difficult tasks even harder and more often than not marking the difference between financial success and failure. Still it was also water, escaping from the firey insides of the earth that found its way into rock fissures and pockets where it deposited the rich minerals it carried, thus forming the very veins men now seek.

It was water, too, that once flowed down immense prehistoric rivers depositing gold in great alluvial fans which during the course of geological history were buried, shifted and eventually raised to mountain top elevations. Then as if beginning all over again, the younger rivers, creeks and streams of our era brought gold down out of the mountains in sufficient quantities to make easy pickings for those who came early enough.

Panning for gold was slow and hard. An experienced miner could barely handle 100 pans in a ten-hour day. This resulted in the introduction of the rocker, which when rocked back and forth would cause the particles of gold to settle as in panning.

The next improvement, called a long tom, was brought to California by miners from Georgia.* It was simply a trough of boards usually about 12 feet long by 8 inches deep. The opening at the head was 12 to 15 inches wide and the entire trough increased in width until it was about 2 feet wide at the lower end; there a piece of sheet iron with holes punched in it was placed so that the finer sand would fall into a sluice box below while the larger rocks would pass on by. The long tom increased production so that a man could work many times as much gravel in a day as he could with a pan or even with a rocker. It also meant he could work poorer ground profitably.

Another innovation was the application of a Brazilian idea. This was the sluice box which consisted of three boards nailed together to form a flume. It was usually fitted with slats or riffles to catch the gold. A number of these units could be fitted together, end to end, to make a long series of sluice boxes and men stationed at intervals along the line could shovel gravel into the swiftly flowing water inside the box.

As you can see, these methods required a steady stream of water and as a result the miners' ditch came into being. The first in California is

---

*A fact often overlooked is that Georgia, South Carolina and other southern states engaged in gold mining befor gold was discovered in California.

Many black men joined the rush to the California gold fields where they worked side by side with white miners. This picture taken at Spanish Flat in 1852 shows two miners using a long tom. The gold bearing earth and gravel is shoveled into the trough where it is washed. Large rocks are removed and the fines are carried down the lower trough and over riffles. The gold, being heavy, sinks and is caught behind the riffles.

Below, a larger company of miners use an expanded version of the long tom as they shovel their gravel into a flume-like structure where it is washed by a continuously flowing stream of water.

(California State Library)

said to have been built in March 1850, at Coyote Hill, Nevada City, to supply the long toms in that area. It was a V-flume about two miles long and was the forerunner of what was to become a huge enterprise in itself, that of supplying water for the miners.

In December of that same year the first system of any considerable length was completed. It was a nine-mile ditch built by the Rock Creek Water Company at a construction cost of $10,000, which was repaid from the sale of water in just six weeks. From there on ditches were built in all of the mining districts of the state. Some can still be seen today and a few, like the Utica conduit of Calavaras County and the Yreka "Big Ditch," which was started in 1854 in Siskiyou County and ran a total of 95 miles to cover an air-line distance of 30, are still in use.

Many of the ditch companies were organized for the sole purpose of delivering water to the miners at a price set by what the traffic would bear. In other cases the miners themselves organized companies and cooperatives to supply their own needs. A story is told of one group of miners who, fed up with the high cost of water, decided to form their own ditch company. This they did by pooling their resources, hiring a surveyor and laborers. As the project progressed the bandit water company watched with mild interest, apparently not willing to believe they would soon be out of business. Finally the day grew near when the miners would be using their own water and a suitable celebration was planned. At the appointed hour the gates upriver were opened and the water was turned into the new miners' ditch. It was all timed so that the water would arrive in town at just the proper part of the ceremony, but the water never came! The people waited and waited, but still no water. Finally in desperation a committee was dispatched to walk the ditch to find out what was causing the trouble. When they saw it they could scarcely believe their eyes. The water had left the dam all right and it had traveled along the flumes and ditches until it reached a point about halfway and there it simply stopped, refusing to go another inch! The solution to this mystery lay in the shenanigans of the opposition water company who had sent men in the dead of night to move the survey stakes of the fledgeling company so that the rest of the flume ran uphill. This they did ever so slightly so the sabotage would not be detected, but over a distance the error would be considerable.

Whether or not this story is entirely true cannot be documented, but it does serve to illustrate the point that with all of the ditch-digging activity there developed many side effect problems such as water rights, right-of-way disputes and exorbitant charges. Many of these disputes resulted in long and costly litigation while others were settled quickly and violently with shotguns and blasting powder.

But back to mining. Sometimes it was necessary to seek out ancient gravel beds and work them by means of shafts and tunnels which followed the gravel down to and along bedrock. Some of these channels were followed and mined for several miles by this method. The Forest Hill Divide in Placer County and Table Mountain near Jamestown, Tuolumne County were two such districts. Some of the gravel extracted from drift mines, as they were called, was so compacted and cemented that stamp mills were often necessary to break it down, however since it was alluvial gravel these underground mines are classified as placer.

Another system, called "booming" or "hushing," was devised to work the gravel in the bed of steep mountain streams. In this method the stream was dammed and when the pond was filled an automatic gate called a "self-shooter" would trip. The large volume of water rushing down the gorge would carry boulders, rocks and gravel until the flow, eventually dissipated, would be led into sluice boxes for recovery of the gold.

Sometimes wooden flumes 18 to 40 feet wide with sides six feet high or more would be used to divert entire rivers during their low water period so that the actual bed of the river could be worked. The Feather, Yuba and American rivers as well as many minor streams were worked in this fashion.

Regardless of the methods used it eventually became apparent that the gold in the river beds, banks and bars was becoming exhausted. The miners then began to follow the tributaries farther upstream where they discovered strata of gravel on the canyon sides and sometimes on benches of land hundreds of feet above the present rivers. These were the telltales of the ancient river beds mentioned earlier and after a little prospecting it

The tools of the placer miner's trade: pick and shovel, gold pan and rocker with the bucket and dipper to supply water to the rocker as needed. If there were an oppressed minority in the California mines it was the Chinese. However, they were thrifty and hard working and many found work as laborers in the diggings. Others organized companies of their countrymen and worked mines of their own. *(above, Bancroft Library; below, California State Library)*

was found that these hillside river beds also carried gold.

Working a placer claim high in the air and far from water presented many challenging problems, but before long some enterprising miner conceived a simple and effective way of working this type of ground. By means of ditches and flumes a stream of water was conducted to the top of the cliff and allowed to flow down over the gravel face. This softened the material and with help from the miner it could be broken off and carried along by the water to a natural sluice on the bedrock below. Thus with proper use of the water and a little shoveling a great deal of gravel could be sent down. This method was called ground sluicing.

From strictly an engineering point of view the most efficient method, by far, was hydraulic mining wherein huge streams of water shot from a nozzle under tremendous pressure would be directed on the face of a cliff, bringing down tons of boulders, gravel and pay dirt. As this muddy tidal wave of rubble roared downgrade through the channels provided, it deposited its gold in sluice boxes along the way. Freed of its gold, but still thick with silt, the "slickens," as the tailings were called, were then discharged into the nearest river, a practice that was eventually to lead to the downfall of hydraulic mining.

Although history credits a Connecticut Yankee named Matteson, who was mining at American Hill in Nevada County, with a "first" in applying hydraulic methods to mining, actually the earliest known approach to this method came in April 1852 when Antoine Chabot, a French-Canadian, used a hose to wash loose gravel into a sluice box on his claim at Buckeye Hill in Nevada County. Anthony Chabot, as he was later called, made a fortune in the Nevada County placer mines and went on to become a great philanthropist and builder. It was Chabot who laid out the beginning of San Francisco's first water supply, built water systems in Vallejo and San Jose. He constructed Oakland's first water system using the water of Temescal Creek and San Leandro Creek and later Lake Chabot, which still bears his name, and he was the first president of the Oakland Gas Light Company in 1866. He made his final gift to the City of Oakland shortly before his death in the form of Chabot Observatory.

Chabot's contribution to hydraulic mining consisted only of using the water to assist in directing the gravel into the sluicebox, thereby saving himself a lot of shoveling. Apparently it never occurred to him to add a nozzle and apply the force of the water to the ground being worked. That remained for the aforementioned Edward E. Matteson to do in 1853 when he brought water from high above his claim through a rawhide hose, at the end of which he attached a tapered nozzle which he carved from a block of wood with a hole bored through the center (some claim it was a sheet iron nozzle). With this crude appliance he was able to direct a strong stream against the face of the bank and wash quantities of pay dirt down and into his sluice boxes. The method worked so well that Colonel William McClure, who had visited Matteson's claim earlier that year, introduced it at Yankee Jim's in Placer County upon his return.

Although stovepipe and canvas hose were used with success in the early stages of hydraulic mining, these primitive materials were discarded as pressures increased. Matteson, who had never thought to patent his new process, soon saw other inventors and manufacturers busy turning out nozzles and other hardware needed to control high-pressure water.

The canvas pipe was needed to provide flexibility at the nozzle end but was soon succeeded by the gooseneck, a flexible iron joint formed by two elbows working over each other. This, in turn, was improved upon by a device known as the radius plate and later the Fisher Knuckle Joint which allowed complete freedom of movement of the nozzle. Attention was given to the design of the nozzles and they acquired powerful and picturesque names such as the Craig Monitor, Hoskin's Dictator and finally Hoskin's Little Giant. It was the latter name that stuck and throughout this dramatic era the huge nozzles were termed simply "giants."

If the miners' ditches were important to the placer diggings prior to 1853, they became big business with the advent of hydraulic mining and there began a gigantic system of dams, lakes, reservoirs, canals and pipelines to supply water to dozens of large hydraulic mines from northern Siskiyou County to Tuolumne County. Hundreds of miles of ditches were built at tremendous costs

In some cases entire rivers were dammed and rerouted in order that their channels could be worked all the way to bedrock. The pictures at left, taken at the Golden Gate and Golden Feather Mining Claims clearly show how the Feather River was made to get up and move over. Current wheels (upper right) were used to drive the pumps that would drain the deep holes and wet spots. Much of the mining had to be done during a single season as the flimsy structures shown in closeup below were sure to be destroyed with the first high water. *(left and below, Bancroft Library)*

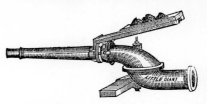
Monitor, Dictator and Giant were some of the names given to the remarkable nozzles that could destroy mountains and as the principal tool of the hydraulic miner they were widely manufactured and advertised. In the advertisements above are the sharp statements made by F. H. Fisher and Mr. R. Hoskin; each claimed to own the Little Giant patent and each claimed to manufacture a better machine. The Giants below are working one of the richest of the California hydraulic mines, the famous Malakoff at North Bloomfield, Nevada County. *(above, Morgan North; below, California State Library)*

even by today's standards and it would not be an exaggeration to say that hydraulic engineering saw its finest hour under the impetus of this type of mining. Textbooks were written and mining colleges taught courses in this branch of engineering. The classic experiments of Hamilton Smith on the flow of water in pipes were made especially for hydraulic miners. Meanwhile the companies themselves made use of every new technological development. For instance, it was only two years after Alexander Graham Bell had received his first telephone patent that the South Yuba Canal Company strung wires along the entire right of way of its system. This was followed the next year by the Ridge Telephone Line which served the ditch companies and mines of the North San Juan district and became one of the earliest long distance telephone installations in the United States.

Some of these water systems brought water from lakes at the very top of the high Sierra and were working examples of engineering skill. The main ditches were usually eight to fifteen feet wide at the top and four to six feet wide at the bottom and ran three or more feet in depth. A wide variety of the engineering devices were used, including tunnels, flumes, pipelines, trestles, and so on. The Miocene mine built a flume designed to carry 3000 miner's inches of water that was suspended by iron slings and brackets from the face of a perpendicular cliff. The Blue Tent Mining Company's ditch, which carried just as great a volume of water, ran a distance of six miles along the face of a cliff. The surveyors had to be suspended by ropes a thousand feet above the bottom of the gorge in order to establish the line. Canyons were bridged by trestle-work and when the width was too great the inverted siphon was used. At Junction City, Trinity County, a mining company laid 5700 feet of siphon pipe to carry the water down a 280-foot-deep canyon and up the other side. An inverted siphon 30 inches in diameter and nearly 2½ miles long was built at Cherokee, Butte County.

One of the large companies in the business of supplying water was the Eureka Lake and Yuba Canal Company. This firm tapped the outlet of four small lakes near the summit of the Sierra and delivered it to North San Juan 65 miles away. Another, the South Yuba Canal Company, was the largest of the water supply companies. They ex-panded their field until at the peak of operations they maintained 450 miles of waterways.

Placer County was served by the Auburn and Bear River Canal, 290 miles long, which cost $670,-000. Amador County had a $400,000 ditch and in Tuolumne County there were the 40-mile big Oak Flat Ditch and the 35-mile County Water Company built at a cost of $600,000 and $550,000 respectively.

Many of these water companies were, of course, continuations of the original placer miners' ditches whose business expanded with the additional demand for water. In the early 1860s it was reported that there were 5328 miles of artificial water courses for miners constructed at a cost of $15,-575,400. This figure increased by many millions of dollars during the next twenty years and it is estimated that at the zenith of the hydraulic mining era the total length of right of way for ditches, flumes and pipelines reached a total of 8000 miles.

Water was not only sold to the hydraulic mines, but to towns for domestic use, lumber and stamp mills for water power, and after eventually seeking its way to lower elevations it was sold for agricultural purposes. With the advent of electric power the water systems were ready-made to provide the prime energy to drive the generators. When the hydraulic era was over many of the aqueducts and canals were taken over by irrigation districts and power companies. The Pacific Gas and Electric Company's records show that a total of 520 separate corporations made up the system of canals and water rights now incorporated in that company's hydroelectric operations.

The basic operation of a hydraulic mine consisted of a huge stream of high-pressure water shooting out of a giant and striking the bank with such force that huge sections of the earth containing boulders, dirt and gravel would crumble before it. So powerful was this solid beam of water that a strong man could not strike a crowbar through a six-inch jet. A fifty-pound boulder placed on the stream of water would be projected with the force of a cannon ball, riding the water for a considerable distance before falling through. An extraordinary though recorded fact shows that men and animals have been killed by the force of the water alone at a distance of 200 feet or more from the nozzle.

The two high pressure pipe lines in the foreground indicate that there were probably additional Giants working farther downline. The Malakoff mine, depicted here, worked a face 1⅛ miles long with any number of the nozzles operating simultaneously. This artistic display of liquid power was probably staged for the benefit of the photographer as the long arcs of water would not provide the most effective usage. During actual operation the large stream of water coming from the right would be from the main mining Giant and would be blasting large segments down from the bank and from a closer angle consistent with the safety of the operator. The three smaller Giants would be used to move boulders and debris and to push the pay dirt and gravel downstream, one Giant picking up where another left off. Finally at the lowest end of the pit the entire flow would drop into a tunnel, much like a giant sink drain, and would be directed over sluice boxes on its way out of the area. This rather all-inclusive photo offers an exceptional cross section of the Tertiary gravel so characteristic in the hydraulic mines of California. Although high in the Sierra these gravel beds are the remains of a prehistoric river which ran in a Northwest to Southeast direction. Known as the Big Blue Lead it is traceable for a distance of 65 miles. (*Morgan North*)

29

This photo taken at a hydraulic mine above Brownsville in Butte County shows the cleanup in progress. The riffles have been removed and the heavy residue is being shoveled into buckets which are hauled away by wagon for further refining. In this network of sluice boxes, sections can be blocked off by gates leaving one set "on line" while the other is being cleaned. However, on this day the entire crew turned out to do the job at one time. *(Wells Fargo Bank History Room)*

31

This derrick and sling is being used to stack boulders out of the way at a hydraulic mine in Siskiyou County, but it is typical of an activity that was common to all of the Calfornia gold counties. Today these pyramid shaped stacks of rocks are still found in ravines and on the banks of rivers and streams. (*California Division of Mines and Geology*)

In this photo of a small hydraulic mine near Columbia the photographer captured all of the components in a single picture. Note the high pressure pipelines, giants, sluice boxes and the derrick for removing boulders. (*Wells Fargo Bank History Room*)

With such power available it is not surprising that the water did most of the mining; however in some cases where the gravel was cemented or compacted tunnels were driven into the ground to be mined for fifty to 100 feet. Then short tunnels were driven off the end at right angles, making a "T"-shaped tunnel. The ends of the tunnel were then loaded with anywhere from 100 to 1000 kegs of gunpowder and fired with a fuse. In this way the area would be broken up and ready for the giant once again.

In hydraulic mining quadruple use was made of the water. Initially the water directed with high velocity was the actual mining agent and then dislodged and mixed with water the earth was transported by gravity to the sluice boxes. As it flowed over the riffles in the boxes the principle of specific gravity caused the gold to leave the solution, leaving the "slickens" to flow on to be eventually disposed of . . . all by the action of the water. Thus with the aid of one man to direct the giant, water actually did the mining, tramming, processing and finally hauled away the tailings. Had the miners been more careful about where the tailings went hydraulic mining might still be a factor in the cheap recovery of gold. In its heyday the California giant mined great quantities of gold and because of its success was soon used in other parts of the world and for other metals that occurred in alluvial deposits. The hydraulic principle is still occasionally utilized by contractors in road and dam construction. It was even used, with some success, in the coal districts of Pennsylvania.

Although the simple act of turning a fire hose-like jet of water on a gravel bank may sound deceptively simple there was a great deal of preparation necessary to starting up a hydraulic operation; not only in bringing in the water, but in making ready the mine site itself. This was done in the following manner: After the ground had been selected one of the first items of business was to drive a tunnel into the gold-bearing gravel at a lower elevation, usually beginning in a ravine, to a termination of maybe a hundred feet below the floor of the mine. This tunnel would slope upward as it ran and would be connected with the mining area by means of a shaft. The combined shaft and tunnel would then provide a giant drain for the water and tailings to flow out. Sluice boxes would

then be installed in the tunnel which would be anywhere from several hundred feet to a mile or more in length. For riffles the sluices used blocks of wood set with the end of the grain exposed, thus making a pavement of wooden blocks. In other cases rocks about the size and shape of ostrich eggs were used. Whether blocks of wood or rocks, mercury would be placed in the cracks to attract and hold the fine gold. Once a month or more often the mine would be shut down or where double sluice boxes were provided the flow merely shifted and the clean-up made. It was not uncommon for these clean-ups to yield $50,000 to $100,000 worth of gold.

Twenty-four hours a day the water shot out of the huge nozzles to thunder against the cliffs with cannon-ball velocity. The pipeman, as he was called, clad in rubber boots and raincoat seemed a strange and lonesome figure as he stood on a platform next to the giant which he directed with deadly accuracy.

Before the days of high-intensity outdoor illumination nighttime operation was facilitated by using oil-burning locomotive headlights strategically placed about the mine.

Naturally the mine owners did everything in their power to make the sluice boxes as efficient as possible for once the tailings left their property they were lost to them forever. Many enterprising miners took advantage of this fact and erected their own sluices in the path of the slickens. Although the tailings had been robbed of most of the gold by the time they reached them, many of these independent operators did quite well considering the small amount of effort and initial investment required on their part.

One of the richest of all the California hydraulic mines was located at North Bloomfield in the San Juan Ridge district of Nevada County some 15 miles from Nevada City. Operated by the North Bloomfield Gravel Mining Company it was known variously as the Bloomfield Hydraulic mine, North Bloomfield and the Malakoff. It was this mine that in 1880 produced the largest gold bar ever shipped from Nevada County. It weighed 510 pounds avoirdupois and at the present value of gold would be worth $200,000.

In 1872, W. Hamilton Smith Jr., a noted mining engineer and manager of the mine, designed and

33

At the Malakoff diggings (top) gold recovery was as efficient as possible and the gold bearing gravel passed over a long series of sluice boxes before being discharged as waste. Center photo shows a high pressure pipeline coming down the face of a cliff and crossing a river via a suspension bridge. The lower picture is of a log debris dam designed to hold back some of the silt which was then beginning to bring discredit to the hydraulic miners. (*upper, Bancroft Library; middle and lower, Morgan North*)

34

built the famous North Bloomfield tunnel which drained the vast Malakoff mine. This tunnel was 7800 feet in length and was considered a marvel of engineering for that time. To dig the tunnel eight shafts averaging 200 feet in depth were sunk approximately one thousand feet apart. Crews dug on two faces in each shaft, making a total of 16 faces being worked at one time.

One of the most vivid contemporary descriptions of the Malakoff comes from a listing in the *Annual Mining Review and Stock Ledger,* an investment publication printed in San Francisco in 1876. Because of its historical interest it is herewith reproduced:

San Francisco 1876

North Bloomfield Gravel Mining Company
320 Sansome Street

Thomas Bell, President°

Hydraulic mine, consisting of 1616 acres, varying in depth from 150 to 400 feet. The mine is situated about 15 miles from Nevada City on the ridge between the South and Middle Yuba Rivers. It is worked through a deep tunnel 8000 feet long with about sixty million gallons of water per day used through three monitors with nozzles varying from five to eight°° inches in diameter, under a pressure varying from 300 to 500 feet. The water supply is furnished from a large reservoir belonging to the Company, containing 1 billion cubic feet of water, which is brought to the mine through a canal 45 miles long, built by the Company at a cost (including reservoir) of about $750,000. The canal has a capacity of about 3500 miners' inches. The mine will consume yearly about 800,000 miners' inches, or say 16,000,000,000 gallons of water. There are no engines or machinery of any kind in use in connection with the operation of the Company. Their works are capable of mining away about 50,000 tons of gravel per day and it is estimated that it will take 50 years to exhaust the mine. The Company commenced operations ten years ago, and have prosecuted the work steadily since they began. They expect to have their mine well opened by the first

_____

°Thomas Bell was an active investor in mining properties at the time. He was also one of the founders of the Bank of California, one of the owners of the great New Almaden and the New Idria quicksilver mines and with Darius Ogden Mills and J. B. Randol owned the Standard mine in Lake County. Bell and some San Francisco associates also owned for a time the famous North Star mine of Grass Valley (see Chapter 12). He was closely connected with San Francisco's infamous Mammy Pleasant and died in the Bay City under mysterious circumstances in October 1892.

°°A five-inch nozzle under a 400-foot head would use 11,250 gallons a minute.

of September this year, and to continue steady at work until their ground is exhausted. In the preliminary work, $426,553 were extracted. Their works are complete in every particular. The deep tunnel, constructed at a cost of $500,000, will answer to exhaust their ground. They own their own water, gravel and outlet, and do not pay tribute to anyone. Their gold saving process, when complete, will enable them to keep control of their material for 2½ miles in distance after it is mined, thus enabling them to save a very large percentage of the gold in the gravel.

The Company have procured a patent from the government of the United States for all their lands. In addition to their own property the Company also own a majority in interest of the Union Gravel Mining Company's property, as also of the property of the Milton Mining and Water Company. In their mining operations at Bloomfield, they make partial clean-ups about every 20 days, a more general clean-up about once every 3 or 4 months, and a thorough clean-up of the entire line of work once or twice a year. The Company are at present engaged in enlarging their Bowman Reservoir by carrying the dam from its former elevation of 72 feet, up to a height of 95 feet. This enlargement, which will be completed this Fall, is being constructed of stone, and when completed will constitute as large and permanent a reservoir as there is on the Pacific Coast.

By the close of this year their entire line of works, from their reservoir to their outlet, will be complete, in every particular, at a total estimated cost of about $2,500,000 gold coin. This amount includes the mine, reservoirs, canal, tunnel, mining appliances, etc., up to the present time. The Company employs 40 to 75 men, and expend $75,000 per year for labor.

With these resources the Malakoff mine became a huge operation. Its water-dug pit which is today a State Park, has a length of 1⅛ miles and a depth of 350 feet at the west end and 550 feet at the east end. The total quantity of material excavated was 41,000,000 yards which yielded during the life of the mine (1862-1884) approximately $4,000,000 in gold.°

Although hydraulic mining may have been an ingenious and efficient method it did not make many friends for the miners, for perhaps in no other part of the world had water been so extensively employed to rearrange nature as it had in

_____

°This figure varies from source to source as do most of the early statistics on mining. The State of California, now operating the Malakoff as a Historic Park, claims land use history indicates the mine grossed $3.5 million between 1866 and 1884 from 30 million cubic yards of gold-bearing gravel.

The pipeman controlled his giant by a rod that connected with the flexible tip of the nozzle. When the tip was turned slightly the deflection of the water would cause the entire giant to turn in a simple application of jet action and power steering. (Wells Fargo Bank History Room)

California, the home of hydraulic mining. Mountains, trees and boulders trembled and disintegrated before the relentless onslaught of this aquatic death ray that washed away the soil and filled the streams and rivers and carried the silt as far as San Francisco Bay and on through the Golden Gate.* Such wholesale misuse of nature caused one traveler to the gold country, Mr. Samuel Bowles, to write in 1868 the following description which was only slightly exaggerated:

> Tornado, flood, earthquake and volcano combined could hardly make greater havoc, spread wider ruin and wreck, than are to be seen everywhere in the track of the larger gold-washing operations. None of the interior streams of California, though naturally pure as crystal, escape the change to a thick yellow mud from this cause, early in their progress from the hills. The Sacramento is worse

*Lindgren's Professional Paper No. 75, "The Tertiary Gravels of the Sierra Nevada," states that estimates based on actual measurements made by his associates between 1895 and 1901 arrive at a "conservative total" of 1,295,-000,000 cubic yards as the amount of debris from the hydraulic mines that was dumped into streams that eventually joined the Sacramento River.

than the Missouri. Many of the streams are turned out of their original channels, either directly for mining purposes, or in consequence of the great masses of soil and gravel that come down from the gold-washing above. Thousands of acres of fine land along their banks are ruined forever by the deposits of this character. A farmer may have his whole estate turned into a barren waste by a flood of sand and gravel from some hydraulic mining up stream; more, if a fine orchard or garden stands in the way of the working of a rich gulch or bank, orchard or garden must go. Then the tornout, dugout, washed to pieces and then washed over sidehills, masses that have been or are being subjected to the hydraulics of the miners, are the very devil's chaos indeed. The country is full of them among the mining districts of the Sierra Nevada, and they are truly a terrible blot upon the face of Nature.

In spite of such attacks as this the hydraulic system of mining gained momentum year after year as more rich gold deposits were found in the ancient river channels running through the ridges of the Sierra. At the peak of the hydraulic era there were 425 such mines operating in California and all were dumping millions of cubic yards of slickens into the creeks and rivers.

The stepped-up pace of this man-made erosion caused great problems downstream, especially among the farmers whose fields were often flooded with gravel and sand when the overloaded rivers left their banks destroying both crops and fields.

The farmers fought back, both as individuals and with their organizations. They even sent armed gangs to the mining country, but their most telling blow occurred on January 23, 1884, when Judge L. B. Sawyer of the United States Circuit Court granted a perpetual injunction against the North Bloomfield Mining Company of Nevada County. This was the famous Sawyer decision that made it illegal to discharge tailings into streams and rivers.

Although hailed by conservationists and socially concerned people as a milestone in the doctrine of the "greatest good for the greatest number" the movement to restrict hydraulic mining was, at the time, pretty much of a fight between two special interest groups, the miners and the farmers. There is no doubt that such legislation was necessary, nevertheless the short-term effects were economically disastrous. The hydraulic mines and allied industries represented an investment of over $100,000,000, a tremendous figure for those days. In short, the hydraulic mines ranked high on the list of national assets and the effect of their closing caused a severe depression in California and a dent in the entire national economy. Whole towns and communities became deserted or completely disappeared from the map as men and their families left the mining districts to seek employment else-where. A few fortunate towns such as Nevada City and Grass Valley had quartz mines to take up the slack and were able to weather this financial setback.

The stakes were high and the hydraulic mining lobby was strong and persistent, but the best they could get in the way of relief was the Caminetti Act of 1893 which permitted hydraulic mining only after the construction of debris-impounding dams under official sanction and under the periodic inspection of a debris commission. The costs of construction and the administration of the program were to be born by a tax on revenue produced by hydraulic mining.

A few attempts were made to operate under these conditions, but they were found to be expensive and generally were not too successful. The farmers had won and agriculture went on to become the number one industry in California, but the spirit of the miner goes on and as this colorful chapter comes to an end we find the dawning of a new era in California mining. This was to be an era of hard-rock or quartz mining assisted by such improvements as newly discovered dynamite, compressed air drilling, scientifically designed mills and recovery equipment. It was also an era that saw the development of the modern gold dredger which since 1897 had been undergoing improvements until these huge machines could work the deltas of ancient gravel beds at costs quite close to those achieved by the now disfavored hydraulic method. Once again the mining world looked to California as the undisputed leader in the scientific recovery of gold.

In the operation shown here rocks are pushed up a wooden chute by the force of the water. These "elevators," though lined with heavy sheet iron, didn't last very long. (California Division of Mines and Geology)

37

Natomas No. 6, the last California operating unit of the Natomas Company lies abandoned and rusting in its own pond east of Sacramento. Stripped of its gigantic buckets, ladder, tailings stacker and spuds it presents a sorry cut-down version of the mammoth floating plant that was once the flagship of the Natomas fleet. This same boat appears in mint condition on page 44.

THE GOLDEN FLEET

GOLD DREDGING 1898 to 1968

Total production by
this method $400,000,000

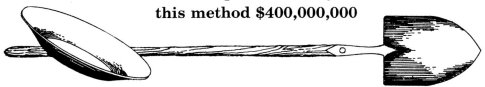

Mining low-grade placer deposits requires the excavating and washing of vast quantities of gravel in order to recover the minute particles of gold. Many original and ingenious devices were invented by the California miners but probably the most complicated and highly mechanized of all is the California gold dredger. In spite of its cumbersome size this monstrous machine can recover gold with tweezer-like efficiency.

Actually among the first ideas that occurred to the early gold hunters in California was the use of a machine to scoop up gravel from the river beds and submerged gravel bars that would have been otherwise inaccessible to them. Many of these early miners had seen steam paddies, as the first steam shovels were called, and other forms of mechanized excavating equipment in use in eastern and European cities, so it was only natural that some of these engineering principles would be brought to the California gold fields. In fact, it was only a few months after Marshall's discovery of gold on the American River that such a machine was shipped around the Horn from New York to San Francisco. It arrived in 1849 and after being assembled promptly sank to the bottom of the Sacramento River.

The following year, 1850, a small river steamer named the *Phenix* was fitted out as a dredge and attempts were made to mine the bottom of the Yuba River at a point about nine miles above Marysville. According to the meager information available from the newspaper accounts of the day the dredging principle must have been similar to

that still in use; that is, an endless chain of buckets bringing up mud and gravel from the river bottom and depositing it in sluice boxes aboard the boat. The fine material was separated from the coarse by screens and the free gold caught by the use of quicksilver. Both the propelling and dredging machinery were steam operated. One writer of the time, J. Wesley Jones, described the *Phenix* as follows: "The *Phenix* dredging machine as seen in the Yuba River, a cumbrous arrangement by which it was designed to drag up sand from the bed of the river and obtain gold in large quantities. It was soon found, however, that this machine dredged more money from the pockets of the owners than it did from the bed of the Yuba, and this kind of dredging was very soon abandoned."

The early dredges tried were generally built along the lines of those used in harbor dredging and were quite unsuited to the entirely different set of conditions met with when digging for gold. During the succeeding years many attempts at gold dredging were made in California and elsewhere in the West, but with the exception of the double lift* bucket elevator dredges of the Bucyrus type that operated at Grasshopper Creek, Montana, in 1894, all proved failures.

Although California was without a doubt the development ground for the modern gold dredger there was a good deal of experimenting and some

*Double lift referred to a two-stage bucket line. First lift to a hopper platform; second lift to screens and shake-out mechanism. In the end the industry settled on close connected single lift; in other words, one bucket line.

The first successful California gold dredge (above) was built in 1898 by the Risdon Iron Works of San Francisco for operation in the Oroville area. In the foreground are W. P. Hammon and Captain Thomas Couch, the owners. One of the two figures seated on the dredge is Frank W. Griffin, also a pioneer in California Gold Dredging. *(Yuba Industries, Inc.)*

After proving itself in the Feather River delta near Oroville gold dredging soon spread to the gravels of the American River east of Sacramento. The early dredge below is Folsom No. 3 of the Folsom Development Company. *(California State Library)*

successful operation of dredgers in New Zealand beginning in the early 1860s. No doubt the first dredging consisted of a man standing in water up to his armpits shoveling gravel into a washing device which was supported on a platform between two canoes. This type of dredging soon gave way to the single bucket or spoon dredge which, as conceived in the land down under, consisted of a bag laced or riveted to a round iron frame, not unlike a basketball hoop, which in turn was secured to the end of a long pole and drawn along the bottom of the river or creek. The bag was counterbalanced so that when it was filled it could be brought up and emptied into a sluice box or rocker. The next step in the evolution of the dredge was to mount the pole and spoon on pontoons or a raft using an auxiliary scow for the washing apparatus. These primitive dipper dredges were at first operated entirely by hand, later by current wheels using the force of the stream and finally steam power was added around 1870.

The first bucket elevator dredge made its appearance in 1867 at Otage, New Zealand, using current wheels for power. In 1881 the first steam-driven bucket elevator dredge was constructed to operate on the Molyneaux River, also in New Zealand. This type of dredge apparently was quite successful as history records that one bucket elevator dredge built sometime around 1882 operated for 16 years. It was, no doubt, because of this record that in 1889 some twenty such boats were built at an average cost of $17,000, each to operate on a branch of the Molyneaux River. Unfortunately these operations were failures. Perhaps it was due to unsuitable bottom conditions or inexperienced management because they were later sold and floated down the river where, under new conditions and ownership, they operated successfully.

It was not until 1897 that a dredge of the single lift bucket elevator type was floated in California. This dredge was built by the Risdon Iron Works for a New Zealander named R. H. Postlethwaite and was put to work on the Yuba River where it was wrecked during the flood season and never recommissioned. Had this same dredge been installed in the Oroville area it probably would have been successful; however Mr. Postlethwaite was not discouraged and remained one of the biggest boosters of California dredging.

A steam gold dredger ascending the Sacramento River in 1849 as envisioned by an artist for CENTURY Magazine. *(California State Library)*

In a manuscript prepared for the California Miners' Association Mr. Postlethwaite presented a good case for dredging by stating: ". . . it may be well to point out that one of the greatest advantages which dredging has over most other classes of mining is its comparative safeness as an investment; for, if the initial prospecting be carried out systematically and honestly, the value of the ground may be very closely determined. Thus, seeing that the cost of handling is now well known, and seeing that the value of the ground can be very closely determined, gold dredging may be considered a business investment rather than a speculation; a position which quartz mining can never attain, as the most careful prospecting cannot possibly determine the permanency of the pay shoot."

Mr. Postlethwaite did learn from his experience with the flood-prone Yuba River and henceforth advocated the beginning of dredging operations from a point well inland rather than in the river itself and in that same paper told how a dredging operation is started, exactly the same method that would be used today. "A small excavation was made (some 3000 feet from the Feather River) about 11 feet deep by eighty feet square, the dredge being built in the dry hole; a pump was erected at the river and, by means of a flume, supplied about one-quarter million gallons of water a day to the dredge. This quantity . . . is sufficient to overcome the seepage, and suffices to keep the water sufficiently clean to operate in. As

The California-perfected gold dredge soon made its appearance in British Columbia and Alaska as well as other parts of the world. Although the basic design remained, constant modifications were made to suit the location. The one above needed such a long reach for its tailings stacker that an auxiliary barge was required to support it. The photo below of the Feather River was taken from the bluff opposite Oroville. Note the gold dredge in the center. The City of Oroville stands on the river terrace to the left. This was where California dredging had its beginning and it remained prime ground for many years. *(above, Morgan North; below, G. K. Gilbert, U. S. Geological Survey)*

regards the advisability of operating on the river or of starting inland, I believe that, where possible, all the advantages are in favor of the latter. The cost of pumping is very small, and the advantage of being able to make your own water-level is often very great. In addition to this, the dredge is entirely independent of floods, which, if not actually dangerous, are always a detriment to working."

Strangely enough the man most responsible for the California gold dredging industry was not a miner but an orchardist with a keen interest in gold mining and a natural knack for promotion. The man was W. P. Hammon, who about 1895 had sunk a large pit in the gravel adjacent to the Feather River. He was convinced by the values recovered that if economically handled these deposits would be of great value. This suggested to him some form of dredging and he proceeded to secure options on several thousand acres of suitable land in the vicinity.

Hammon then consulted with F. T. Sutherland. Sutherland wasn't too familiar with the New Zealand dredges, but he was aware of the successful bucket elevator types that had been operating at Bannock, Montana, and he was also familiar with the almost ideal dredging conditions that existed in the Oroville area of California where the rushing Feather River enters the Sacramento Valley and over the centuries had deposited untold millions in gold. Sutherland succeeded in interesting Capt. Thomas Couch of Butte, Montana, in Hammon's proposed venture. Meanwhile Hammon himself had been talking with W. H. Cristie of the firm of Cristie and Lowe, general contractors, who were at that time engaged in canal and jetty work in the East. Their experience in handling large quantities of sand and gravel economically was useful and perhaps could be adapted to the California gold fields. Their interest, too, was aroused and Cristie and Lowe dispatched a Mr. Brown to make an examination of the ground and to report on the practicability of its being worked by dredges. Mr. Brown's report was indeed favorable and soon afterward Capt. Couch agreed to finance a dredge. The Risdon Iron Works of San Francisco was awarded the contract for the building of the first bucket elevator dredge in the Oroville district.

Operation was begun in March 1898 and the enterprise was successful right from the beginning.

Soon other companies and dredges were operating in the Oroville area. In fact, throughout the history of dredging in California the Oroville district has probably floated more dredges and seen more dredging companies than any other area in California.

The Oroville gravel was so rich that one company, so the story goes, offered to buy the city of Oroville, lock, stock and barrel, and set it up on another location for the privilege of dredging the land on which it was built. The offer was declined and today Oroville still rests in its original golden setting.

Stories of the wealth-collecting abilities of the Oroville dredges apparently reached the ears of one ambitious robber who, under the cover of night, boarded one of the huge clanking boats. Suddenly, striking a menacing stance in the center of the dredge, he ordered the crew to break out the gold, not knowing that the recovered gold accumulated in a locked area inaccessible even to the operating crew. At the "hands up" order one quick-thinking dredge man threw the main light switch, plunging the boat into total darkness. The robber, in strange surroundings anyway, was terrified at being in the center of that huge machinery where one false move would mean a horrible death by mangling. As soon as his eyes could locate the dim outline of an opening he made a dash for it and disappeared into the night, thus ending in dismal failure his ill-conceived plan for the first (and as far as I know the last) great dredge robbery in the history of mining.

Most of the early California dredges beginning with Hammon and Couch's were steam operated. Fans of the steam engine might be interested in the following description of the power plant from R. H. Postlethwaite's "Notes on Dredging for Gold":

"The motive power to operate the dredges is in most cases steam (author's note: gasoline engines were tried also). A compound condensing, vertical engine, indicating about forty horsepower, running the whole dredge, except the electric light plant and winch, which have separate engines. The power is transmitted to the buckets by ropes and gearing, a friction clutch being placed on the countershaft so that, instead of breaking anything, in the event of the buckets running up against solid,

Dredge No. 15 of Yuba Consolidated Gold Fields is shown above operating at Hammonton, Yuba County in 1934. Below, Natomas No. 6, completed in July 1938, was once the pride of the Natomas fleet. She came to a clanking halt in February 1962 and as of 1969 was a rusting hulk visible from Sunrise Avenue east of Mather Field near Sacramento. *(above, W. D. Johnston, Jr., U. S. Geological Survey; below, E. G. "Dick" Smith collection)*

hard bedrock or other obstruction, the clutch merely slips and continues to slip until the winch man eases the strain, when the bucket belt starts again.

"Steam is supplied by a horizontal return tubular boiler, burning 2¾ cords of wood per day. The condenser is placed in the suction of the main pump, thus doing away with the necessity of a circulating pump; a vacuum of twenty inches is obtained.

"The operating crew consists of two men per shift, one engineer and one winch man. The winch man has complete control of the dredge, his winch having six independent drums; one being for the ladder line, one for the head line, and the other four being for lines connected to the four corners of the boat and fastened to deadmen on shore. By means of these lines the dredge can be made to take up any position required."

With the exception of an increase in the size of the crew (three to four men are usually used on the dredges of today) and the substitution of electric power* (1901) for steam, dredging is still conducted almost exactly as outlined by Postlethwaite. Naturally capacity has increased with the growth and development of the dredge. Whereas the first Risdon boats operated at a depth of thirty feet and with a bucket capacity of 3½ cubic feet worked 30,000 to 35,000 cubic yards a month, a modern dredge has buckets of 18 cubic feet capacity and can work 124 feet below the water level handling 125,000 cubic yards a week!

Along with the American characteristic of large-scale operation special attention has been given through the years to the efficiency of the gold recovery equipment aboard the dredge. This has been perfected to the point where a large dredge can profitably work gravel with a gold content of 10 cents to 15 cents a cubic yard. With operating costs running 5 cents to 10 cents a cubic yard this brings the operating efficiency close to that achieved by the hydraulic miner.**

---

*Shoreside power is delivered to the dredge through long flexible waterproof cables.

**These are outdated figures purposely left intact for comparison. Present-day costs of dredging in California are now 12 cents to 15 cents per cubic yard, due largely to increased labor and other overhead costs. Since the gold content of even good dredger ground runs from 10 to 25 cents a cubic yard there isn't much left for the operator.

Prior to 1903 the principal gold-dredging areas of the state were located along the Feather and American rivers. The Yuba River had long been known to contain great possibilities, but was considered too difficult because of the depth of the deposit. The deepest practicable dredging at that time had been forty feet and the Yuba gravels would require a 65-foot dredge at least. John Hays Hammond,** the famous mining engineer, was so convinced that these mechanical difficulties could be overcome he took an option on a thousand acres of land in the heart of the district and retained another famous mining man, Fred W. Bradley, to test it for him. Bradley and Hammond became involved in a bitter dispute with the result that the option was never exercised and the property was acquired by W. P. Hammon. As successful a dredge man as he had been, he now realized that the Yuba River operation would require greater capital and involve greater risk than any of his previous projects. Even San Francisco capital was reluctant to enter such an untried field and Hammon was forced to look elsewhere.

He finally turned to a group of Boston capitalists he had met a couple of years earlier while they were investing in some of the smaller dredge operations on the Feather River. The group included Messrs. Clark, Coolidge and Holden and had been successfully involved in a number of large mining ventures, including the Island Creek Coal Co. and the United States Smelting & Refining Co. These men were joined by Mr. R. D. Evans, then president of the United States Rubber Company. Evans, who by this time, had acquired considerable confidence in Hammon, formed a syndicate, holding the major interest himself, which included the aforementioned men plus John Hays Hammond and his British associates. Approximately $100,000 was spent in testing the 3000 acres involved in the project and by August of 1904, the first two dredges, the Yuba No. 1 and No. 2, costing approximately $90,000 each, were put into operation. Thus began activity in what Hammond described in his autobiography as "the most profitable dredging area in the world."

**Hammond had won fame and fortune in the South African gold fields and at that time maintained an office in London.

The anatomy of a dredge. The winchman controls all machinery and movement from the lever room which is perched like a pilot house high above the bow of the boat. Motor controller adjusts power to the bucket line. The three meters, upper center of photo, monitor current to the main motor and require constant watching in hard ground to prevent overload. The winches (below) operate independently and are connected to the ladder line, head lines and lines connected to the four corners of the boat and fastened to deadmen on shore. By paying out and taking in on the various lines the dredge can be made to take up any position required. With the exception of clearing the right-of-way, moving the power cable occasionally or advancing the deadmen most of the activity occurred aboard the dredge. (upper, California State Library; lower, Yuba Industries, Inc.)

Head-on view of the bucket line taken from shore. Photo directly below shows the bucket line ascending its ladder. At the top of the ladder the buckets dump their load into a hopper which in turn feeds into a rotating trommel (upper right). Inside the trommel (center) high pressure water jets break up and wash the material. The oversized rocks roll onto a conveyor belt and are dumped from the end of a long boom called the tailings stacker. The fines fall through screening and are directed over a series of riffles (lower right), a refinement of the sluice boxes previously described. *(upper left, Yuba Industries, Inc.; others, California State Library)*

At the top is an overall view of the Natomas Company's dredge headquarters at Natoma just west of Folsom. Once boasting its own U.S. Post Office Natoma is no longer on the map. At left is the office building; the small house in the center is the retort house where the gold was melted and poured into bars, the large building in background is the machine shop. Center, is an aerial view of the Benicia plant of Yuba Industries, Inc. Here dredges were designed and built for use all over the world as well as for its own mining subsidiary, Yuba Consolidated Gold Fields. Dredge below is Y.C.G.F. No. 20, one of the big Yubas which operated at Hammonton, Yuba County. It was designed to dig 124 feet below water level and to work against a bank 50 feet high. Each bucket had a capacity of 18 cubic feet. *(center and lower, Yuba Industries, Inc.)*

By 1909 gold dredging had become big business and although there were a number of small one-dredge operators, the bulk of the land was now controlled mainly by three large companies: Oroville Dredging Ltd., financed by British capital, Natomas Consolidated, financed by San Francisco capital, and Yuba Consolidated Gold Fields, largely financed by Boston capital. The first two represented consolidations of a number of smaller operations while the latter was a single enterprise involving most of the important dredging acreage on the Yuba River. Meanwhile Hammon, because of his early experience at Oroville and his wise acquisition of property secured an interest in and was directly associated with the operations of all three of the major companies, which at this time represented a capital investment of $9,000,000 and were returning millions of dollars in gold.

However, the gold dredging industry alone was not a broad enough outlet for all of W. P. Hammon's energies. The dredging companies with which he was associated were running smoothly in 1910. Even his Hammon Engineering Company was in capable hands; so Mr. Hammon turned his energies to a variety of other fields, including gold dredging in Alaska, tin dredging in Portugal, railway and power construction in California, oil in Southern California and copper mines in Arizona. Truly an amazing man, this former orchardist became the father of gold dredging in California and the founder of a dozen other industries still flourishing throughout the world.

Meanwhile the design and erecting facilities such as the Western Engineering and Construction Company and the dredge manufacturing works of the Boston Machine Shop, pioneer firms of Oroville, were acquired and consolidated by the Yuba Company. When, in 1913, foundry facilities for large steel castings became available in California, Yuba undertook the manufacture of the heaviest known dredge machinery used in the industry.

Most of the operating life of Yuba Consolidated Gold Fields centered around the Hammonton property on the Yuba River. Only one piece of Yuba River property other than the original parcel was acquired during the company's life and that was twenty years after operations had commenced. This was a thousand acres adjoining Yuba's own property and was the only large piece of dredg-able land remaining in the district. It formerly belonged to the Marysville Dredging Company and was acquired by outright cash purchase in 1921.

In 1927 Yuba did set out to acquire some land outside of the Marysville area when they formed the Capital Dredging Company for the purpose of taking title to some 2200 acres of land on the American River near Folsom. This property they then equipped with four dredges named Capital No. 1, No. 2, No. 3 and No. 4.

Their next acquisition took place in 1930 when the company purchased about 950 acres and a small dredging company that had been operating on the Merced River.

As of 1968 the Yuba gold property consisted of 9700 acres of leased and owned land. The total gold production during the history of the company comes to about $130,000,000.00.

From time to time throughout the history of Yuba Consolidated Gold Fields, estimates have been made as to the probable life of the gold operations of the company. It was at first thought that about ten years was all that could be counted on. When this period ran out in 1915 some of the more optimistic gave it another ten years, but when 1925 came around and the property was still far from exhausted the termination date had to once again be revised . . . and so it went throughout the years.

After emerging from a reorganization the Company now operates as Yuba Industries, Inc., and is mainly engaged in the manufacturing of heavy equipment. Gold dredging was carried on by the Yuba Mining Division.

Although the Capital properties near Folsom have been shut down for some time, the original Yuba River land that was the birthplace of the company continued to produce revenue for Yuba, showing a net profit in 1965 of $373,000, $482,000 in 1966 and an estimated net of $400,000 in 1967. This in spite of continuous dredging in the same ground since 1904, a real tribute to the increased efficiency due to improvement in design throughout the years.

In January 1967 Yuba No. 20 was shut down and on March 6 Yuba No. 17 completed its profitable operation at the present price of gold, leaving No. 21 as the last operating gold dredge in Cali-

Yuba's dredge No. 17 was hardly a year old when this photo was taken at Hammonton in 1935.

Below is an aerial view of dredge tailings near Folsom. From a distance they look like the tracks of a giant earthworm. Dredged property, once considered virtually destroyed, is now leveled and quite suitable for housing and industrial sites. *(above, W. D. Johnston, Jr., U.S. Geological Survey; below, Bob Baker)*

fornia. But she was soon to join her sister ships and on October 1, 1968 the grinding, squeaking and scraping sounds of the giant buckets ceased and another era passed into history.

Yuba Industries, however, will continue to make dredges for other minerals as well as heavy equipment of all sorts at their historic° though modernized plant at Benicia, California.

Another large company whose name was synonymous with California gold dredging is the Natomas Company which, for the most part, operated along the American River in the Folsom area and in fact almost to the very city limits of Sacramento, where the big buckets of Natomas No. 6, the last operating unit, creaked to a stop in February 1962.

Of more than passing historical interest is the fact that the Natomas Company operated on a huge tract of land that was originally a grant from the Mexican government and whose various owners are familiar names in the history of early California.

To begin at the very beginning one would have to go back even before the discovery of gold in California, when only a few adventurous spirits had penetrated to this wonderful country, then so far from civilized centers. One of the men who came to California in this pre-49er period was William Leidesdorff, the son of the governor of the Danish West Indies. Earlier young Leidesdorff had set out to seek his fortune and had landed in New Orleans in the early 1830s where, so the story goes, he had a love affair which ended disastrously for him when the lady's family discovered that he carried a strain of Negro blood. Seeking to leave this unfortunate episode in his life as far behind as possible, Leidesdorff left for the wild and undeveloped West. Arriving in California aboard his own schooner, the *Julie Ann,* he was immediately impressed by the beauty and fertility of the land which lay east of the present city of Sacramento and visualized that some day this garden spot would be settled with small farms. Leidesdorff lost no time in applying to the Mexican govern-

ment for a grant to an area of eight square leagues or 46,000 acres. This property, which had the American River for its northern boundary and the Sutter grant for its western neighbor, was called the Rancho Rio de Los Americanos and was granted to William Leidesdorff by Manuel Micheltoreno, then governor of California, on October 8, 1844.

Whatever plans he had for the Rancho Rio de Los Americanos, will never be known for on May 18, 1848, four months after the discovery of gold on the banks of the American River, Leidesdorff died in the city by the Golden Gate.

In 1847, just a year before Leidesdorff's death, Captain Joseph Libby Folsom, U.S.A., arrived in California with the Stevenson Regiment and at the conclusion of the Mexican War decided, as did many others, to remain in San Francisco. It was Folsom who next acquired the Rancho Rio de Los Americanos, but was soon to be beseiged with difficulties associated with the settlement of Leidesdorff's estate. It was a complicated matter consisting of entanglements and conflicts of Mexican, American and Danish laws which were to keep it in litigation for over a decade. Some say the responsibilities of the court battle and the debts he incurred to finance them were too much and he, too, died at age 38 without ever seeing the development of the Rancho Rio de Los Americanos, a part of which became the town of Folsom which he had dreamed would some day exist.

In 1853 the Natoma Water and Mining Company was organized with the purpose of bringing water to the area from the South Fork of the American River for mining and other uses. This Company had bought the eastern portion of the Rancho Rio de Los Americanos from Folsom prior to his death and in 1854 built the Natoma Canal and the first dam on the American River. Much of the work was performed on a deferred payment basis by miners who were anxious to obtain water and who later took their pay in that commodity. Later the company allowed miners to work their property in return for the water they bought.

Another man with faith in the Folsom area was Horatio Gates Livermore. He dreamed of an industrial city using the water-power possibilities of the American River similar to the mills and factories he had seen in New England. By 1862 Livermore,

---

°Historic in that it occupies the site of one of California's earliest industrial centers. The property, situated on the Carquinez Strait, was the California terminus and repair depot for Gold Rush steamers operated by the Pacific Mail Steamship Company from the East Coast via Panama. One of the old brick-walled buildings is still being used.

This photo of Yuba No. 20, the world's largest gold dredge, clearly shows it in operation. The dredge is held in position by shore lines and a huge spud, that vertical column at the stern. The ladder and bucket line has been lowered and is operating well below the water level. Rocks and gravel can be seen dropping from the end of the tailings stacker and the muddy runoff from the riffles is being discharged from chutes on both sides of the boat. Gold dredges not only worked river bottoms, but also operated well inland, taking their own ponds with them by the simple expedient of cutting from the front and filling in at the back. (*Yuba Industries, Inc.*)

who was now joined by his two sons, acquired control of the Natoma Water and Mining Company. Looking ahead to the depletion of gold the company decided to use its water for agricultural purposes and planted orchards and a vineyard, the latter at one time being the largest in the state. In fact, so extensive was the fruit-growing end of the business that it was operated separately under the name Natoma Vineyard Company.

In addition to the vineyard the company also operated the Natoma Development Company which was organized for the purpose of dredging placer gravels by this new method of mining that was making itself known in California.

About 1902 an outside group which called themselves the Folsom Development Company entered the picture and began to acquire dredging ground. This company then organized two subsidiaries, namely the Folsom Rock Company, which erected a rock-crushing plant, and the Folsom Machine Company, which built large shops for the repair and maintenance of their dredging equipment. Both the rock company and the shops were located at Natoma, just west of Folsom.

The controlling interest in the Folsom Development Company was held by the Armour meat packing people and as the predominant color used by this company was yellow, all of the buildings at Natoma were painted yellow, with the result that the employees were dubbed the "Yellow Town Kids."

Dredging the Folsom area had by now proven itself to be a highly profitable proposition and since the vines of the old Folsom Vineyard were becoming diseased it was decided to return these properties to mining and to acquire additional land for this purpose. It was further decided to combine the various independent dredging companies that were operating in the Folsom area.

Thus was organized the Natomas Consolidated Company of California, incorporated on November 25, 1908, with an authorized capital stock of $25,000,000. The new company combined under one ownership and management the Natoma Development Company, Folsom Development Company, El Dorado Gold Dredging Company and the Feather River Development Company. Later reorganizations of the company saw the name change from Natomas Consolidated Company of California to Natomas Company of California and finally to simply Natomas Company.

Gradually Natomas Consolidated bought up land in addition to the original acreage acquired from the Natoma Water and Mining Company until, as of 1910, 30,000 of the original 46,000 acres granted to William Leidesdorff were back under one management and the old water rights were being used for irrigation as well as for dredging.

Over the years dredge operators have taken their share of criticism over the way they left the land, literally turning it upside down, and since you can never seem to put back into a hole all of the dirt you take out, the dredged lands are always ten or more feet above the rest of the terrain. However, by using the rock for aggregate and leveling the tailings, the land is certainly not lost in today's land-hungry economy.

Natomas began selling off some of its property starting with a huge tract during World War I, on which Mather Air Force Base was built. Since that time the Federal Government has acquired 4000 additional acres for the establishment of one of the major training fields in California. One of Sacramento's largest industrial plants, Aerojet General, is built on 7500 acres purchased from Natomas in 1951 and since that time Aerojet has acquired a total of 13,000 acres from the Natomas Company either by direct purchase or option to buy. Parcels have been sold to the Douglas Aircraft Company and others who have built huge plants that have added materially to the rapid industrial growth seen in the Sacramento area since World War II. Even the old shop buildings at Natoma with their many coats of white paint over the original Armour yellow have been sold to an electrical contractor.

In 1956, the same year gold dredging ceased in the Folsom area, a plan of reorganization was consummated whereby Natomas Company acquired the assets of a holding company consisting of approximately 48% of the outstanding capital stock of the American President Lines, formerly the Dollar Steamship Company. Today the revitalized Natomas Company is a highly diversified operation with major interests not only in APL but Americal Mail Line and Pacific Far East Lines as well. It also owns the new International Building in San Francisco, West Indies Oil Company Ltd., which refines and markets petroleum products in the West Indies, Isle of Man Petroleums Ltd., and more recently has acquired large offshore petroleum interests in Indonesia.

Still intrigued by gold mining, the company's one operating dredge is in the high Andes of Southern Peru where Natomas Company of Peru produced some $694,246 in gold bars during 1966, a marginal operation as business goes today, but still a reminder of how it all began.

An even smaller division is the Company's pear orchard adjoining the American River Parkway in Sacramento County which produces about 1000 tons a year of excellent table pears marketed under the Natomas brand. This well-maintained oasis in a sea of industrial tracts is all that remains of William Leidesdorff's dream to make a garden land of the Rancho Rio de Los Americanos.

One of the few remaining buildings at Eagle-Shawmut is this solidly-built storage house. Typically "Mother Lode" in construction, with stone walls and iron door, it was used to store oil and lubricating supplies during the operation of the mine.

CHAPTER 3

EAGLE-SHAWMUT
CIRCA* 1860-1947
Jacksonville, Tuolumne County
Vertical depth 3,550 feet
Total production $7,500,000

At the foot of the Shawmut Grade, three miles south of Chinese Camp (Tuolumne County), one can see huge terraced concrete foundations that would first appear to be the ruins of some ancient civilization. A second glance reveals extensive mounds of rock, unmistakably the dump of a large mining operation. This is the Eagle-Shawmut mine where many miles of underground workings have produced huge amounts of low-grade ore. Although the mine was opened at a very early date most of the extensive work was done since the turn of the century.

Some information has been written in mining journals on the latter days of the Eagle-Shawmut, but little is recorded of the mine's early history except to say that it was the consolidation of two mining claims, the Eagle and the Shawmut.

The Eagle mine, located on Blue Gulch on the east vein of the Mother Lode, first appears in the *Mining and Scientific Press* for April 28, 1866, when that paper reported that "the Eagle Gold Mining Company near Jacksonville has one of the most promising locations on the Mother Lode." We further learn from the article that a Mr. Peter Musser is superintendent and most, if not all, of the stock is owned by residents of Philadelphia.

*The actual discovery of gold in the area occurred in 1848 at Woods Crossing on Woods Creek. Gold in quartz was found at an early date with some operation around 1860. The Eagle and Shawmut claims were first worked as separate mines. The two properties were combined sometime around 1895 and from then on the Eagle-Shawmut became one of the big operations of Tuolumne County.

Apparently this was not the first company to operate the Eagle because the writer states that ". . . a tunnel 125 feet long was run by the former owners of the mine." He also goes on to say that at the end of the tunnel a chamber had been excavated of sufficient size to accommodate a "whim" and Mr. Musser had sunk a winze on the vein to a depth of ninety feet. A whim is a horse-operated windlass and by so situating this original "hoist" Mr. Musser must have set a trend approved by all of the mining engineers who followed him because an underground hoisting works was to be a feature of the Eagle-Shawmut all through its productive years.

Musser's first quartz was struck at a depth of thirty feet and at the bottom of the winze the vein was three feet wide which he estimated would pay $50 per ton. For milling, the company had erected a good ten-stamp mill which was water driven, using an overshot wheel forty feet in diameter.

Little else is known of operation, owners or results at the Eagle mine until 1884 when the December 20th issue of the Tuolumne *Independent* tersely reported: "We learn that the old Eagle mine at Jacksonville on the Mother Lode, which was sold for $300,000, is now bonded to Charlie Tozier."

We'll never know how Charlie Tozier made out, for nine years later, in 1893, we find the mine in the hands of John Rosenfeld & Sons of San Francisco. The little ten-stamp mill had been kept fully employed through those years, working on rock which paid handsomely. The general average of

The original Eagle mine on Blue Gulch is shown here reproduced from a painting, artist unknown. Further information and exact date are also unavailable although it was probably in the 1860s. The water wheel in all likelihood drove a primitive 10-stamp mill or an arrastra, both of which were known to have operated on the property during its early years.

The over-all view below shows the Eagle-Shawmut as it looked in 1895. The large building housed the mill which consisted of 20 stamps at that time. A later photo shows the building enlarged and mining reports written around 1900 refer to a 40-stamp mill then being operated on the property. Boarding houses can be seen in the upper center. The cottages at the top of the photo were for workers with families. Cottage at the extreme right is the only building in this picture still standing, and is the home of James H. Nickley, Sr., the last remaining employee of the Eagle-Shawmut mine. *(above, Bancroft Library; below, James H. Nickley, Sr. collection)*

the rock on the dump yielded above $25 per ton. In fact it was thought by many experienced miners to be one of the best mines on the Mother Lode. Three years later, according to the October 10, 1896, issue of the Sonora *Union Democrat*, 75 men were employed on the Eagle and the Shawmut claims and new shafts were being sunk. The one on the Shawmut end of the property was down 125 feet while the new one at the Eagle had just been started.

By 1900 the property was referred to as the Eagle-Shawmut and many extensive changes had been made. It was now beginning to take on the appearance of a major mining operation. In fact it showed such promise that the *Mining and Scientific Press*, one of the leading journals of the day, devoted considerable space in its January 27, 1900, issue to describe the operations of Eagle-Shawmut thusly:

> The plant is extensive and excellent and is housed in ample buildings. The power employed is water under 480-foot fall, transmitted by wire from a seven-foot Pelton wheel, but there is a large steam plant in reserve. The mill contains forty stamps and 16 six-foot Frue concentrators. Below there is a Gates sulphuret saver with forty tables. The ore is drawn by mules through a 3000-foot tunnel in the face of which a hoisting station is located. The tunnel strikes the ledge 500 feet from the surface and a shaft extends into the mine from this point. Each car of ore is weighed and sampled before being dumped into the mill. Two electric dynamos supply power for the machine shop as well as lights for the entire mill, works and village. The machine shop is extra large and well equipped. There is a large two-story change building at the entrance to the tunnel containing private rooms for the foremen. Nearly 200 men are employed. E. Dorward is superintendent, C. Jackson, foreman.

The early years of the new century were busy and productive at the Eagle-Shawmut. The records for 1901 show 250 men on the payroll, heavy equipment such as a new hoist being installed, and a 100-stamp mill was under construction. An incline tramway was also being built that would take ore from the No. 2 shaft at the top of the hill to the mill. By the following year 260 men were employed and the new mill was crushing five tons per stamp per day. A chlorination plant was built on the west bank of Woods Creek, directly across from the mill and the two were connected by an aerial tramway.

For a number of years the Eagle-Shawmut ran like clockwork night and day and became known as one of the big mines of the Mother Lode. There is no doubt that it was the largest in Tuolumne County, and the deepest. Its payroll was the longest, its 100-stamp mill the largest, and it required the most power to operate. Its extraction of ore was the heaviest, up to 150,000 tons annually. It also took shrewd management and the expenditure of a large amount of capital, for Eagle-Shawmut ore was of very low grade, rich rock being unknown. What it lacked in quality it made up in quantity, but still required high operating efficiency at all levels to make it pay. Although costs obviously did not remain constant, it is interesting to note that in 1905 the total expense for extracting and reducing the ore was $1.46 a ton.

In 1907 a strike made below the 1800-foot level was said to surpass all previous discoveries on the property and possibly with the anticipation of increased activity the owners purchased a 200 hp Ingersoll-Sergeant air compressor and a triplex electric pump was installed on the 600-foot level. By 1909 another find of high-grade ore, this time on the 2200-foot level, was of such unusual richness that the management decided to continue sinking the shaft still deeper. This shaft was eventually connected with the old shaft 400 feet below the surface.

In 1913 the Eagle-Shawmut Company purchased the machinery of the Tarantula mine, which adjoined their property. Unlike the Eagle-Shawmut which has only changed hands twice since 1883, and was privately owned each time, the Tarantula mine, at various times, was a stock company. Neither its ground nor its prospects were ever very good, a sordid fact that required bringing in fresh money from time to time. To take care of such emergencies a supply of real showy ore, a rarity at the Tarantula, was kept always on hand; then when the promoters would see an expected party of prospective stockholders coming down the Shawmut Grade to visit the mine, the word would be sent up to the diggings to "put in the good stuff" so as not to disappoint the city folks.

Some years later the Tarantula mine was purchased from the United Mining and Milling Company of Paris by Henry T. Gage, a former governor of California. Mr. Gage also owned the Jones

Miners pose at entrance to the No. 2 Adit of the Shawmut mine in 1890. In 1914 this tunnel was enlarged considerably to accommodate electric locomotives and larger cars.

The chlorination works built around 1902 was located on the west bank of Woods Creek directly across from the mill. Concentrates were transported from the mill to the plant by means of an aerial tramway. One of the buckets can be seen suspended from the cable at the right of the picture just above the creek. The cable in the center supports a pipeline. The horizontal line running across the picture between the creek and the plant was the grade of the old Yosemite Short Line Railroad which proposed to run a 30″ gauge railroad from Jamestown to the Yosemite Valley, but never got much past Jacksonville. In 1908 the Y.S.L. built a siding at the Eagle-Shawmut, however soon after that the railroad was abandoned. This photo was apparently taken sometime after the rails were pulled up. *(above, Tuolumne County Museum collection; below, Donald Segerstrom collection)*

mine adjoining the Tarantula and planned to work the two in conjunction. For a time S. C. Thompson and associates of New York were interested in the two properties along with Mr. Gage, but true to their history these mines never became profitable producers.

This was not the case at the Eagle-Shawmut for in 1913 more rich ore was discovered and the following year a new electric generating plant was completed at a cost of around $200,000. By 1915 work had progressed to 2450 feet below the surface with three veins opened. That year the ore was running above average and 52,382 tons of ore yielded 5985 tons of concentrate, running on the average, $39 a ton. Eighty-five per cent of all the gold recovered came from the concentrate. Silver was present but amounted to only pennies per ton.

In 1917 the Rosenfelds leased the property to the Tonopah-Belmont Development Company of Nevada and for a time the mine was called the Belmont-Shawmut with G. F. Williamson in charge.

The Belmont Company, old hands at the mining game, pitched right in and continued to improve the property, investing additional capital as required. These developments are perhaps best told in the Tonopah-Belmont Mining Company's annual report for 1917:

> During the past year the main three-compartment shaft was sunk and heavily timbered from the 16th level to a further depth of 409 feet, from 1834 to 2243 feet, measured from the adit level; and the new 17th and 18th levels were turned off the shaft at 150 and 350 feet respectively below the 16th level. Stations and ore pockets were cut on No. 16, 17 and 18 levels and the two latter were driven. At the adit level a large room was excavated and timbered and a large electric hoist installed. An underground headframe was built in a suitable excavation and new skips, cables and an electric bell signal system were installed in the shaft. An adequate electrically driven pump was put in on No. 16 level and a smaller pump on No. 18, these being connected to pumps on the levels above by proper water columns. Power transmission cables connecting up the hoist and pumps were installed. A large amount of work was done on general repairs underground. Old stopes were put in shape for production; levels that had been crushed were opened and timbered, ventilation connections made, etc. Development has not been and cannot be of a character to definitely block out reserve ore. The drift levels cannot be driven on the ore because of heavy and caving vein material. They must be carried in or partly in the front hanging wall. The full extent of the ore can only be determined by crosscuts. A great deal of laboratory work on the ore was done and a process of combined gravity and oil flotation process was developed. For comparison an actual mill test was made using the old system before deciding and from the results obtained gravity concentration followed by oil flotation was decided upon and the remodeling of the old 100-stamp plate and vanner mill was undertaken. Seventy of the original 100 stamps were used. The daily capacity is expected to be 400 tons. Gold production is expected to begin in May 1918.

The Tonopah-Belmont Mining Company operated the mine for seven years and although they began with great expectations increased costs after World War I seriously cut into the mine's earnings, for then, as now, the price of gold was fixed by the government and unlike other businesses it was not just a simple matter of marking up the selling price of the product whenever production costs took a jump. An example of the financial pressures is contained in these figures compiled by the mine management for the last half of 1918 and reported to the State Division of Mines: Wages for miners increased 26%, mill men and mechanics 38% from 1917, efficiency of labor at the same time decreased 65% of normal effort, and the labor turnover reached 280% in one month. The cost of mining supplies averaged 27.7%, the cost of water jumped from 12½ to 37½ cents per miner's inch daily, electric power cost increased 36% and freight rates and smelter charges were raised to such an extent that concentrate, which contained most of the gold produced, could not be profitably shipped.

What was happening was, of course, not a new story in mining ventures. All too often the increased costs of labor and materials runs headlong into the selling price of the product or the ability of the property to produce, with the result that the mine becomes economically unsound to operate.

The Belmont Company discontinued operations in 1923 when they turned the mine back to the owners, who operated it until the early part of 1926 when the mine went idle. At that time the total recorded production from 1897 to 1926 inclusive came to $5,380,000. In 1929 the mill was cleaned up and most of the machinery sold.

Piecing together the story of a mine and the men behind it from old reports and publications is

Here is an 1895 photo of the mill at the Mammoth mine which was situated between the Eagle-Shawmut and Jacksonville. This mill reduced ore from the Mammoth as well as the Republican and Orcutt mines nearby. Although neighbors of the Eagle-Shawmut, none of these mines were great producers. Below is a view of the Eagle-Shawmut mining district. Eagle-Shawmut mill is the white building in the center of the photo. Smoke to the right is the chlorination works. White building to the far left is the Trantula mill. Note schoolhouse in the lower center. *(above, James H. Nickley, Sr. collection; below, Donald Segerstrom collection)*

not only difficult but is apt to make pretty dull reading. For this chapter on the Eagle-Shawmut I was most fortunate in obtaining the firsthand observations of a former employee and a resident at Eagle-Shawmut for many years. He is James H. Nickley, Sr., who at the time of my visit in May 1967 was living on the property as caretaker. Mr. Nickley tells us in his own words what life was like during the peak of operations.

I came to Shawmut in May 1914 from Sutter Creek, Amador County, with my father who came here to be underground foreman. Also . . . Jack Noce, mining engineer, Emmet Noce, miner, Al Prothers from Angels Camp, mining engineer, and several other recruits from the Calavaras and Amador mines: Alvin Cook, Frank, Dick and Lou Scott. I believe Lou Scott had lost one leg and went on to be tunnel superintendent for the P. G. & E. and built up a big record as a tunnel construction superintendent.

The reason for hiring the men mentioned was the transition of ore handling from the top of the mountain and gravity tramming to the mill in the valley to the installation of an underground hoist and crushing plant on the 500-foot adit level and the opening up of small five by seven-feet adit to the underground hoist to eight by ten feet and putting in a ten-ton electric haulage locomotive and five-ton side dump ore cars.

At this time or the previous fall there was a change-over from water power to electricity for the mine hoist, mill and crushing and haulage of ore. The compressor remained on water power for several years. Water power was supplied by pipeline to a reservoir. The line, a 20-inch riveted pipe beginning at the mill, ran up the mountain to the surface hoist and then northeast to the reservoir, 8500 feet from the mill. This was a graduated pipeline, 36 inches at the reservoir outlet and stepping down to 30 inches from there to 24 inches, and finally to twenty inches at the outlet or service end. Pipe was buried in a trench where possible or rock walled and earth covered. The original ten-stamp mill, was situated near the Dore Shaft, which was the main entrance to the mine. This shaft was sunk on the vein of quartz ore which was free gold milling ore from the surface of the 500 level or waterline of the mine. I have no definite information as to the time this was abandoned and the 20-stamp mill was built on Woods Creek at the present adit level.

From the copies of correspondence from the mine superintendents to the owners dated previous to 1890 and 1900 there was much reference to the fact that production was stopped for the time due to the shortage of water for power during the dry season. All records of this nature along with most of the maps and assay records were destroyed by fire in 1935.

The only owners that I knew (other than the present owners) were the Rosenfeld Brothers of San Francisco; Louis Rosenfeld being the only one I can remember. George F. Williamson was the superintendent, George Porter, chlorination superintendent, James Daley, master mechanic, A. E. Vasper, bookkeeper and office manager. A Mr. Brown (initial unknown) was mill superintendent.

Charles E. Uren was the engineer for the mine and also deputy U. S. Surveyor. As there were about 250 employees on the payroll there were a number of married men with families. There were 32 houses, a schoolhouse, U. S. Post Office and a recreation room and barber shop-store combined. All pay checks were in the form of a voucher payable at Saul Morris' grocery store at Chinese Camp. The charge of $1.00 per day for board and rooms and $1.00 per month for doctor's fees was deducted by the Company. At this time the roads were bad and there were few autos, so on paydays there was a marching horde on the foot trails between the mine and Chinese Camp. As no alcoholic beverage was allowed to be sold on Company property, the big drunks were in Chinese Camp. There was a large turnover in underground labor and the best miners were termed ten-day men, that was due to the fact that they could go from mine to mine in the area and to work at any time. Miners were paid $3.50 per day, ten hours, so at the end of a ten-day period they would have some $24.00 cash and would take a few days with the bars, gamblers and girls, and then show up at some mine and go to work again. Muckers and other laborers earned $2.50 for a ten-hour shift.

The mine being predominantly a sulfide ore operation, the concentrates were smelted and chlorinated at the chlorination plant across the creek from the mill, concentrates being transferred by aerial cable tram between mill and roasting plant. The road from Chinese Camp to the Shawmut mine was a private road built by the Company to transport timbers, supplies and crude oil for the smelter. It was engineered for 20-horse teams of which the Company operated two teams and was two feet of dust in the summer and a sea of mud in the winter. This road, the well-known Shawmut Grade, was deeded to the County of Tuolumne in 1917 and deeded by the County to the State in July 1926.

Bill Poole was the teamster foreman and Leu Eggling was the horseshoer and veterinarian. The stables were on the flat near Woods Creek below the Company office. Directly below the stables was the Mexican settlement of five houses.

Directly above the adit level portal on the hogback ridge (about 250 feet above) there are a series of dry masonry foundations and level fills. This was the site of a small arrastra operated by the Spanish or Mexican miners in the early days of lode mining. The area north of the outcrop of the lode, the glory hole, was high-grade quartz in flat floor seams in the slate and was very rich in content. These quartz floors were from one-half to four

This photo of the Eagle-Shawmut mill was taken by Lester Uren, son of the mine superintendent, in 1901. The grading for the foundations was done hydraulically with 400 pounds of nozzle pressure. When completed the machinery was also run by water power with water purchased from the old Sierra and San Francisco Power Company.

At the Eagle-Shawmut mill, the revolving cams alternately lifted and dropped the stamps which were located on the level below. When operating, the 100 stamps each weighing a thousand pounds created a deafening roar. Note the bull wheels which were built of wood by millwrights on the job. *(both, Tuolumne County Museum collection)*

inches in thickness and contained very coarse gold. There is not much to substantiate the existence of this arrastra except one of the muller stones with the eyebolt at the site and the presence of quartz tailings on the hillside below the site and in the gulch coming down below. Judging by the size of the muller stone this was not a very big arrastra; probably used to process the high-grade quartz from the floor seams in the surface workings on top of the hill above the site.

Many references have been made about the existence of a large arrastra in Blue Gulch Creek at a site east of the Shawmut outcrop, but I failed to come up with any definite evidence of this. The arrastra was probably operated by Spaniards about 1860. Mining was carried on very extensively on the surface and by tunneling on the vein on the top of the hill north and west of the Dore Shaft. This surface enrichment opened up about 250 to 300 feet in width and extended to the property on the west, extending across the adjoining Tarantula property which was also surface mined in the early days of quartz mining.

With a keen memory assisted only by notes, carefully kept, on detailed matters, James Nickley has contributed a valuable eye-witness account of the Eagle-Shawmut mine which has been both his home and livelihood for thirty-eight years. (1913-1915 — 1932-1967).

In 1936, the present owners, H. G. Miller and George W. Clemson, bought the mine and operated it from 1938 until October 1947 with Daniel C. Peacock as manager. After an early period of experimental work in both mining and metallurgy the mine produced 730,000 tons of ore which grossed over $2,000,000 and returned a profit to the owners. During this last period of operation most of the ore was taken from the upper workings of the mine, that is, up inside the hill and above what is now the main haulage tunnel, Adit No. 2. In fact, much of the ore came from just below the old shallow workings and glory holes at the top of the mountain. Because much of the ground in the Eagle-Shawmut is broken shale and caves easily, concrete mucking chambers were used and the ore was scooped up from these by mucking machines and loaded into cars.

The largest production year was 1942. After 1942 less than half of the mill capacity was used for gold as copper and zinc from the Penn mine in Calaveras County, also owned by Miller and Clemson, was treated at Shawmut. The Eagle-Shawmut concentrates, at that time, carried two to three ounces of gold per ton and were hauled by truck to the smelter at Selby, California.[*] The fact that this type of concentrate was needed there at the time made the Eagle-Shawmut one of the few gold mines allowed to operate during the war. Even so, operation was restricted and wartime conditions and shortages prevented the necessary development of the mine. After the war increased costs made it unprofitable to continue so all work was stopped November 1, 1947,[**] and the equipment dismantled and sold.

Twenty years later co-owner George Clemson, living near San Diego with his mining days behind him, summarized the Eagle-Shawmut operation for the author with this concise and informative statement:

> Our operation was based on block caving the black slate vein fill between the two quartz veins that were mined to a great depth.
>
> We discovered a way, by selective flotation, to recover the sulphides in the graphitic slate in a concentrate that could be smelted at Selby. Based on this we re-opened the adit tunnel and gradually built production to 500 tons of ore a day, mined on two shifts and milled 24 hours a day.
>
> As we mined [we] did a lot of core drilling both above and below the adit and proved up a great quantity of ore which still remains in the mine.

At the time of the closure manager Daniel C. Peacock also stated that the mine was far from worked out and that considerably more ore remained in the mine, some of a higher grade than any worked since 1938, but because of paradoxical economic conditions the treasure of the Eagle-Shawmut lies deep inside the mountain, effectively sealed by a final charge of dynamite that purposely caved the main tunnel when the mine was shut down.

Now a further fate awaits the Eagle-Shawmut as construction of the new $98.5 million Don Pedro dam on the Tuolumne River, a joint project of the City and County of San Francisco and the Turlock and Modesto Irrigation Districts, will eventually flood the entire canyon completely obliterating the little remaining evidence of a bygone era during which men toiled underground for a yellow metal called gold.

---

[*]American Smelting and Refining Co. at Carquinez Strait, upper San Francisco Bay.

[**]The very last activity at the Eagle-Shawmut was in June 1948 when old chlorination tailings were trucked to the Sierra Railroad at Chinese Camp for shipment to the Selby smelter for use as flux.

Many mechanical aids came to gold mining during its later years such as this Eimco mucking machine shown at work in the Eagle-Shawmut prior to its closing in 1942. In operation the machine runs on rails and works ahead of the ore cars. Operator directs the machine at the tunnel face or in the mucking chamber as the case may be. When the scoop is filled the arms raise it completely over the machine and dump its contents in the waiting ore car. In the center photo the camera has reversed its position and is looking inward over the almost full ore car showing that the scoop has gone back in for another load. *(James H. Nickley, Jr., collection)*

Left, one of the electric haulage locomotives used at the Eagle-Shawmut mine. It was used until the mine closed down. In 1947 it was sold to the Vanadium Corp., Bishop, California.

64

This close-on view of the Eagle-Shawmut mill in 1901 shows the ore receiving bins, tramway with ore car and water tanks at lower right. The mill had apparently just been completed as scaffolding is still in place. (*Tuolumne County Museum collection*)

Seen from the Shawmut grade across the canyon (lower) the foundations of the Eagle-Shawmut mill appeared in 1969 like the ruins of some ancient civilization.

This miners' rooming house at Carson Hill was built in the 1890s to replace an earlier one built in the sixties. The famed glory hole of the Morgan mine can be seen in the background. It was in this mine that the world's second largest nugget was found. It weighed 195 pounds and at $35 an ounce would bring $74,000.

a source of trouble as in diggings as rich as this it was the feeling among the California miners that 25 feet per man was an equitable distribution and Col. Morgan and his group had no right to control property that under their code could take care of a hundred and sixty miners. There was much grumbling and feeling ran high, an ideal situation for a strong personality to capitalize on and as usually happens in matters of this kind there was one ready to seize the opportunity. He was Billy Mulligan, a former member of the "Hounds," a disreputable gang of hoodlums down in San Francisco, about which history has nothing good to say. Taking to the hills to avoid the Vigilantes, Mulligan had gone to Columbia to make an easy dollar by gambling, promoting prize fights and any other enterprise that did not involve hard labor. When he heard of the rich Morgan mine and the situation at Carson Hill, Billy Mulligan saw a tailor-made opportunity for personal gain. He lost no time in rounding up a small army of roughneck friends and they marched on Carson Hill. There was no attempt made to find facts or argue the case, nor is it recorded that Mulligan was playing the part of the fearless defender and acting on behalf of the grieved miners. Billy simply wanted the mine and was going to have it. What's more he took it and he and his gang operated it as their very own for two years or more. Finally after many pitched battles, both in and out of the courts, Billy Mulligan and his gang were expelled in 1853 by court order.*

Although their property was restored to them, Morgan and his partners had become thoroughly sick of the long struggle which had completely occupied their time when they might have been operating the mine. Morgan left for England to try to sell the property and during his absence production dropped to almost nothing.

As it turned out Col. Morgan's buyer was not in England and the mine was acquired by James G. Fair who at that time was engaged in small mining operations and other business enterprises at Shaw's Flat and Whimtown. Fair's ownership of the Morgan gave him sufficient capital to go on to other ventures, and eventually he became one

of the Comstock silver kings and a social lion in San Francisco.

It was during his stay at Carson Hill that James Fair* met and married Tessie Rooney, whose mother ran a miners' boardinghouse.

However, even a shrewd businessman like Fair sometimes has his problems. Fair almost met his match in William Irvine whom he hired to mill the ore. Through some technicality Irvine tried to claim an interest in the mine and while the two men fought in the courts for ownership the mine remained closed. Fair apparently won the case as title remained with him and his heirs until 1918.

William Irvine came into the news in a similar way some time later when he became the principal figure in a western style "land war" that shattered the quiet of the town of Carson Hill. It all began when Irvine produced a registered homestead certificate for 143 acres comprising the Carson Hill townsite on which the other residents apparently had not filed properly. Irving lost no time in evicting many of the original families including the Tarbots, Cordes, Rooneys (James Fair's in-laws) and the Allisons, many of whom had lived at Carson Hill for more than twenty years in homes they had built.

John Tarbot, owner of the Finnegan mine and one of those affected, volunteered to represent the entire community at a hearing in San Francisco, but died of a heart attack the night before he was to have left for the City. In a fine example of small town cooperation the community helped build a house for Mrs. Tarbot and her eight children at the base of her husband's Finnegan mine. The house still stands near the Carson Hill roadside rest area.

William Irvine still maintained his hold on the town and even changed the name to "Irvine Hill," an action that caused shots to be fired at his house on several occasions. Little damage resulted for the shots were probably designed to frighten the Irvines away. They did leave, but not until 1902 when they moved to San Francisco, leaving the property to a son, Louis. In 1909 the matter was finally resolved by the Morgan Mining Company for $500 in gold coins and feuding and fighting

---

*Years afterward Billy Mulligan fatally shot two men while in a drunken state and was himself killed by officers of the law.

*James Fair was 26 years old when he came to Carson Hill.

Irvine Hill once again became pleasant and peaceful Carson Hill.

In the late 1850s G. K. Stevenot, grandfather of Fred G. Stevenot and Archie D. Stevenot, came into possession of the Morgan mine. It was Stevenot who began the glory hole and brought Carson Hill quartz mining out of the arrastra stage when he erected the first stamp mill near Carson Creek. It was a crude three-stamp machine which was shipped all the way from England; however, it performed satisfactorily until it was destroyed by a flood in 1862. Not long after that the Melones and Stanislaus Mining Company was organized with Stevenot as manager. This company worked Melones and Stanislaus claims to a depth of 250 feet and a length of 400 feet, dry-grinding the ore in a wooden tub-like affair and shipping the concentrates all the way to New York. Production was later improved by the erection of an eight-stamp mill.

In the 1860s and early 1870s the mines were closed most of the time as the result of litigation and milling problems, and were not to be opened until 1876 when both the Morgan and Melones mines were operated intermittently through the 1880s by the Melones Mining Company.

In 1889 an English firm doing business as the Calaveras Consolidated Gold Mining Company, Ltd. and locally referred to as the "Old English Company," bought the claims owned by the Stevenot family and began the first large-scale operation involving low-grade ore ever tried in the area. They erected a 20-stamp mill and worked ore worth only $3 to $5 a ton. By 1898 this company had reached a total depth of 500 feet below the outcrop. Nothing more was heard of this operation and little more of the area until 1917 when Carson Hill Gold Mines, Inc. was organized by W. J. Loring with A. D. "Archie" Stevenot as mine superintendent.

Meanwhile on the south side of Carson Hill a company that had begun prospecting the Stanislaus claim in 1895 was working the Melones mine. Known as the Melones Consolidated Mining Company, headed by W. G. Devereaux of New York and with W. C. Ralston, son of the San Francisco banker, as superintendent, the firm listed Messrs. Grayson and Boland as chief stockholders. By 1898 they had driven the tunnel a distance of 5166 feet

on the middle vein and 1407 feet on the east vein with a small shaft sunk in the east vein to a depth of 200 feet. In addition to the Melones and Stanislaus claims this company also added the Enterprise, Keystone, Last Chance, Mineral Mountain, Reserve and later the adjoining South Carolina mine was taken under option. A tunnel had previously been run 1080 feet on the South Carolina and the Melones Consolidated continued this to a length of 3030 feet which brought them to within forty feet of the Morgan line.

Prospects looked good and in 1899 a mill was started and work was begun on the 1100-foot tunnel. By October 1901 this tunnel was 4200 feet long having crossed the vein 4000 feet from the portal. At the place where the adit crossed the vein an internal shaft 5 by 17 feet was sunk at an inclination of seventy degrees to the 1050-foot level and from there to the bottom (3000 feet by that company) the shaft continued on a fifty-degree inclination.

Along with all of the underground work and mill construction an extensive project was under way to supply water to operate the mill. This was to be delivered via a flume three and three-quarters miles long, having a capacity of 5000 miner's inches. As the mill was designed to operate under low head, meaning with a large volume of water at low pressure, the flume was a large one. One early photograph shows the Melones flume under construction with a horse and wagon operating comfortably inside.

By 1902 the mill was completed, water had arrived by flume and the first sixty stamps began crushing ore. One hundred stamps were operating in 1905 and 120 in 1914. The mill reached its maximum output in 1918 with 245,000 tons milled. Each stamp weighed 1050 pounds and dropped a distance of seven inches at the rate of 102 times a minute. The total average recovery of the mill was from 83% to 85% with 92% saved from the concentrate, the latter yielding from $25 to $44 a ton in gold. Silver was present in very small quantities.

The Melones mine was always known as a low-grade producer, with ore carrying only $2 to $3 a ton in gold, so it was imperative that all mining methods be as efficient as possible. As the result of careful planning and good engineering the Melones mine was worked at probably the lowest cost per ton of any other large lode mine in California. During the period between 1908 and 1910 operating costs were $1.08 a ton. By 1914 costs had risen to $1.60 a ton. During and after World War I they continued to mount until the Company reported it was costing about $20.00 an ounce to produce gold. The price of gold at the time was $20.67 an ounce. The Melones Consolidated Mining Company closed the mine in 1918, although the mill, which ran on water power until the end, operated until 1919 on ore previously mined. During its lifetime the Melones Consolidated Mining Company produced about $4,500,000 in gold although there is no public record of any dividends paid. In fact, the stockholders lost their equity entirely when the bondholders, who hadn't been paid either, ordered the property sold to satisfy their first claim of $499,200.

Ironically the Melones Consolidated never discovered the upper part of the famous hanging wall ore body. When this rich shoot was finally discovered in the neighboring Morgan mine in 1919, just after the Melones Company gave up, it was found that it was separated from the old Melones workings by just six feet!

It was this ore body that was now to enhance the fortunes of Carson Hill Gold Mines, Inc., which had been operating the Morgan mine since 1917. In 1919 ore from this discovery averaged $14.95 a ton from the first 60,000 tons crushed. With this sort of showing development was rapid. The Melones mine, which had been inactive since its former owners closed down, was taken over and along with other properties was consolidated into the operation. In the next few years this new ore body was mined to a depth of 4550 feet and yielded over $5,000,000. A new thirty-stamp mill was built west of the highway at Melones which handled 9000 to 15,000 tons a month and operated until 1926 when the operation was discontinued. Production under this company during its seven years of operation was $7,000,000.

In 1933 the Carson Hill Gold Mining Corporation was organized by A. O. Stewart with Charles H. Segerstrom, an influential financier of Sonora and San Francisco, as president and manager and John A. Burgess, mine superintendent.° This company also included the Morgan and Melones operations which by this time covered the whole of

The flume which carried water from the Stanislaus River to the Melones mill was large enough to comfortably accommodate a horse and wagon as shown in this 1902 construction photo. *(Morgan North)*

Carson Hill. Work was started in April 1933 in the heart of the depression; however, as times were hard, costs and wages were proportionately low. Much of the equipment necessary was already on the property and it was found that even after a seven-year shutdown repairs to mine workings and equipment could be made for $100,000.

Work was naturally begun where mining could be done for the lowest cost. This meant glory hole and surface mining by power shovels with a limited amount of work underground. The old 1100-foot level Melones tunnel was repaired and connected with the surface by the Morgan shaft sunk from the bottom of the Morgan glory hole. Ore from the surface workings could then be dropped

°Officers and department heads as of 1935:
Pres. and Mgr., Charles H. Segerstrom, Sonora and S. F.
Vice Pres. and Dir., Lawrence Monte Verda, Angels Camp
Sec., M. D. Jones, Sonora
Gen. Supt., John A. Burgess
Engineer, Max Peterson
Underground Supt., Frank Wagner
Mill Supt., Jerry Maroon
Cyanide Plant Supt., H. T. Libby
Mech. Eng., Al Wisebacker

Looking south along Highway 49 toward Carson Hill, the building on the left is the old bunkhouse. The glory holes of the Morgan mine and other early operations can be seen in the hill above. In the 1933-42 operation a shaft was sunk at the bottom of the Morgan cut and the ore was dropped down an ore pass to trains in the Melones tunnel below. They were then pulled by electric locomotives (lower) to the mill on the south side of Carson Hill.

through an ore pass down to the Melones tunnel and into ore trains. The trains were then hauled about a mile through the mountain by fifty-ton electric trolley locomotives to the mill just west of the bridge at Melones. Early in the operation the price of gold increased to $35.00 an ounce and underground mining progressed as far as the 3500-foot level. The mill was improved and in June 1934 was reported to be handling ore at the rate of 20,000 tons a month. During this period 160 men were employed.

Across Coyote Creek at Melones one sees a huge pile of mill tailings, over 3,000,000 tons. Most of this was from ore processed by the Carson Hill Gold Mining Company since tailings from the old Melones Company operation were simply discharged into the Stanislaus River.

The Carson Hill Gold Mining Company operated in this fashion until May 1942, when the stamp mill was destroyed by fire. If the Company entertained any hopes of rebuilding they were dashed to pieces five months later when the government issued its L-208 wartime order which declared gold mining a non-essential industry and required their closing. Like so many other California gold mines the Carson Hill mines never reopened. However, the Carson Hill Gold Mining Company fared better than many another mining enterprise for during their nine years of operation the mine produced 2,840,000 tons of ore from which a total of $6,500,000 was recovered. Out of this amount the company paid wages, taxes, power and other operating costs, paid for the purchase of the mine and declared eleven dividends.

OVERPAGE, top photo shows the buildings and installations at the portal of the Melones tunnel. Tunnel entrance is at the left. Some of the ore cars can be seen in center background. A few of these cars are still being used as ballast cars on the Roaring Camp & Big Trees Narrow-Gauge Railroad, a tourist attraction in the Santa Cruz Mountains. The curving track going down to the left corner of the photo leads to the mill across Highway 49 which is in the foreground.

Lower photo is a panoramic view of the Carson Hill Gold Mining Company's surface operations on the south side of the hill. The Stanislaus River runs along the bottom of the photo, with Highway 49 bridge at lower left and a portion of the river lower right. The building above the bridge is the mill. The dump and group of buildings in the center mark the portal of the Melones tunnel previously described. Trains ran from here to the mill. Building on the left was the cyanide plant. *(Donald Segerstrom collection)*

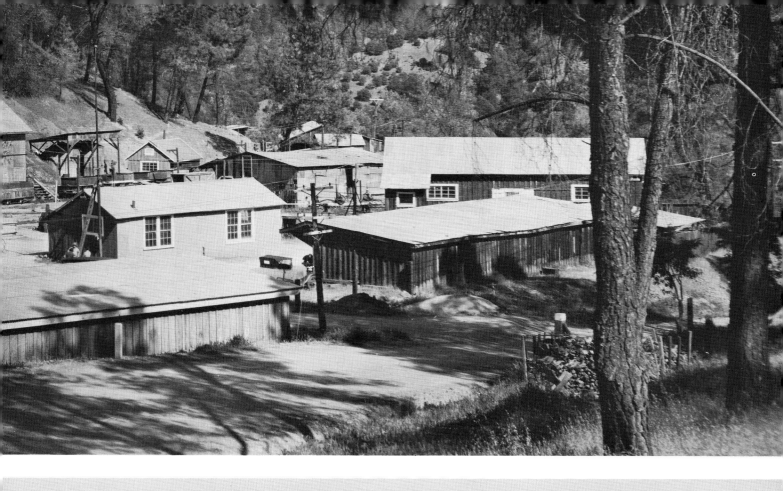

This exceptional photo of the Carson Hill Gold Mining Company's mill was taken in 1934, on the occasion of its grand opening. Guest cars are parked in the foreground. The rail line from the Melones tunnel can be clearly seen as it terminates at the crusher house. A covered conveyor leads from the base of the crusher to the top of the mill where the ore was conducted mainly by gravity through the various processes of reduction. This mill ran continuously until May 1942 when it was destroyed by fire. *(Donald Segerstrom collection)*

77

The Carson Hill Gold Mining Company's mill as the interior looked in 1934, showing the battery of 30 stamps, belt driven from below. At the upper right is one of the ball mills which further pulverized the rock after it left the stamp mill. The base of the stamp mill is on the level above. On the castings is the lettering "Angels Iron Works, Angels Camp, Cal.", one of the Mother Lode foundries that specialized in mining machinery. Below at right are the concentrating tables over which the highly fluid pulp flowed and dropped its particles of gold. *(Donald Segerstrom collection)*

The Mother Lode settlement of Angels Camp contained a number of gold mines all concentrated virtually in the center of town. Today there is little left to show for all of this activity. Even the largest, the Utica and the Gold Cliff, are totally unrepresented by the usual relics of headframes, buildings, machinery, etc. The subject of this painting is the compressor at the Lightner shaft, which together with the remains of the hoisting machinery unused since 1920, lies rusting just below Highway 49 and just north of its nearest neighbor the Utica which is now a city park.

CHAPTER 5

THE UTICA MINING COMPANY

Angels Camp, Calaveras County

THE UTICA 1849 to 1916   THE GOLD CLIFF 1850 to 1920

Combined
total production $19,834,000

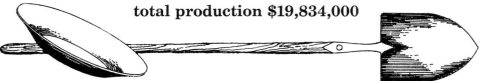

In the celebrated Mother Lode town founded in 1848 by Henry Angel and made famous by the tall stories of Mark Twain and the rough, romantic yarns of Bret Harte, there existed a group of mines crowded together; virtually all within the city limits of even so small a town as Angels Camp. Situated just 3.8 miles north of the fabulous Carson Hill this group had such names as The Mother Lode Central, Angels Deep, North Star,[1] Sultana, Lightner, Gold Cliff and the Utica. By far the largest of these operations and the last to survive were the Gold Cliff and the Utica, both owned by the Utica Mining Company. As is usually the case the Utica mine was a consolidation including the Utica, Stickles, Raspberry and six other claims. The Gold Cliff was also a combination of about half a dozen early-day mines.

Although the Utica had yet to prove itself when James G. Fair came up from Carson Hill, he decided to invest some of his Morgan mine profits in it. However, he didn't hold it long as he was soon able to talk someone into buying it from him for $37,000. Fair would eventually discover that he sold out too soon, but the Fair luck wasn't all bad for even as he had gained a wife at Carson Hill it was at Angels Camp that fate was to introduce him to John W. Mackay with whom he was later associated in the great Comstock bonanza which made them both millionaires many times over.

The exact discovery date of the Utica mine is somewhat vague although it is reported that the surface workings of the Utica claim were worked during the early part of the gold rush, when the ore was milled in arrastras; so we will set it as circa 1849. The Stickles claim was worked during the 1860s and there is evidence that it had been developed to a depth of 240 feet by 1871 when there was a ten-stamp mill on the property.

During the early life of the Utica it had passed from hand to hand until it came into the possession of Charles D. Lane.[2] Lane had his share of discouragement and would also have disposed of the mine had it not been for a fortuneteller who advised him to hold onto the property.

There were still to be some years of doubt as the shaft seemed to be headed for China without any appreciable returns. It was probably in an attempt to share the responsibility that sometime during the 1880s Lane brought in Walter Scott Hobart[3] and Alvinza Hayward[4] as partners. These two men controlled numerous mines in the area and together they organized the Utica Mining Company. Under this new impetus the company

---

[1]This should not be confused with the large North Star mine at Grass Valley which will be covered in Chapter 11.

[2]Mr. Lane later went to Alaska where he invested and lost heavily in mining and railroad ventures.

[3]Pioneer lumberman and mine owner who acquired wide interests in California, Hobart Mills, Nevada County, Hobart Building, San Francisco, etc.

[4]Well-known mine investor. See Central Eureka and Plymouth. Mr. Hayward is not to be confused with hotel owner William Hayward for whom Hayward, California, was named.

In 1899 the Cross Shaft, the newest of four, was being pushed to the depths of the Stickle mine, one of the properties of the Utica group. It remained until the end the main working shaft. *(Earle R. Edmiston collection)*

began to acquire and develop adjacent claims, including the Gold Cliff in 1884, and operation was conducted on a major scale.

The new company lost no time in upgrading the mine which included the sinking of a new shaft and other works. It must have been a busy time for Angels Camp according to this report from the *Mountain Echo* for September 26, 1888: "Preparations are making for the erection of the new hoisting works on the south shaft of the Utica mine. The derrick to be used for raising the large timbers into place was put into position during the week. The works to be erected on the shaft will be of the same dimensions as those on the north shaft. Messrs. Rider and Lee are now at work framing timbers for the new forty-stamp mill to be built in addition to the twenty now in use. A scene of general activity prevails at the Utica night and day."

At this state of the mine's development the mill was run by water power and the hoisting works run by steam. The mine was not very wet, making about 15,000 gallons of water a day. No pumps were used, the management bailed it with water barrels, each holding about 150 gallons, and raised them by hoist. During the 1890s the Utica was known as one of the most productive mines in the nation and had more than 500 men on its payroll.

Things were not all smooth sailing for the Utica, for in July of 1895 a fire occurred between the 800 and 900-foot levels of the Stickles mine. A strong draft through the open workings caused the fire to spread rapidly and as it soon became evident that no ordinary means would extinguish the flames, the shafts were all tightly bulkheaded and the entire available water supply, amounting to nearly 20,000,000 gallons in 24 hours, was turned into the mine. For ninety hours this cataract fell into the workings, which caused some caving, but extinguished the fire.

Then the tedious work of unwatering the great stopes began. Night and day for eight weeks pumps and bailing skips, both regular and extra, were kept constantly employed. When the water was finally emptied it was discovered that the damage by fire had been confined to the small stope in which it had started and the water damage was not nearly as bad as it had been feared; so with only a brief setback the Utica was once

again a producing gold mine. The following year, however, when a field representative of the California Division of Mines visited the property the superintendent refused all information. This was not unusual for in those days gold mining was a close-mouthed business.

As mentioned before, early hoisting at the Utica was powered by steam and later on we will see how electricity came to the area. In between there was a period when water power hoists were used. This fact is brought out by J. H. Collier, Jr. in an 1899 article titled *Deep Mining at the Utica,*[*] which further describes the machinery and operations of the day as follows:

> Each shaft is supplied with a double acting water-power hoist. Two Dodd water-wheels, nine feet in diameter, are placed on the pinion shaft in reversed position, so that the power may be applied to run the hoist in either direction. The water is applied through three nozzles, so that the power can be readily proportioned to the load. The nozzles are served by a ten-inch wrought iron pipe, which delivers the water under a head of 420 feet, giving a standing pressure of 180 pounds, which falls to 130 when the hoist is in operation.
>
> Wire ropes, one inch in diameter, are used on five-foot drums. The ropes, which last from three to eight months, are inspected daily, and at the least sign of failure are condemned and removed. The rope passes from the drum over a seven-foot sheave wheel at the top of a gallows frame eighty feet high.
>
> Two skips are used, each covered by a sheet-iron bonnet and supplied with an automatic safety clutch. When the skip descends faster than a certain rate of speed, which can be regulated, a parachute under the bonnet raises and releases the clutches which grip the guides, and so arrests the descent of the skip. [Two of these skips now form the entrance arch to Utica Park in the center of Angels Camp].
>
> The Rock skip is constructed of sheet-iron of two-ton capacity. It is loaded from the chutes in the shaft at different levels. At the surface it is dumped automatically by means of a curved switch.
>
> The water skip is also made of sheet-iron, three feet square and eight feet long, holding about 500 gallons of water. The tank is filled through a butterfly valve in the bottom; when it reaches the surface, one wing of the valve is opened automatically by a system of levers, which are activated by a bumper on the gallows frame and the water is discharged into a tank at the side of the shaft.
>
> The drainage of the mine is further provided for by a pumping plant consisting of two seven-inch

California Mines and Minerals, published by California Miners Association, San Francisco, 1899.

Earlier shafts were the South Utica, which was sunk on the ledge and about 900 feet deep in 1899, and the North Utica (lower). The heavy timbers being delivered by 14-mule team will be stored in the timber yard to the left for eventual use underground. (*Earle R. Edmiston collection*)

bucket and one eight-inch plunger pumps. This plant is run by a six-foot Dodd wheel, geared to a long reciprocating rod in the shaft, which supplies the power to the pumps at the several stations in the shaft. The capacity of this plant is about 75 gallons per minute from a depth of 900 feet. Most of the water is still handled, however, by the water skip.

. . . In all there have been four shafts sunk on this property [1899]; the North Utica, sunk a short distance back in the footwall, is still a good shaft. The South Utica, about 900 feet deep was sunk on the ledge, and, after being kept open to hoist ore through only, at a large expense, had to be abandoned, and now gives difficulty in stoping around it. The Stickle Shaft, 1,000 feet deep, was sunk on the ledge and has been almost entirely re-timbered twice, at considerable expense, at one time necessitating the shut-down of the Stickle Mine and Mill for about a month.

Profiting by the experience with the other shafts, the new Cross Shaft, which it is intended to sink to a depth of 1500 feet, on the Stickle Mine, has been sunk at a safe distance in the footwall from the stopes.

To supply the sixty-stamp mill with about 300 tons per day requires two shifts of 45 men each, consisting of miners, helpers and shovelers working on ten-hour shifts. The two shifts alternate on night and day shift, changing every two weeks. Each shift consists of approximately 12 miners, each with a helper, about 15 shovelers and six men running cars on the level. This division of the working force is not constant, as it depends on conditions in the mine which are constantly changing. When the broken rock is plenty and easy to get at, some of the miners may be put to shoveling pay rock and some of the shovelers put to work stowing. On the other hand, if rock is short, some of the shovelers may be added to the force of miners.

The miners are paid $3.00 a day. Helpers, shovelers and car men $2.50. In addition to these two shifts a crew of ten timber men is necessary at $3.00 per day.

In order to insure their water supply, in 1890 the Utica Mining Company purchased the stock of the Union Water Company, which had operated about twenty miles of miners' ditch bringing water from the North Fork of the Stanislaus River to the mines around Murphys. Soon after taking over the physical properties of the company the Utica Mining Company built a masonry dam on Silver Creek in the high mountains of Alpine County which formed the Silver Valley Reservoir, now known as Lake Alpine.

In 1895 the Utica Mining Company, using its newly acquired water rights, built one of the first hydroelectric plants in California. It was a modest installation located in Angels Creek about a mile and a half east of Murphys. Designed to supply electricity for lighting purposes only, it consisted of a single Westinghouse alternator driven by a Pelton water wheel. The electricity generated was transmitted the 8½ miles to Angels Camp at 2500 volts. Actually it was probably a pilot plant to acquaint the company and personnel with electric generation and transmission. At any rate it successfully served its purpose and in 1899 was replaced by a larger plant. The new plant, which ran for many years, consisted of two 750-kilowatt alternators direct coupled to Pelton wheels with a heavy flywheel between the two. Power was generated two phase at 500 volts which when connected to six single-phase step-up transformers in Scott connection emerged for transmission as 16,500 volts, three phase.

As a wholly owned subsidiary of the Utica Mining Company, the Utica Power Company's primary purpose was to generate power for the Utica, Lightner and Gold Cliff mines; however, since there was a surplus it was a simple matter to supply neighboring mines, as well as the town of Angels Camp. Later, under an arrangement with the newly organized Standard Electric Company, Utica power was fed into that company's Calaveras line to serve San Andres, Mokelumne Hill, Jackson, Sutter Creek, Amador City and other towns in the area.

The late A. J. Gianelli, a long-time resident of Murphys and for over forty years a member of the Calaveras County Board of Supervisors, played a part in the construction of the Murphys powerhouse and recalled that the building was built with stone quarried at the old Adams Ranch which was later known as the Kenny Ranch. One end was left unfinished because it was planned to install two additional generators, but this was never done. The heavy machines were shipped by the Westinghouse Company to a point near Stockton and were brought up to the then remote location of the plant by extra heavy horse-drawn wagons, a journey of several days.

Mr. Gianelli also remembered the early days of operation, before better protective devices had been developed, when sometimes during lightning storms the interior of the powerhouse would be a blue haze from electrically charged atmosphere.

After the Utica shut down in 1918 the Gold Cliff became the only operating property of the Company. However, two years later the Gold Cliff became unprofitable and its demise marked the end of mining activities for the Utica Mining Company. Picture above shows the property in 1924 after abandonment while lower photo was taken during operation. Note electric locomotive, at the far end of the track, just coming up the canyon as the picture was snapped. *(top photo by A. Knopf, U. S. Geological Survey; lower, Earle R. Edmiston collection)*

Most of the time the Utica power plant used the water directly from the headwaters of the North Fork of the Stanislaus River diverted into the Utica Conduit; however during periods of low water, usually October and November, the waters of Alpine Lake and the Utica Reservoir could be used as a reserve. There was a time, however, during 1913 when work was curtailed for almost six months due to a shortage of water. Not only did this affect the Utica but many other mines in the area also which depended on the Utica Company for water.

The problem apparently was caused by flume and ditch trouble, perhaps due to winter damage; at any rate the records show a virtual shutdown of mining activity, with all hands repairing flumes and ditches.

Through it all the Angels Camp and Gold Cliff mines managed to operate by obtaining their water from supplies usually reserved for domestic purposes and by running their compressors on power temporarily obtained from the San Francisco and Sierra Power Company, a newcomer to the electrical transmission field, then being formed by the United Railroads to supply power for their San Francisco street cars. Meanwhile the damaged seven miles of main flume were rebuilt and enlarged to seven feet wide by four feet deep, and by July the camp was operating as usual. The mules used in hauling ore cars underground, apparently the only ones to profit by the vacation, were once again sent down hole to resume their labors in a world of darkness.

By 1916 fortunes began to show signs of changing. For one thing the new Cross Shaft, which had recently set records in shaft sinking, was closed down temporarily and only in preparation to sinking it still deeper management said, but still in a mining town such things cause talk. Then there was the Utica mine itself, quiet for some time although still milling reserve ore. Reports there indicated that after cleanup of current milling, underground operations would continue, but with fifty less men . . . and so it was that the crew was put to work deepening the mine in the hope of striking the Gold Cliff lode.

Although right next to each other and interconnected by over a hundred miles of workings, the Gold Cliff and the Utica mines were in different ground geologically speaking. The Gold Cliff was considered to be a part of the Mother Lode whereas the Utica was thought to be an extension of the Carson Hill lead. Although this theory had some validity, at the surface where the two branches were 3000 feet apart it became a matter of much argument when it was found that at a depth of 2700 feet the veins actually did meet. The theory had been that if these two veins did intersect a veritable bonanza could well exist. However, when the huge bulk of ore men had learned to expect in such a situation was not to be found in this case it became evident that the Utica, which for thirty years had been one of the most successful mines on the Mother Lode, had played out. It must have been a sad day that Christmas in Angels Camp for it was on December 25, 1916, that the remaining 100 men were paid off and the Utica mine ceased to operate.

There was still the Gold Cliff; so a bulkhead was installed where the two mines connected to keep the abandoned Utica from flooding its neighbor. Superintendent Fred J. Martin now turned his full attention to the remaining operation. Twenty stamps at the old Utica mill were now dropping on Gold Cliff ore milling about 6000 tons a month and the comprehensive prospecting and development plan which had been under way at the Gold Cliff was meticulously reviewed.

The Gold Cliff was still a good mine, but would never be the producer that the Utica had been. Martin must have known that, for in September 1918, after the last of the machinery at the Utica had been sold, Fred Martin, who had been superintendent for so many years, turned the remaining Gold Cliff mine over to the charge of A. C. Wilson and retired from the mining business to a ranch in Arizona. The end was now in sight, for two years later in 1920, the Gold Cliff reached that point in the life of a mine where the gold it contains is no longer worth what it costs to mine it. The Utica Mining Company, once one of the largest operations in California, had seen its last days.

Oddly enough, the Utica Mining Company was never a corporation, but all through its active years was jointly owned by Hobart, Hayward and Lane and extending, with their deaths, to their heirs. Around the period mining activity ceased

87

The Stickle mill near Angels Camp is pictured above. Lower photo shows the extensive chlorination works of the Utica Mining Company. The plant, used to chemically treat ore from the Utica group, was the largest in the West. *(lower, Stuart Library of Western Americana)*

the owners were the Hobart Estate Co., Emma Rose and Anna G. Lane.°

The company did have one asset left in the Utica Power Company and though there were no longer mines to be supplied it still lighted the town of Angels Camp and vicinity as well as supplying domestic water. Thus the Utica Power Company continued to operate as a miniature hydroelectric utility with pioneer equipment and veteran employees.

In 1946 the company was purchased by the Pacific Gas and Electric Company. Most of the employees continued in their former jobs and although the P. G. & E. invested over one million dollars improving the little system, most of the money was spent in rebuilding the Utica flume —

°Property is now owned by a local group doing business as the Gold Cliff Development Company mainly engaged in real estate.

the old alternators continued to hum as before. It was not until 1954 that the old Murphys powerhouse was replaced with a new $1,335,000 plant built just a half-mile downstream.

On February 19, 1954, in a civic ceremony the late A. J. Gianelli, who helped build the plant 55 years earlier, closed for the last time the valve he had turned so many times during his years as an operator and supervisor. As the water ceased flowing the deafening roar of the machines died down, the great armatures slowly came to a stop and the swinging needles on the dials at the control board fell dead. For the first time since 1899 both machines lay quiet and electric power no longer flowed out over the wires from that old stone building in the canyon. As the lights dimmed to darkness perhaps Gianelli could hear in his mind's ear the diminishing tempo of distant stamp mills as they slowed to a stop just as they had in reality nearly 35 years before.

This interior of the hoisting works at the Cross Shaft shows the cable winding drums, engineer's platform and the huge horizontal steam cylinders in the foreground and at the opposite end of the room. This plant was designed to operate on steam or water power and would shift from one to the other depending on the season. *(Morgan North)*

89

Built in the high Sierra in 1890 by the Utica Mining Company this stone dam created Lake Alpine as a source of water power for the Company. For many years the Utica flume brought water to Angels Camp for use in the mines. After the mines closed the entire system was surveyed as a possible source of water for the City of Stockton. It remained, however, under Utica ownership until 1946 when it was acquired by the Pacific Gas and Electric Company. Since then it has been rebuilt and is still used for power generation and for domestic water in Angels Camp. At left, the author walks the Utica flume in 1969. *(upper photo, P.G. & E. News Bureau)*

90

The Murphy's powerhouse built by the Utica Mining Company in 1895 was one of the early hydroelectric plants in California. Lower, interior photo shows generators and switch gear. From here the electricity ran 8½ miles to Angels Camp where it powered the Utica. Lightner and Gold Cliff mines. (*P.G. & E. News Bureau*)

This headframe still stands over the main shaft of the Argonaut mine high on a hill overlooking the Mother Lode town of Jackson, California.

CHAPTER 6

THE ARGONAUT
1859 to 1948
Jackson, Amador County
Vertical depth 5,570 feet via 63-degree shaft
Total production $25,179,160.43

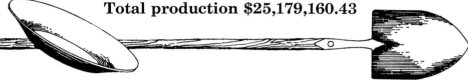

"CLEAR MAIN LINE OF ALL TRAFFIC. MINE RESCUE CAR RUNNING SPECIAL."

That brief order flashed over Southern Pacific telegraph wires by the dispatcher at Sparks, Nevada, in August 1922, started one of the greatest railroad races in the history of steam and dramatically figured in one of the country's worst mine disasters . . . a tragedy of such epic proportions that it never left the front pages for over 22 days and focused the attention of the entire world on the mining town of Jackson, Amador County, California, and its now famous Argonaut mine.

We'll finish that story, of course, but first some background on the area and the early history of the Argonaut mine.

Let's start with Amador County with its western border just 25 miles east of Stockton and with Jackson,* the county seat some 47 miles by highway. Like the other counties along the Mother Lode, Amador participated in the gold rush and later became famous for its deep quartz mines.

Amador County was active in the field of mining. The California Division of Mines lists 251 quartz mines, 44 placer and 96 miscellaneous, varying all the way from coal to marble, a total of 391 separate mining operations.

Mining was the chief industry for many years, followed by logging and agriculture, primarily stock raising. Today with gold out of the picture

the mining consists of more prosaic minerals such as potter's clay and lignite. Although timber products and cattle are just as important as ever, the tourist dollar now plays an increasingly important part in the economy of the county.

During the height of mining activity along the Mother Lode the deep mines of Amador County had been the most productive. This was mainly due to the fact that the ore continues to a great depth without radical change in its nature. Mining men had long predicted that only increased costs of operation due to great depth and the difficulty of holding the ground open would eventually prove to be the limiting factors.

The ten-mile length of Lode in Amador County between Plymouth on the north and Jackson on the south produced over half the total yield credited to the entire Mother Lode gold belt. It contained most of the mines with the highest individual outputs and the deepest ones — those exceeding 4500 feet vertical depth. Among them were such fabulous producers as the Argonaut, Kennedy, Central Eureka, Old Eureka, Keystone and the Plymouth. We will cover all of the these mines beginning at Jackson, where we first come upon two of the most famous of all the California deep mines, the Argonaut and the Kennedy.

The Kennedy, which at the time of its closing was the deepest mine in North America and with every evidence that the gold was going still deeper, was the nextdoor neighbor of the Argonaut mine. Both were situated on a hill just north of Jackson and within sight of the town.

---

*Jackson was named for Colonel Alden Jackson, a famous Indian fighter as was Jacksonville near the Eagle-Shawmut mine in Tuolumne County.

Early photos of the Argonaut mine were taken both above and below ground. The picture above was of the mine between 1900 and 1910, as later a steel headframe and a new hoisting works were built and in 1912 a large mill and other buildings appeared on the hillside (see page 96). The lower photo clearly shows the size of the timbers required and judging from the depth the year would be about 1915. *(California State Library)*

The Argonaut was second only to the Kennedy in size, depth and production and together they must of necessity head the list of any grouping of mines in the Amador region.

Little is recorded of the early history of the Argonaut, although we do know that work was begun in 1850 on a small scale on the property, known then as the Pioneer claim, and continued in a desultory way until 1893.

In 1893 the Argonaut Mining Company was incorporated and development was begun in earnest. In April 1896 the Amador *Record* reported that the Argonaut shaft was down 1220 feet and was still being sunk at the rate of 2½ feet a day. One curious feature of that shaft which, according to the *Record,* made it ". . . the only mine that was ever sunk in the country nearly so deep as it is without stations, crosscuts or drifts." However, by 1898 we find another entry stating that the Argonaut shaft is now 1710 feet deep although mining at that time was being confined to and above the 1200-foot level. We can only conclude that during the two years that elapsed between these two statements the mine management saw fit to add a few drifts and crosscuts in the upper levels.

The 2500-foot level was reached in 1907 with good ore encountered along the way. By 1917 the Argonaut shaft had reached 4300 feet and required an elaborate pumping system. All in all it was a profitable operation, producing during its bonanza period, between 1914 and 1919, the best average grade of ore of any mine along the Mother Lode.

By this time the shaft had reached a 63-degree incline depth of 4800 feet. Then in the spring of 1919, fire, believed to have been of incendiary origin, was discovered on the 4000-foot level.

In a short time the fire was thought to have been surrounded and under control and work was resumed. However, in March 1920, almost a year later, fire was discovered on the 3000-foot level of the adjoining Kennedy mine, having presumably eaten its way through old workings and caved ground.

On March 17th the Kennedy management began filling the mine with water and as the two mines were connected at that time, the lower lev-

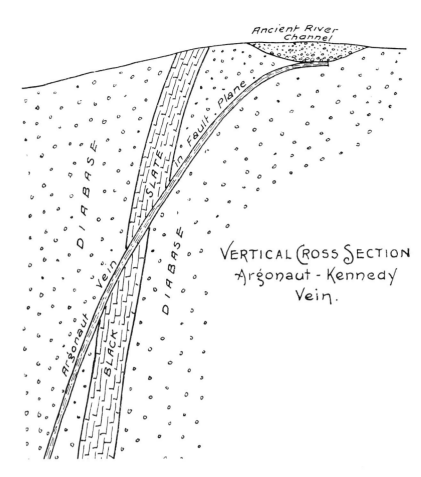

VERTICAL CROSS SECTION
Argonaut - Kennedy
Vein.

els of both were flooded and water rose to within fifty feet of the 3150-foot level of the Argonaut.

Unwatering began at the Argonaut early that summer, but they found it too much for their plant and the Kennedy joined in the work, which was not completed until April 1921. Naturally this meant a costly setback to both properties; however work was going ahead at the Argonaut after the unwatering under encouraging circumstances, and ore from the 4800-foot level was keeping the sixty-stamp mill busy.

But bad luck is said to come in threes.

It was shortly after midnight on the morning of August 28, 1922, when shift boss Clarence Bradshaw, Steve Pasalich and Michael Jago came to the surface. As they climbed, almost falling out of the skip, it was immediately apparent that all three were on the verge of collapse. Before Bradshaw could speak he dropped in his tracks; however, he was soon revived and told the bloodcurdling story of fire raging deep in the mine and

95

What was later to become a four lane section of Highway 49 was only a dirt road when this photo was taken. Wooden headframe, upper left, marks the site of the shaft which served throughout the life of the mine. The smaller headframe, just right of center, is the Muldoon shaft, an auxiliary shaft used for ventilation. The trussed bridge carries the tramway from shaft to dump, and the hoisting works is just below the last span of the bridge. Held up by idler wheels on towers, the cable crossed the road to the headframe. Below, in a later photo of the Argonaut mine, the large mill has been built on the top of the hill with a steel water tower for pressure. Mill and shaft are connected by an inclined tramway. Headframe has been rebuilt of steel and a larger hoisting works is situated in the same location as its predecessor. Note growth of dump since the photo above was taken. *(San Francisco Chronicle)*

how he and the two men had experienced a nightmare of being pulled through several hundred feet of burning shaft timbers, barely escaping with their lives.

Later, in a more detailed report, Bradshaw described his experience thus: "I was at the 4200-foot level at 11:40 (that would be the night of Sunday, August 27, 1922) when I noticed smoke. Within hailing distance were a couple of skip tenders known as Steve and Jocko, but all the rest of the shift were in other parts of the mine. I yelled to the skip tenders to get out as fast as possible, and with them ahead of me, we made for the shaft. Thicker and thicker the smoke drove around us, getting worse with every foot we made. We were nearly choked to death at the 3000-foot level. Without smoke masks we were compelled to hold our nostrils and mouths. There were flames, too, at the 3000-foot level. How we ever got by and out of the mine alive is a miracle."

However, Bradshaw was a game one for as soon as he had recovered he and Foreman Sanguinetti started back down hoping to be of assistance to the men still in the 4650 and 4800-foot levels of the mine. They got as far as the 2800 where they were turned back by an impassable barrier of fire and smoke.

By this time it was clearly apparent that with 47 men still underground, trapped below a raging inferno, the situation was indeed serious. Virillio S. Garbarini, superintendent of the mine, was immediately notified and he rushed to the scene.

From far below came the frantic ringing of signal bells as the terrified miners appealed for help, but further efforts to descend the shaft were deemed futile.

It was then that Garbarini, in one of those "battlefront" decisions that life requires some men to make, gave orders that the plant supplying air be operated to full capacity. This was a calculated risk as he knew full well that the life-giving air which he sent to the men trapped below would also feed the flames, but if the fire could soon be extinguished there might still be a chance.

Garbarini had come to the Argonaut from the neighboring Kennedy and was a mining man of considerable experience and his experience told him that this situation called for all the help he could get. Even though it was still the early hours

of the morning, he lost no time in notifying the State Bureau of Mines which rushed from Berkeley a full set of rescue equipment. The Federal Bureau of Mines also dispatched men and equipment from the famous mine rescue station then operating at Grass Valley.

During that terrible lull while waiting for trained rescue crews to arrive, assistant foreman Floyd Murphy endeavored to lead a party down the shaft, but after a brave attempt was driven back by the fury of the fire. He reported that the intense heat had badly twisted the rails in the shaft and that the skip in which he rode had almost jammed.

There was also an attempt to lower a skip full of water but this too was unsuccessful.

News of the disaster did not spread to Jackson until early Monday morning when the day shift reported for work. Upon hearing of the accident virtually the entire district ceased work and went to the site. The wives and children of the trapped miners were among the first on the scene and there was such a rush for the mouth of the shaft that it was necessary to establish a guard of deputy sheriffs to hold them back.

Quiet sobbing mingled with the chatter of of strange tongues since over half of the unfortunate miners were foreign-born. The work force in the mines then consisted mainly of Slavs, Italians, Poles, Irish and Cornishmen.

The Amador County Red Cross sent workers to the scene and from the immediate area over a thousand men volunteered their services, but they could not be used for lack of organization and plan.

At one point a small boy scurried from the mine to the office twenty yards down the hill crying: "There is one man just brought up . . . and he is dead!" At these cruel words three women, who had been patiently waiting for word, pitched forward and fainted. As it turned out the boy's report was false. A man had been brought out of the shaft but, although he was badly gassed, he was not dead. He was Joseph Garbarini, one of the rescuers and brother of the superintendent of the mine. He was immediately removed to his home where, between gasps of pain, he told the hair-raising story of how he, Superintendent Garbarini and his son, in a desperate attempt to battle the

Rescue workers getting ready to go down into the Kennedy mine. Not knowing when they would be needed, relays of these men with their oxygen equipment were always on hand at the 3900 station ready to go into the Argonaut as soon as the connection was made.

The faces of the group below, waiting in the station, clearly show the strain they are under. The man at the left is Argonaut shift boss Pete Akers with assistant shift boss Dan Sanguinetti sitting beside him. The rest of the men are part of the U. S. Bureau of Mines rescue team. *(San Francisco Chronicle)*

fire, almost fell into the raging furnace. Persuaded to describe the incident only by the argument that the public should know of the heroic efforts being made to save the men below, Garbarini haltingly pieced together the following account: ". . . I got down the shaft about fifteen feet below a water skip. When they opened the valve and shot that volume of water, it sent the gas up along the sides of the shaft in one great wave.

"We had made our way clear below the 2700-foot level and it was getting very hot. We had no masks. We were a hundred feet below telephone communication. I had noticed little puffs of gas and once or twice had felt a little weak in the knees.

"Just before the water fell, I foresaw the danger and tried to shout across to my brother, the superintendent, who was on the other side of the shaft, but there was all kinds of noise and he did not hear. The water splashed past. I heard it hiss in the flames below. At the same instant I felt an overpowering wave of gas. Immediately I started to climb the ladder. My feet were very heavy, and my legs and hands were numb. I held my mouth and nose shut with one hand and hooked the other around a signal wire, feeling my hand become paralyzed as I did so.

"It was simply a question of whether I could climb up through that gas cloud before I would again have to breathe.

"I made about five feet and then I was aware that my nephew, Earl, was climbing down the ladder above me. He tried to reach down to me just as I weakened and was nearly torn from the ladder.

"I was almost unconscious, but began to feel purer air. Somehow I had the strength to climb about fifty feet with Earl's help, and that of my brother, who managed to get across the shaft. He had been partly gassed himself. Suddenly I became totally unconscious. I knew I had fallen. They told me later that I fell forward over the lip of the 2700-foot level, where Earl was able to hold me until both men pulled me up."

Actual firefighting began with the arrival of the official party Monday afternoon. By then over twelve hours had elapsed since the discovery.

Rodney Hecox, foreman of the Bureau of Mines rescue crew, concurred with Garbarini and other mine officials in that it would be necessary to extinguish the flames before anything could be done in regard to the men.

The possibility of reaching the miners from the depths of the Kennedy mine, less than a mile away was suggested. The two mines formerly had connected and in fact were the subject of a long-fought legal action famous in mining circles, but now like two quarreling neighbors were separated by a concrete bulkhead at the 3900-foot level of the Argonaut mine.

It was also suggested that communications might be made with the trapped men through the Muldoon shaft of the Amelia mine, now owned by the Argonaut. This shaft was equipped with a blower to force fresh air into the Argonaut.

Both of these suggestions were not considered expedient at this time because it was feared that the opening of these vents would only serve to operate as a flue, drawing the fire from the 3000-foot level 900 feet nearer the miners on the levels below. In any event Superintendent Garbarini said that the levels on which the men were trapped could not be reached through either the Kennedy or Muldoon shafts.

Meanwhile the Bureau of Mines crew began experimenting with canary birds to see how far down the shaft it was possible to go. The birds were lowered into the shaft and careful measurements made as to the depth descended. Some of the canaries came up weakly moving their wings, but alive, while others came back dead, depending upon the depth descended. By this method it was determined that the fire had evidently burned itself out somewhat and life was possible in the 2700-foot level. Two men equipped with breathing apparatus were immediately sent down followed by skips full of water with siphon hose. The men could only work for 15 minutes at a time and a fresh crew was sent down. This method was admittedly hit or miss, but it was the best that could be devised.

Twenty-four hours had now elapsed but the rescuers still clung to the slight hope that the miners might still be alive.

Two huge air compressors at the surface continued to pump fresh air down the shaft through steel pipe, but there was no way of knowing if the pipe had been fused through by the fire or

Rescue workers are waiting to descend the Kennedy shaft during the Argonaut fire of 1922. Below, Argonaut miners are posed for this photo during shift change sometime during the 1930s. Note 60 degree shaft as indicated by the slant of the skip seen suspended by cable in the background. This was the mouth of the three-compartment shaft which descended to an incline depth of 5,700 feet and was the main entrance to the mine. The mine itself contained 8 miles of drifts, crosscuts and tunnels, 4 miles of raises and 50 miles of stope floors. (*A. "Babe" Garbarini collection*)

destroyed by a cave-in; then, too, it might be just adding oxygen to the flames.

Mine experts and government officials were rushed to Jackson for whatever assistance they could offer . . . and by the fastest transportation available. For instance, H. M. Wolflin, Superintendent of the Bureau of Safety of the State Industrial Accident Commission, was flown to the scene from Crissy Field, San Francisco, in a World War I biplane, making the 100-mile air-line distance in just 1 hour and 15 minutes . . . a near record in 1922.

Another record run was made by a Southern Pacific train crew hauling a specially equipped mine rescue car which had been stationed at Sparks, Nevada. With signals green and all main-line traffic cleared, the mercy train left Sparks at 10:20 a.m. Tuesday, August 29th. With whistle screaming the special flashed through Reno like a thunderbolt. Up the eastern slope of the Sierra Nevada mountains it roared. Lurching and swaying around the dangerous curves of Donner Summit, it then began the long descent to the floor of the Sacramento Valley. Passing through Roseville with the brake shoes glowing red hot, the train stretched out for the long straight run to Sacramento. At Sacramento it was switched to the Valley line and raced south toward Stockton with more tangent track ahead. Just north of Stockton the train left the main line and headed east to the little foothill town of Ione. Here the Southern Pacific rails ended, but the train didn't stop long for waiting patiently with a full head of steam was another locomotive, a toy by mainline standards, but the pride of the 12-mile Amador Central.° Moments later the precious equipment was rolling up the steep grade behind the puffing shortline locomotive, arriving at Martell, within sight of the burning Argonaut mine, in a total elapsed time from Sparks, Nevada, of six hours flat.

Rescue crews were now equipped with oxygen breathing equipment, but even so were limited to two hours exposure in that smoke-filled hole.

The men worked under the direction of Byron O. Picard, Chief Engineer for the United States

_____
°Built in 1905 as the Ione & Eastern, it was reorganized and renamed the Amador Central after bankruptcy in 1909. The railroad still operates bringing in carload freight and returning with lumber from the mill at Martell.

Bureau of Mines for the California, Arizona and Nevada District, assisted by R. B. Hecox, Foreman Miner with the Bureau.

Also on hand and assisting in the work were engineers and picked miners from the Kennedy, Melones, North Star, Empire, Plymouth Consolidated and Fremont mines.

Early in the effort a high command was established to direct the rescue work consisting of E.C. Hutchinson, President of the Kennedy Mining Company, V. S. Garbarini, Superintendent of the Argonaut Mine and F. L. Lowell, Engineer, Industrial Accident Commission.

One of the trapped miners, Ernest Miller, had survived a mine fire at Butte, Montana, and it was felt that his experience would surely lead the men to establish a barricade against the gas and with mine water readily available it would be possible for the men to live without food for a number of days. But the question on everyone's mind was just how long?

By Tuesday (August 29th) hope began to fade and an air of gloom settled over the rescue workers and waiting families alike. Few words were spoken, but the worst was known when shift boss Peter Akers and a crew of four returned to the surface after a five-hour battle with the fire. They reported hearing gas explosions from the drifts below them and looking down the shaft with the aid of a 300-foot searchlight beam saw a grim spectacle of destruction, the shaft filled with tons of rock, rubble and burning timbers.

With all other methods now closed to them, the only alternative lay in penetrating the barrier between the two mines. At a hurried midnight conference officials from the Kennedy and Argonaut, forgetting past grievances, brought together for the first time the maps of both mines in an effort to plan a rescue approach.

It was immediately announced that an attempt would be made to enter the Argonaut from the Kennedy at two underground points, the 3000 and the 3900-foot levels.

A careful measurement of the maps showed that just 21 feet of slate separated the two mines at the 3600-foot level. Of this distance 15 feet were on the Kennedy and six on the Argonaut.°

_____
°With all due respect to the maps this figure was revised several times.

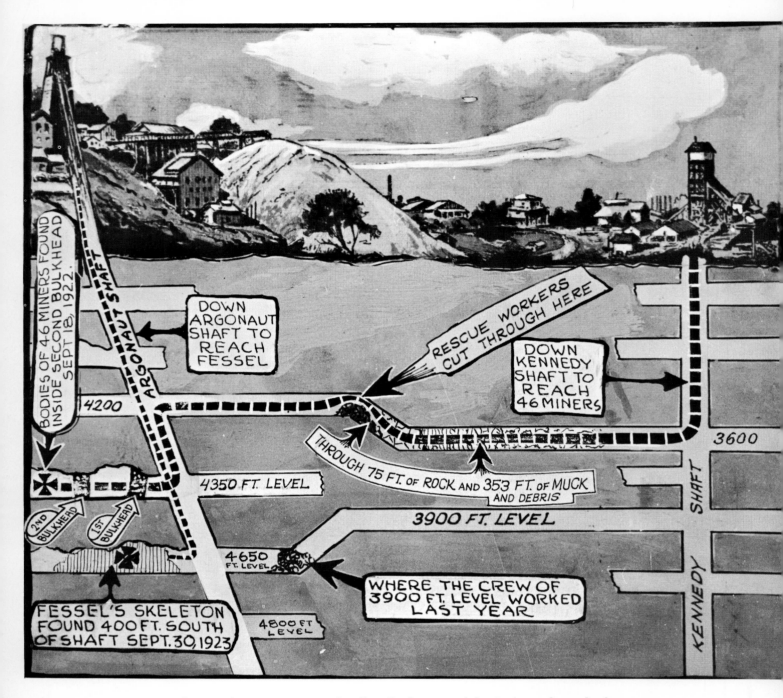

This artist's cross-section graphically tells the story of the Argonaut fire and subsequent events. Mine at the left is the Argonaut and the Kennedy is at the right of the drawing. On the night of August 27, 1922 fire broke out on the 3,000 foot level of the Argonaut trapping the crew working below that level. It was soon determined that it would be impossible to reach the men via the Argonaut shaft and rescue workers concentrated their efforts in the neighboring Kennedy mine in an attempt to connect the two mines at either the 3600 or 3900 foot levels. Finally after 22 days of constant work rescue crews broke through into the Argonaut only to find 46 bodies behind a makeshift bulkhead. Another man who was separated from the others was not located until a year later. (San Francisco Chronicle)

The 3600-foot level of the Kennedy mine would strike the Argonaut just 38 feet below the 4200-foot level; not an impossible penetration, but one that the engineers estimated would require at least three days to accomplish.

No time was lost in assaulting that wall. Six crews of thirty men each were put to work in four-hour shifts. Unsparingly they gave of themselves as they blasted, drilled and carried out the rock in a record-breaking attempt to tunnel through that barrier while hope of life still remained.

Sunday, September 3rd . . . a full week since the fire was first reported. Special prayer services were held in the Jackson churches.

September 4th . . . five muffled sounds like blasts were reported by the crews in the 3900-foot drift of the Kennedy. These were taken by the men to be signals from the entombed men, though the committee in charge discounted them.

September 6th . . . two more blasts, this time more distinct, were heard by the early morning shift. All interest was now centered on the drill crew on the 3600 and 3900-foot levels of the Kennedy.

September 8th . . . rescue workers in the 3600 and 3900-foot levels were working valiantly but against great obstacles.

September 10th . . . the rescue crew at the 3900-foot level struck a rock barrier 141 feet thick . . . a bonus of $5000 was offered by mine officials to the crew to first break into the Argonaut. A welcomed prize to be sure, but hardly necessary as an incentive since both the 3600 and 3900-level crews worked feverishly toward their goal. Their distance covered was almost a tie.

September 14th . . . some doubt was cast as to the accuracy of the measurements. Progress was slowing due to the hardness of the rock.*

September 15th . . . the crew in the 3600 reported they were in the area, but later checks revealed they had penetrated an old caved area that was so choked with timbers and rubble that it was faster to strike diagonally upward, thus avoiding the area completely.

_____
*After the breakthrough final figures showed the distance to have been 428 feet at the 3600-foot level of the Kennedy (4200-foot level of the Argonaut). Of this 75 feet was in solid rock and 353 feet of muck and debris according to newspaper accounts.

September 16th . . . so near and yet so far. It now appeared 49.7 feet remained.

The crews worked even faster, if that was possible, smashing all known records for tunneling through rock.

In their eagerness for speed, miners Ben Fuller and Dan Murphy were overcome by powder gas when they rushed back into the hole too soon after a blast.

All during the rescue efforts the Red Cross had been in attendance at an emergency station above ground; now it was necessary to set up a first aid station underground. This was done by Dr. E. E. Endicott of Jackson, assisted by rescue workers because nurses were not permitted below. If any of the entombed men were alive they would have to be given a considerable amount of treatment before they could be brought to the surface. The second stage would be to gently raise them to the surface where a warehouse at the shaft head had been cleared and supplied with beds and the latest hospital equipment.

Everyone was at their posts and ready for the zero hour of "breakthrough." The crowd at the surface was larger than ever. They welcomed the oncoming crew, shook them by the hands and wished them "good luck."

But more hours of frustrating delay lay ahead.

September 17th . . . as it turned out it was the drill operated by Joe Miller that first broke through into the Argonaut mine. Miller, who lived at Jackson Gate in a stone gold rush house built in 1852, was acting as driller on the shift that had gone to work at one in the afternoon and was due to quit at 7 p.m.

It was just before quitting time when Miller felt the machine surge forward. It was through! But Joe Miller was in for a further surprise for when he withdrew the drill there swirled a miniature windstorm through the two-inch hole, making a furious sucking sound. Since the draft flowed from the Kennedy toward the Argonaut the phenomenon tended to prove that the air in the burning mine was light and gas laden.

Naturally the men on Miller's crew were anxious to open up that two-inch drill hole and quickly tamped in a dynamite charge. However, when the explosion went off, the draft suddenly stopped!

Shift boss Peter Akers, the man at right, appears on the surface to report progress of the rescue team. Other men in the picture are left to right, B. O. Pickard, District Mining Engineer of the U. S. Bureau of Mines, F. L. Lowell, Mine Inspector of the State Industrial Accident Commission and E. A. Stent, Vice President of the Argonaut Mining Company. Below, a message from the dead written with the soot of a carbide lamp. At first it was assumed that William Fessel, a utility man who was known to have been working on that unlucky shift, had written and signed the "last message," however, only 46 bodies of a 47 man crew were brought up. The missing 47th man was William Fessel. Funeral services at Jackson buried 46 men and a full scale mystery developed around the missing miner. He was reported to have been seen in Susanville and a bus driver claimed to have seen a man of his description in Arizona. It was not until a year later that his skeleton was found on the 4,650 foot level, 300 feet below the bulkheaded "death chamber" that held the 46 other men. The only possible explanation was that since Fessel was a maintenance man his duties took him all over the mine. It would, therefore, not be unusual for him to leave the regular crew in order to make his rounds. The real author of that farewell message was probably trying to leave word that Fessel was elsewhere in the mine, but was overtaken by death before he completed it. *(San Francisco Chronicle photos)*

When Miller came to the surface to report he said that he thought his drill had merely penetrated a crevice that eventually led into the Argonaut mine but was not completely out in the clear. The blast, then, had filled the crevice with muck causing the flow of air to cease.

They were close, eight feet someone estimated, and everyone believed the long-awaited moment was now within reach. Final preparations for an early breakthrough were quickly made. Canned milk and other provisions were taken down to the 3600 level. Rescue workers from the Bureau of Mines took down sledger poles to be used for building an emergency bulkhead and the crew slated to be the first to enter the Argonaut stood by near the shaft ready to descend on a moment's notice.

Also waiting were two Catholic priests, Father Michael O'Connell of Sutter Creek and Father M. J. Kearney of Jackson. Both were ready to go underground to administer extreme unction to any man, conscious or not, whose body yet contained life.

Tension mounted . . . and then the telephone in the hoist room gave a sudden jingle. Foreman William Sinclair darted from the telephone to the skip and was immediately dropped to the "36." A murmur came from the previously silent crowd. "They've broken through" someone said and the rumor swiftly spread.

But they hadn't broken through. In fact, they were lost.

James Spiers, superintendent of the Kennedy, then went into the mine, to return a short time later with Sinclair, Shift Boss Dan Murphy and a mucker. The four men held a hurried conference with E. C. Hutchinson, President of the Kennedy, and Fred L. Lowell of the State Industrial Accident Commission.

The survey had been carefully checked and re-checked for the umpteenth time, but the facts now showed that there were not eight feet to go, but eleven . . . four feet in an upward direction and seven feet laterally before a connection with the Argonaut mine could be expected.

At 1:00 a.m. the shift reluctantly came to the surface showing keen disappointment on their faces. Theirs would not be the honor of "breaking through."

At midnight a bulletin was issued stating that the last remaining few feet would be drilled through by 4 a.m.; however the aperture would not be passable until at least two blasts were set off.

Wearily the men trudged to nearby beds for a few hours' sleep.

Because of the drama that was taking place on the 3600-foot level the second crew, busily working in the 3900 level, had been all but forgotten. Nevertheless fourteen men had been constantly working at that level, progressing at the steady rate of four feet per shift. They still had fifty feet to go.

Meanwhile up at the Argonaut shaft a scientific crew was keeping a careful watch on the air in the 2400-foot level, as it was fully expected that when the two mines were connected a rush of deadly gases toward the surface would occur . . . perhaps even causing an outbreak of the fire still smouldering in the shaft.

Another worry that the men now began to consider was the probability of the Argonaut mine being flooded since none of the pumps had been working as the fire had severed both pipes and power cables. Knowing how much water the Argonaut mine made, this prospect was frightening indeed.

Because of extensive news coverage the entire world was breathlessly waiting for the breakthrough . . . the moment of truth that would reveal the fate of those 47 men who had been entombed without food for 22 days.

Everyone sensed that the end must soon be in sight, but strangely enough, unlike the first few days of the disaster, none of the families of the trapped men were to be seen at the mouth of the mine. Perhaps they couldn't bear to face the actual climax after so many days of hope and torment. Perhaps they felt a foreboding of tragedy and sensed they would learn the fate of their loved ones soon enough.

All through this dramatic sequence of events an entire press corps was in constant vigil at the mine. Typewriters clacked and blended with the sharp staccato noise of Morse sounders as bulletins were telegraphed directly from the spot. Yet with all of the detailed coverage, of what must have been the journalistic cliff-hanger of all time, ru-

Three burly hard rock miners, typical of those who worked the deep mines, solemnly pose beside the Argonaut shaft. Note ladder in skip on which men sat one above the other when changing shifts. (San Francisco Chronicle photo)

A view of the Argonaut hoisting works which shows the herringbone drive gears, brake drums and shoes (center) and the two circular dials on pedestals which are depth indicators. (California State Library)

mors began to spread. Started, perhaps, by someone eager to be the first with the news, false reports raced up and down California like wildfire. Watsonville, San Jose and Salinas all had untrue reports of a breakthrough. Stockton was full of "authentic" and "confidential" reports that the rescuers had entered the Argonaut. San Jose had it that 37 men had been found alive. Unfortunately none of this was true. Drilling, blasting and mucking were still going on deep underground.

Meanwhile the crews that had been making four feet a shift in the 3900-foot level had struck heavy going and were now almost at a standstill, showing but 11 feet during the past 24 hours or an average of two feet nine inches a shift. At that rate it would take them another five days to reach the predicted point of intersection.

Finally early in the morning of Monday, September 18th the passageway from the 3600-foot level of the Kennedy was holed through to the Argonaut. A few more hours were required to enlarge it and timber it so that it would be usable.

Shortly after 11 o'clock the official rescue team, which had been waiting at the surface, was summoned. They immediately leaped into the cage eager to accept the honor of being first into the Argonaut.

But as a matter of fact they were not the first. Two of the local miners, names unknown, made good the often repeated pledge that no outsider would ever enter the mine first in search of their missing comrades. Perhaps it was local pride, or maybe it was in the spirit of camaraderie that only a miner would understand, that prompted the two men to dash into the 4200-foot level of the Argonaut the moment the rock was penetrated. It was a bold, almost foolhardy deed, for they were without breathing equipment of any kind. However, they managed to make it clear to the main shaft of the Argonaut and returned with the news that they could find no sign of men in the drift.

Now came the official mine safety party led by Rodney Hecox and for a time the hoist at the Kennedy was busy hauling stretchers and other equipment of both a grim and hopeful nature.

The Hecox party also made it to the Argonaut shaft at the 4200 level and reported that since the fire was far above there was still hope that life might be possible.

Another crew was hastily summoned and set to work building a bulkhead across the shaft to shut off this portion of the mine from the fire in the upper levels.

The Argonaut was surprisingly dry considering the amount of water known to be pouring into the shaft. This could only be due to the fact that the upper part of the shaft was plugged by a cave-in.

At 3:40 that afternoon it was announced that a thorough search of the 4200-foot level had failed to turn up any sign of the miners and the rescue team would descend to the 4350-foot level. An hour later Hecox's crew reported that all was well at the 4350-foot level and requested the reserve crew to join them. At 12 minues past 5 Hecox himself arrived at the surface with the word that his men had encountered a strange, newly built bulkhead blocking a passage on the 4350 drift. Behind it — they knew instantly — was locked the secret of the Argonaut.

Losing no time in breaking down the barrier they were greeted by a rush of foul air and when at last they were able to enter the chamber they found farther down the tunnel a second barricade. This one was even more crudely constructed and as a barrier against gas was useless, although the miners' clothing had been used in an attempt to seal the cracks.

It was with considerable restraint that the rescue crew refrained from smashing down that second barrier, but trained men that they were they felt that the air was already too foul to risk venturing further into the unknown. As the result another hour went by while a compressed air hose was run in from the Kennedy mine.

At long last the barrier was broken and Byron O. Pickard, Chief of the Federal Bureau of Mines for the district stepped a few cautious paces into the drift and then he came upon the bodies of the men they had worked so hard to save.

In orderly rows they had lain down to die. Many of them were naked as they had used their clothing in a desperate attempt to caulk the makeshift bulkhead.

Charles and Arthur Oberg, father and son; the two Leon brothers and the others lying side by side . . . many unidentifiable because of decomposition.

This, then, was the end of 22 long days of grief, hope and tortuous labor and the end to 47 individual lives — men who left behind families and loved ones.

How long had the miners lived entombed? There was no need for idle speculation on that score for one of the dead men had written a last message on the rock well using the smoky flame of his carbide lamp. Like a message from the grave it read: "Three o'clock. Gas getting strong. We are going to leave you . . . "

There was one other note. Written on paper and unsigned. It read. "Three o'clock. Too much gas." Below was a shakily scrawled figure "4," indicating the passing of another hour no doubt. So by these messages it was determined that the miners had existed in that deadly atmosphere barely five hours. Perhaps it was better that way.

Now up from the Kennedy — once the legal enemy of the Argonaut, but now more like a needed friend and good neighbor — there slowly came a long series of canvas wrapped corpses. At the surface they were placed in caskets and taken to the Argonaut mill where the giant batteries, unstilled for years, now stood in silent tribute as the flag-draped boxes were placed side by side.

Silent grief descended over the community and spread across the nation. Church and firehouse bells rang throughout the land to announce the tragic end of the story that had held an entire populace enthralled for three long weeks. In San Francisco memorial services were held in the Exposition Auditorium while the funerals were held at Jackson at the Catholic, Protestant and Serbian churches.

Once the dead had been cared for, people then began to consider the living. All during the rescue period the miners' families had been receiving triple wages and now they were entitled to death benefits from the State Workmen's Compensation Fund in amounts up to $5000.

Benefits were given to raise funds for the miners' families. In San Francisco huge benefit balls were held simultaneously at the St. Francis, Palace and Fairmont Hotels. The rescue crews were brought down to march in a parade that ran from the Ferry Building to the City Hall to publicize the fund-raising event.

Naturally official hearings on the cause of the fire were held and pages and pages of testimony given, some of which suggested arson. Such was the conviction of foreman Ben Sanguinetti who testified that he was sure the fire was incendiary. He cited the 1919 fire which was proved to have been set and told of evidence found on the 4000-foot level at that time, consisting of a candle in a forked stick set in a pile of inflammable material so as to form a crude timing device. In the more recent case the fact that the shaft was passed through at 11:05 p.m. with no sign of fire and by 11:45 p.m. three sets of timbers were found to be burning vigorously was indeed suspicious. Had the fire been started shortly after midnight all of the men would have been out of the mine and the fire would have blazed away undetected for perhaps several hours. It was the foreman's feeling that the arsonist had planned to destroy the mine in this fashion, but a miscalculation in timing caused the device to fire while the shift was still below. This was never proven, however, and by and large the Argonaut fire was put down as one of those unfortunate accidents that sometimes occur in the hazardous business of mining. Some recommendations on mine safety were made, but no real finger of blame was pointed. So the record closed on what was surely the most tragic episode in the history of California mining . . . ranking high on the list of mining disasters of the world . . . the now famous Argonaut fire of 1922.

Damage from fire, water and cave-ins was severe and rehabilitation was a slow and costly business. Clearing out the rubble and retimbering the main shaft took seven months. Repairs to the pumping, electrical system and pipelines required additional time. All in all the Argonaut was out of production for a full year following the fire.

When the operation was resumed about 200 men were employed. The Company, which was known as a regular dividend producer up until the fire, resumed payment in 1925 when the 106th dividend was declared. In 1927 they passed the dividend as the expenses of twice unwatering the mine and repairing the shaft after the fires had begun to be felt.

From 1923 to 1936 a considerable amount of gold was recovered from tailings produced in earlier years of operation. These were treated by a separate company, known as the Amador Metals Reduction Company, in a plant built especially for the purpose.

Prior to 1936 milling was done in a sixty-stamp mill. In 1936 ball mills and floatation cells were installed, making possible a recovery rate of 94%. In addition further advances in recovery techniques were made at the Argonaut which were applied with profit all up and down the Mother Lode.

In 1941 the Argonaut Mining Company constructed a cyanide plant to treat concentrates from the Argonaut mill as well as those from the Plymouth Consolidated mine which it also operated.

Production at the Argonaut had been continuous from 1923 until 1942 when profits declined due to the high costs of materials, scarcity of labor and the wartime restrictions on gold mining.

On March 28, 1942, the wheels stopped turning and the remaining miners were paid off. At that time both the men and the owners felt it would be only a temporary wartime shutdown. "Just for the duration," they said, and optimistically kept the upper part of the mine unwatered and in repair in the hope of reopening. In December of 1947, after five long years of waiting, the directors, upon close examination of the prospects for gold mining, recommended dissolution of the Argonaut Mining Company* and by February 1948 the majority of the stockholders had given their consent.

The total mine production at the Argonaut to December 31, 1942, was 2,759,000 tons of ore from which $25,179,160.43 was recovered. Dividends of $3,789,750 were paid on an original capitalization of $1,000,000.

It is interesting to note that part of the liquidation settlement was the distribution of 10,500 shares of General Motors and 4900 shares of Chrysler stock which the Company held as an investment. The cost of the shares was $413,000 and at the 1948 market they were worth $885,000.

During the dissolution of the corporation the physical property was purchased by Messrs. Bernard Monte Verda and E. C. Taylor and the machinery was removed and sold. The real estate, which has lain idle for years, will one day be developed and then little will remain to mark the spot of the once famous Argonaut mine.

---

*A publically owned corporation with 200,000 shares outstanding. Controlling interest was held by the White Knob Copper and Development Company of New York.

(A. "Babe" Garbarini collection)

The Kennedy mine at Jackson was the deepest mine in North America at the time of its closing in 1942. The wheel in the right foreground is one of four 58 feet in diameter that were used to elevate mill tailings over the hill for disposal.

CHAPTER 7

THE KENNEDY

1856 to 1942
Jackson, Amador County
Vertical depth 5,912 feet
Total production $34,280,000

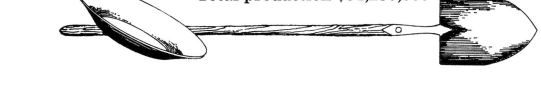

Although hard put to equal the neighboring Argonaut mine when it comes to dramatic story material the Kennedy was nonetheless one of the two big mines at Jackson and for that matter one of the largest in California. For one thing it claimed the distinction of being the deepest mine in North America* and its total production over the years came to nine million dollars more than the Argonaut, its arch rival. This plus the fact that the Kennedy mine paid out over five and one-half million dollars in dividends on an original capitalization of $100,000 leaves little doubt that it qualifies for a place among the most famous of the California mines.

The original Kennedy was located in 1856 by Patrick Kennedy (some accounts called him Andrew, others John) an Irish immigrant, and with several additional claims was consolidated to form the Kennedy mine in 1860.

During its early years the mine was worked on a small scale using a whim for hoisting. In 1871 the first powered hoist and a twenty-stamp mill were erected. In 1872 the property was patented and by 1873 two promising ore shoots were being worked; the Kennedy on the north and the Pioneer at the south end of the mine, with 170 feet of the vein lying within the Kennedy property. It was this 18-foot wide Pioneer vein that led into the Argonaut mine and was to be the cause of years of litigation between the two mines.

*This was true at the time the Kennedy closed. Since that time the record has been held by the Homestake mine, at Lead, South Dakota, down to a vertical depth of 6800 feet as of 1969.

Although production records show that the Kennedy produced $300,000 up to a depth of 600 feet, by 750 feet the ore in the south shaft gave out. This in itself would have been bad enough, but as though to add insult to injury the ore reappeared just inside the Argonaut line. It was discouraging enough to cause the shutdown of the Kennedy mine.

During this period the mine had been worked by several companies, including Burgin, Fuller, Flemming and Company, The Richard Hickman Mining Company and others. Finally after a long period of inactivity it was purchased in 1885 by a new group organized by F. F. Thomas, a mineralogist, and the mine began its long career as the Kennedy Mining and Milling Company.

Under this new ownership the South Shaft was sunk 200 feet deeper, where it once again encountered profitable ore.

The following year a forty-stamp mill was erected which operated steadily through the 1900s processing approximately 36,000 tons of ore per year with the sulphrets running up to $150 a ton and said to be the richest on the Lode.

During 1890 the Kennedy Mining and Milling Company paid three dividends amounting to $15,000.

By 1891 the North Shaft had been sunk to 1300 feet, but not without a great deal of difficulty caused by the volume of water encountered. This water continued to pour in at the rate of 75,000 gallons a day and was removed from the mine without the use of pumps, being bailed entirely by water skips each with a capacity of 550 gallons.

Waste was trammed to the dump from the North Shaft of the Kennedy mine. The South Shaft can be seen to the right. The town of Jackson, much smaller then, is in the background.

Below is an early photo of miners at the 1300 foot level of the Kennedy mine. Note illumination was supplied by candles at that period. Many mines sent down miners' lunch containers in the skip and then hauled them up after lunch so that highgraders could not smuggle out jewelry rock in their lunch buckets. *(both, California Division of Mines and Geology)*

The hoisting works and mill machinery were run by water power at this time. In fact, seven Pelton water wheels were in use throughout the plant with the largest, a six-footer, operating the stamps and a four-foot wheel the concentrators. As the Company did not operate its own ditch system water was purchased from the Blue Lakes Water Company.*

Two forty-horsepower steam engines remained on standby at the mouth of each shaft ready to take over in the event of an interruption in the water supply. By and large, however, the Kennedy had become a fairly smooth operation with many improvements being made in both mine and mill as suggested by operating conditions.

The Kennedy was not only a well-operated mine, but it was a good producer for the stockholders as well, for dividends were paid with the regularity of clockwork. On December 1, 1891, the company reported that so far that year it had disbursed over $300,000 in dividends and exclusive of the regular fourth quarter dividend, which would be payable later that month, an extra Christmas dividend of $30,000 was declared by the Board of Directors. This fine showing was made without depleting the treasury or violating the Company's policy of always keeping a $100,000 contingency fund on deposit with the bank. Basically this prosperity was, of course, due to the rich ore being encountered although the mining and financial press did not fail to recognize the efficient management of the mine under the superintendency of J. F. Parks. At any rate in the face of this success the Kennedy Mining and Milling Company became one of the blue chip investments of the day and its stock was always in demand.

By 1898 the North Shaft had reached an incline depth of 2400 feet (2150 feet vertical). There a large ore body was discovered that assured additional life for the Kennedy mine. It was noted at that time that since 1860 the Kennedy mine had yielded $8,000,000 in gold and had paid out nearly $3,000,000 in dividends.

*The Blue Lakes Water Company was another descendant of the early miners' ditch companies. In 1887 it was acquired for the purpose of bringing water from Amador County to the City of Oakland, but many years were to pass before that became a reality. Around 1896 Prince Andre Poniatowski and his California Exploration Company entered the picture and the system became the foundation of the Standard Electric Company.

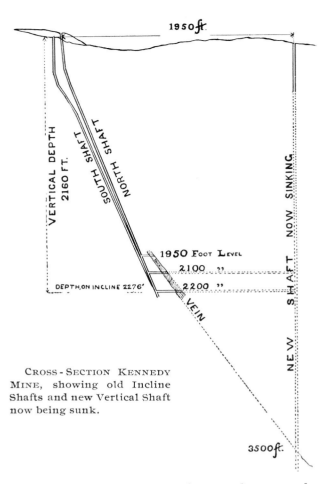

CROSS-SECTION KENNEDY MINE, showing old Incline Shafts and new Vertical Shaft now being sunk.

Results were now so satisfactory that an ambitious expansion program was launched under the direction of E. C. Hutchinson, president of the company.

One of the new projects was a shaft started in 1900 about two thousand feet east of the North Shaft. It was intended that it should cut the vein at some point deep in the mine. The engineers were not disappointed for it did just that, intersecting the east vein at 3680 feet and the west vein at 4000 feet. This new shaft became the main working shaft and the marvel of the Mother Lode. It was sunk with such precision that a plumb-bob dropped down the shaft would not be off one thirty-second of an inch. Looking up from the bottom the shaft opening appeared as a tiny square of light high overhead. It was a three-compartment vertical shaft that eventually reached a depth of 4764 feet, but the mine didn't stop here for an inclined winze descended still deeper until the record vertical depth of 5912 feet was reached.

An enclosed headframe and hoisting works were features of the South Shaft of the Kennedy. After 1900 most of the operations centered around the new vertical East Shaft which was sunk about two thousand feet east of the North and South shafts. Lower photo shows the timber yard, mill (center) and the wooden headframe of the East Shaft. *(upper photo, California Division of Mines and Geology; lower, Arthur B. Foote)*

V. S. Garbarini, who later became superintendent of the Argonaut, was given the task of building a permanent hoisting works. The plans called for a 1000-horsepower hoist capable of raising five-ton skips from a maximum depth of 5000 feet.

At the same time superintendent J. F. Parks had crews grading for the new stamp mill which first called for forty stamps, then twenty more were added and finally in 1904 the old forty-stamp mill at the North Shaft was moved, making a total battery of 100 stamps at the new mill site adjoining the new east shaft.

Although the ore continued good, the year 1906 brought a scarcity of men and materials due to the great reconstruction following the San Francisco earthquake and fire. This affected other mines along the Mother Lode as well as the Kennedy. Although the wage scale for miners ranged from $3.00 to $4.50 a day, many men deserted the mines attracted by the $4.00 a day offered in San Francisco for hod carriers and helpers. Cement was also a scarce commodity, notwithstanding the large production in California even at that time, and the Kennedy mine was forced to delay the placing of their new compressor for want of cement for the foundation.

Some of the problems faced by the Kennedy through the years were the direct result of having another operating gold mine as a neighbor. For instance, as early as 1884 the Argonaut Mining Company brought suit against the Kennedy Mining and Milling Company in a case involving the question of trespass into Argonaut ground. In this it was the Argonaut's charge that the Kennedy people had been working the Argonaut side of the Pioneer claim on many of their levels, taking out a large quantity of rich quartz. The suit was to be a great inconvenience and expense to the Argonaut Mining Company for in order to prove their case they were forced to discontinue sinking the large incline shaft while they set to work following the Pioneer vein in order to establish to the satisfaction of the court that it continued on through to its apex in Argonaut property. In 1912 the Kennedy filed a countersuit and the legal battle grew more and more complicated. As late as 1914 it was still in the courts and today in the Amador County Museum the visitor may see a sectional model of the disputed portion of the

mine that appeared as "exhibit A" in this famous case.

The end result of all of these suits was that the court decided that the Argonaut Mining Company had proved its case and they were awarded heavy damages against the Kennedy Mining and Milling Company. Oddly enough over the years the disputed Pioneer mine had been offered several times to the Kennedy company for the nominal price of $30,000 but it had been rejected, an ironic footnote to the years of costly litigation.

The Kennedy's tangles with the Argonaut were not to end here, for like Siamese twins the fate and fortunes of one affected the other.

In the spring of 1919 a fire, thought to have been of incendiary origin, was discovered on the 4000-foot level of the Argonaut mine. Within a short time the fire was thought to have been brought under control and work was resumed; however, early in March, 1920, one year later, fire broke out in the adjoining Kennedy mine, having presumably eaten its way through old workings and caved ground. When all standard fire-fighting procedures failed to contain the fire the Kennedy management began flooding the mine with water and as the two mines were connected the water rose in the Argonaut as well, coming to within fifty feet of the 3150-foot level which caused all operations to cease.

Unwatering began at the Argonaut early that summer (1920), but the load was soon found to be too much for their plant alone and the Kennedy joined in the work, which was not completed until April 1921 and it was not until the end of the year that the connection between the two mines was bulkheaded and operations were back to normal in both mines.*

Eight months later fire again broke out in the Argonaut. This time it was the tragic holocaust of 1922 that was reported in detail in the previous chapter, and once again the Kennedy found itself involved in the affairs of its neighbor. The cooperation of the Kennedy management in dropping all normal activity to deploy men and machines in the rescue effort was commendable as was the releasing by both mines of the maps and surveys that had still been kept top secret because of the

---

*It has been estimated 190,000,000 gallons of water flowed into both mines before the fire was extinguished.

This complicated-looking wooden headframe stood over the Kennedy vertical shaft from 1900 until 1926 when it was replaced by a steel structure 100 feet high. The steam hoist (below) was also replaced with a new electric hoist at that time. Both hoists were double drum on a single shaft and operated counter-balanced cages, that is one would be at the bottom of the shaft when the other was at the surface. Notice in this photo the drum on the left is wound full while the one on the right is nearly empty. *(Arthur B. Foote)*

long history of litigation. The Kennedy was again shut down, for a short time, while the more severely damaged Argonaut required a full year to be rehabilitated. As the result of these fires both mines suffered severe financial setbacks.

In spite of large losses the Kennedy now began a program of development under the superintendency of Webb Smith. This included expenditures for improvements in the hoisting plant and a refuge chamber, accessible in time of accident from both the Kennedy and the Argonaut. The condition of the mine as regards ore prospects was more promising than ever and once again the Kennedy settled down to a steady operation.

In November 1926 the Kennedy main shaft was changed over from steam to electric power with the installation of a thousand horsepower electric hoist and a new electrically driven air compressor, although the steam engines were left intact for emergency use. The old wooden headframe was replaced with a beautifully engineered steel structure 100 feet high. With the new headframe and equipment it was now possible to raise skips with a capacity of 32 men up the shaft at the rate of 2000 feet a minute* The following month (December) the North Shaft, which had still been using water power, was changed over to electric power, making the Kennedy 100 per cent electrically powered as were the other mines in Amador by this time.

On September 7, 1928, the Kennedy mine was to become once again the victim of fire. This time entirely on its own property a disastrous blaze destroyed all of the surface plant except for the mill and main office building. The plant was rebuilt in 1929.

In 1939 E.C. Hutchinson, who had been president of the Kennedy Mining and Milling Company for many years, was succeeded in that office by Joseph R. Knowland, publisher of the Oakland *Tribune*.

The mine was closed in November 1942 in compliance with the U. S. Government's wartime

---

*By comparison the high-speed elevators in the new 52-story Bank of America Building in San Francisco can do 1600 feet a minute. The ones in the 110-story World Trade Building in New York will approach 2000 feet a minute. Of course, the greater the length of the shaft the higher the possible speed, but 2000 feet per minute is considered very fast even today.

order L-208, from which it never recovered. After the War, between 1948 and 1950, the tailings were worked intermittently by several lessees, and in September 1950 the Kennedy Mining and Milling Company went out of existence.

Mark Eudey, who had been superintendent from 1939 until the very end, purchased the property and remained at the mine for several years. Since then the mine has been acquired by Mrs. Sybil Arata, who spent her childhood in Jackson although she is now a Bay Area resident.

Though the Kennedy is not operated as a tourist attraction, Mrs. Arata has conducted occasional surface tours of the property during the summer months and has also presented weekend theatricals in the old change house. Good use will eventually be made of this beautiful California hillside land, but economic conditions would seem to indicate that it will never in our time replay its role as a major producing gold mine.

One of the distinctive features of the Kennedy mine readily accessible to the visitor is the famous tailing wheels. These huge wheels, four in number, are located at the southern end of the Kennedy property at Jackson Gate one mile from the town of Jackson. Often depicted in booklets and articles on the Mother Lode, these wheels have now been acquired by the County of Amador as a public monument and judging by the number of tourists, artists and photographers who make the short detour from Highway 49 to visit the wheels, they are indeed a popular attraction.

Since the wheels are located a considerable distance south of the Kennedy mine some confusion has existed as to just what function these giant structures performed in the mining process. The simple explanation is that they were elevator wheels* which, when equipped with redwood buckets (long gone) along the outside perimeter of the wheel, would boost the semi-liquid residue from the mill approximately half the diameter of the wheel before it was dumped on its downward sweep. In this way a series of four wheels with a diameter of 58 feet, each one taking over where the other one left off, would raise the tailings a total of 176 feet; however, in this case the wheels were not closely connected. In fact, wheels No. 2 and No. 3 were separated by a flume 800 feet long

---

*The only ones in California.

At left is a close view of two of the amalgamating plates at the base of the stamps at the Kennedy mill. Stamp mill castings indicate the machinery was built by "Knight & Co., Sutter Creek, Cal." The lower picture is an exterior shot of the 100-stamp mill. Ore cars from the East Shaft were trammed over the trestle at the right of the photo to the top of the mill. (*Arthur B. Foote*)

which crossed the Jackson Gate road on a high trestle. In order to keep the thick solution, consisting of crushed quartz, sand and water, moving it was necessary to provide the flume connecting the wheels with a downhill grade of seven-eighths of an inch for every running foot. Naturally this caused a loss in some of the height gained during the elevation. Taking this into consideration the net vertical lift provided by the four wheels would be 128 feet. This was carefully calculated to be just the proper elevation needed to lift the tailings over two small hills to the tailings pond provided by a dam on the other side.

To the modern engineer this may seem like a Rube Goldberg way to elevate material, but at the time this system was devised there were no centrifugal pumps generally available that would stand up to the abrasive action of finely ground quartz.

Prior to the wheels, the Kennedy mine merely deposited its tailings in the valley at the base of the mill where much of the liquid found its way into the North Fork of Jackson Creek. With increased quartz mining activity in California at the time, this type of disposal was getting the deep mine operators into precisely the same kind of trouble as the hydraulic miners faced a few years earlier. Finally in 1912 the California state legislature passed an act which compelled all mining companies to impound their tailings or cease operations. This was a "no nonsense" law and its immediate effect was to cause the shutdown for want of a disposal site of the famous old Zeila mine, located within the southeast City Limits of Jackson. It forced the Argonaut mine to move its mill from a site below the present Highway 49 to the top of the hill (about the location of the present telephone company microwave installation) where the tailings would be conducted by gravity to a valley west of the mine, and it caused the Kennedy Company hurriedly to seek an acceptable solution if they were to stay in business.

Thus it was that when the Kennedy management learned of a wheel system being used in Montana for a similar purpose, they dispatched a mechanical engineer named James Spiers* to report on its feasibility. His findings were favorable and upon his return he was authorized to design a series of elevators for use at the Kennedy.

The wheels were laid out and constructed on the flat area of the waste dump at the mine under the charge of Mr. Elbridge Post, the mine's master mechanic, and the construction foreman, Mr. William Daugherty.

In the meantime the sites had been graded, foundations poured and timber supports built large enough to accommodate the heavy main bearings, hub and the shaft, which was 11 inches in diameter, and, of course, the weight of the wheel itself.

When this was completed the wooden wheels were plainly marked, dismantled and hauled by wagons to the permanent site, where they underwent final assembly.

A laminated wooden pulley forty feet in diameter was built into the wheel structure. This powered the wheel by means of a canvas belt three-quarters of an inch thick, twenty inches wide, 125 feet long and weighing approximately 800 pounds. Its area of contact with the pulley was at least 270 degrees, which was more than ample in achieving an efficient transfer of power. The driving end of the belt was a cast iron pulley four feet in diameter which was in turn connected by means of gears to a 25-horsepower induction motor. The diameter of the pinion gear was 16 inches, the master gear 48 inches and the ratio was three to one. The wheels rotated 14 revolutions per minute and at that speed the 208 redwood buckets very nicely handled the entire tailing output of the 100-stamp Kennedy mill, a matter of some 850 tons every 24 hours, not counting the water content.

When completed each wheel was enclosed in its own corrugated iron building for protection against the weather; and so they operated 24 hours a day from the day they first began in 1914 until the closing of the mine in 1942, 28 years continuously performing the task they were designed to do.

The wheels would have chalked up a 100 per cent record in the service of mankind had they

*Mr. Spiers later became superintendent of the Kennedy and the Central Eureka. Although there were undoubtedly tailing wheels in use in Montana at the time, T. Calvert Slater, who was engineer, geologist and later superintendent at the Central Eureka, recalls Spiers telling him that the wheels were modeled after a system being used in South Africa.

119

On September 7, 1928 the Kennedy mine was hit by a surface fire that destroyed the classic wooden headframe and all of the plant buildings except the mill and main office, but they were rebuilt and back in operation by the following year. However, shortly after completion another fire destroyed the new headframe and adjacent buildings (above). Lower, the Kennedy surface plant as rebuilt. Large building is the 100-stamp mill. The second steel headframe with ore bins and primary crusher, built at a cost of $210,000 is right of center. Hoisting works, shop buildings and change house are to the right of headframe. The main office building with its wide veranda is in the center of the photo. *(upper photo, A. "Babe" Garbarini collection; lower, California State Library)*

not shown their steel teeth to one of their masters. It was a bitterly cold night in January 1930 when Ed Purcell reported for the night shift. After exchanging a few comments with the man he was relieving, Ed was left alone. Although there was a wood fire blazing in the stove it was still not warm enough in the drafty building to dispense with his overcoat. It was this bulky old overcoat that somehow got caught in the big gears and pulled Ed into the menacing teeth. Although badly mangled he managed to escape and started toward the distant mine to obtain help. The next morning when the day man reported for work he found the big wheels steadily turning, but there was no sign of the operator and the stove was stone cold, indicating that he had not been there for some time. Quickly the morning man went from wheel to wheel and there, about halfway between wheel No. 1 and No. 2, lying in the snow, was the body of Ed Purcell.

A shift stands ready to descend to the depths of the Kennedy. One cage is at the bottom of the mine and the other one can be seen at the surface landing. The long, narrow sheet iron box to the right of the cage is a water bailer and is lowered in the shaft to collect water. Some mines can be kept dry by this method instead of pumping. The numbers on the vertical board with the arrow pointing at "43" indicate the height of water in the sump at the bottom of the shaft. (A. "Babe" Garbarini collection)

The picture below, looking roughly southeast, gives a clear idea of the route taken by ore from the vertical shaft of the Kennedy. Hoisted from the depths of the mine and dumped into the bins attached to the headframe, the ore was first crushed and stored waiting transport to the mill. Ore cars then made the short haul from the bins to the mill over the connecting bridge. The material was further crushed by the stamps and processed in the mill. After being relieved of the gold the semi-liquid residue went by pipeline and flume to the bottom of the little valley below. From there it was lifted over the hill to a more suitable storage area by means of a chain of elevator wheels. These wheels were enclosed in a series of four large buildings which can be seen to the right of the photo just above the mill.

Both the Kennedy management and the manufacturer, Allis-Chalmers, were justifiably proud of the immense hoist shown at right, built entirely to Kennedy specifications in 1929. Powered by an 800 horsepower electric motor this model plant provided high speed vertical transportation in the mile deep East Shaft. This drawing, made for an Allis-Chalmers advertisement appearing in the technical press at the time, was designed to inform the engineering world of the achievement.

At lower right are familiar Kennedy tailings wheels which have been used by many artists and photographers to provide an interesting foreground to pictures of the mine. In distance can be seen the headframe, office building and the 100-stamp mill now in a state of complete collapse. (below, *Stuart Library of Western Americana; top right, Morgan North*)

At left is the main office building of the Kennedy Mining and Milling Company photographed from the headframe in 1967.

This spool-shaped construction is the tailings dam which was built around 1914 to provide storage area for the Kennedy tailings.

For forty-two years mill tailings were lifted by the Kennedy wheels and allowed to fill a small valley east of the town of Jackson and south of the mine. After World War II this huge quantity of previously milled quartz was reworked for the values it still contained. Above is the cyanide plant operating at the site between 1948 and 1950. *(Mrs. Emmet H. Garbarini collection)*

On the side of Sutter Hill, just below the steel headframe which once presided over the Central Shaft, can be seen (1970) the ruins of the Central Eureka mill. Here 40 stamps steadily dropped on Eureka ore which, when ground fine, yielded its gold with 95% efficiency.

CHAPTER 8

THE CENTRAL EUREKA
1855 to 1958
Sutter Creek, Amador County
Incline depth 4,855 feet (65 degrees)
Total production $36,000,000

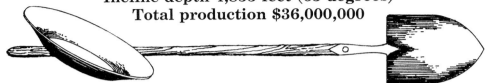

One of the most picturesque little towns along the Mother Lode is Sutter Creek with its iron-shuttered buildings and veranda-covered sidewalks. It is also one of the cleanest, thanks to the city's long-established custom of hosing down its main street every Friday morning, but perhaps the best thing to be said for Sutter Creek is that in spite of its authentic Gold Rush appearance, it has not yielded to the temptation to become a tourist attraction. Although rich in the part it played in the golden days of California, it has not commercialized on its past and today remains a quiet town of freshly painted houses set back among brightly colored flowers and velvet green lawns.

Without acquiring the ugliness of most mining towns, Sutter Creek became the center of an amazing concentration of some of the most active and profitable of the deep quartz mines of the Mother Lode. Associated with the town and the mines there was an equally amazing array of personalities whose names will be recognized by anyone familiar with California history, beginning, of course, with the man who lent his name, General John A. Sutter.

Sutter had a saw mill there in 1846, long before the excitement of gold was in the air, but moved it to Coloma to be closer to his New Helvetia (Sacramento Valley) holdings. Sutter had no way of knowing that his new mill site would be the location of the discovery of gold in 1848 and that men seeking the yellow metal would one day overrun California, trampling in the dust his dream of a vast agricultural empire.

By 1851 the hard-rock era of California gold mining had just begun and one of the leading prospects in the Sutter Creek district was the Union mine. It boasted one of the first stamp mills in the area and had high hopes for the future.

Most of the investors were local people although there were some outsiders, including a man named Leland Stanford. Stanford had done some mining at Michigan Bar but gave it up and moved down to Sacramento, where he had been doing very well in the grocery business. Stanford's interest in the Union mine, renamed the Lincoln in the late 1850s, was sufficiently large so that when the mine began to lose money he came up from Sacramento to do something about it.

Not one to send good money after bad, Stanford intended to cut his losses by unloading the mine at almost any price; perhaps recovering something from the machinery and calling it a day. He set his bailing-out price at $5000.

R. C. Downs, a local resident and also a stockholder in the mine, felt it was a mistake to give it up and finally persuaded Stanford to give it one more chance. Together they bought out some of the smaller discouraged stockholders and Stanford returned to his store in Sacramento, leaving Downs in charge of the mine.

The gamble paid off, for in less than a year the vein was found again and the Lincoln mine went into a bonanza period, producing between 1860 and 1873 $2,200,000 in gold. Stanford finally sold out, but this time for $400,000, and went on to become one of the builders of the transcontinental

Left, steel headframe, hoist house, primary crusher, ore and waste bins at the Central Eureka mine, Sutter Creek. Just down the hill from the Central Eureka was the Eureka mine (center), sometimes called the Old Eureka or the Hetty Green after its one-time owner. The huge pile of rock at the southern end of the town of Sutter Creek is the dump and all that's left of the Eureka mine. Photo below shows the headframe with steam hoisting plant at the South Eureka. *(top, L. A. Norman, Jr. collection; center, A. "Babe" Garbarini collection; bottom, Arthur B. Foote)*

railroad, a governor, senator and founder of the world-famous Stanford University.

Another prominent name associated with Sutter Creek was Alvinza Hayward.* It was said that at one time his personal income amounted to over $50,000 a month. The brick building that was once Hayward's office is still standing at Sutter Creek along with the old Masonic Hall, the Keyes Building and other structures of that era.

But success was elusive for Hayward, and he went broke several times before his luck began to change and his mining ventures started to pay off. He was still trying to put together the foundation of his mining empire when he acquired an interest in the Badger mine, which had first been worked in 1853.

Hayward now owned the largest interest in the mine and for a time was encouraged by the prospects; however in 1857 there came a time when a barren streak of over 400 feet was encountered where the quartz was of such low grade that it failed to pay expenses. Each month there was a growing deficit and finally Hayward reached the limit of his resources and credit. At this point Oscar Chamberlain, an old friend and partner with whom Hayward had come to California from Maine, stopped by to say goodbye to Alvinza.

Chamberlain had also failed in mining and out of desperation turned to raising potatoes, from which he had cleared over $6000 in three years. Now he was going to return to Maine to claim "the girl he left behind" and settle down. Hayward, hating to see his old friend go, especially with the $6000 in potato money, argued that Chamberlain should remain in California and invest his money in the mine. The amount was just enough to buy a half interest in the property, Hayward stated, and he even promised him a job as hoisting engineer which would bring in eating money until the investment paid off. Chamberlain finally weakened and turned his money over to Hayward with the observation that if they lost they would have to start another potato ranch.

The sinking of the shaft was now vigorously pushed with Chamberlain's money, eventually striking a pay shoot that was a veritable "treasure vault" and in a short time a half million dollars

was taken out. Two years later the "Hayward Quartz Mine" was consolidated with the Wolverine and the Eureka to become known as the Old Eureka, one of the most fabulous of the mines of Sutter Creek.

In the meantime Chamberlain married the girl, built a handsome house in Sutter Creek where his children were born, and settled down to live as befits a successful mining man.

One of his children became the Baroness Von Saelhors and lived in Germany for many years prior to World War I. After the war she returned to Sutter Creek with her son. Broken in health and stripped of her fortune, she died there in 1920. Her son, Eric, for a time resided in Ross, Marin County, California.

In March 1869 Hayward and Chamberlain's Old Eureka mine was sold for $750,000 to the Amador Mining Company. This company had as an investor and member of its board of directors an Easterner by the name of Edward H. Green. Mr. Green was the husband of the famous Hetty Green, the richest and most highly publicized woman of her day.

Born of Quaker stock, Hetty's father acquired a fortune in whaling and in the China Trade in the days before the Civil War. He died in 1865 and by his will she received about one million dollars outright and a life interest in nearly five million more. About the same time a maiden aunt died in New Bedford leaving Hetty a life estate in perhaps a million and a half additional.

Hetty had married Edward Green, a man of some means himself, and all during their marriage they had managed their fortunes separately; nevertheless Hetty came West with her husband while he supervised his investment in the Old Eureka.

The story is told that they lived in nearby Jackson for a time and Hetty herself worked around the mine during the six years her husband's company operated the property.* But the venture was not especially successful and between 1878 and 1886 the shareholders were forced to pay many assessments just to keep things going.

Green's failure to meet his share of the assessment payments caused the forfeiture of 12,000 of his 30,000 shares of stock, leaving him with an

---

*See also the Utica and Plymouth which were all highly profitable holdings of Alvinza Hayward.

*This may be a local legend as there is no mention of this in biographies of Hetty Green.

Left, main hoist and compressor room at the Central Eureka mine. Reproduced from the Annual Report of the Central Eureka Mining Company, April, 1933. *(L. A. Norman, Jr., collection)*

A distant view of the Central Eureka mine shows the steel headframe over the Central shaft and associated buildings at right of center surrounded by mine dump. The 40-stamp mill is the large building to the left. *(California State Library)*

ownership interest of 18,000 and then only after getting into some of his wife's money. It was at this point that Hetty banished her husband and closed the mine in 1881.

In the East Hetty was highly successful as a trader in the stock market and as a real estate speculator. Her holdings were many times the deciding factor in proxy fights involving some of the nation's leading corporations and her reputation as an "operator" gained her widespread publicity as the richest woman in the United States. To some extent she became the victim of a newspaper-invented personality that was partly brought about by her own eccentricities.

Many stories have been written and told about Hetty Green and like the aura surrounding any colorful figure, some have to be taken with a grain of salt. One of these stories, for instance, claims that once Hetty found it necessary to get from Philadelphia to New York in a hurry or lose a large sum of money. Taking the cue from other flamboyant characters of her era she chartered a special locomotive and car to make the high-speed run into New York City, but when she heard how much the railroad was charging her for the car she canceled the order and rode the entire distance in the cab of the locomotive.

Although no longer interested in California gold mining, Hetty continued to hold onto her husband's Old Eureka stock until 1916* when she sold it to the Old Eureka Mining Company for $500,000. Six months later Hetty Green died in New York City at the age of 81, leaving an estate of $100,000,000.

Needless to say mining promoter Alvinza Hayward, mentioned earlier, would have been the last person to sell off a property of value, so when Jerry Mahoney, fresh from Ireland, agreed to pay Hayward $1000 for a mining claim, Hayward must have thought he had really found a "live one." The mine in question was next to Stanford's Lincoln mine, which at that time wasn't doing very well either. But Mahoney's luck of the Irish saw him

*Hetty was not very popular in Sutter Creek for allowing the mine to remain idle for so long. When it became known that she had finally sold and a new company planned to start up again there was much excitement. A torchlight parade was staged with a band playing a popular tune of the day and the marchers singing their own version: "Goodbye Hetty, it's nice to see you go."

through and the "Mahoney Mine," as he now called it, proved rich almost from the beginning.

With his new property's earnings Jerry Mahoney sent for his four brothers and as partners they earned rich dividends for many years. Finally, following the death of his brothers, Jerry Mahoney sold the mine to a company headed by Senator Stewart of Nevada, who operated it until 1906, when it was acquired by the California Consolidated Mining Company. In 1914 the mine, along with the Wildman and the Lincoln, was purchased by a Duluth Syndicate.

The Mahoney brothers are buried in the old cemetery yard beside the little church of the Immaculate Conception, which they generously helped to build. A memorial window, still to be seen in the church, is dedicated to the memory of the Mahoney Brothers of County Cork, who made their fortunes in the new world and lived and died as good citizens of Sutter Creek.

One of the most dramatic and potentially dangerous episodes in the history of Amador County was the Miners' strike of 1891.

At that time the Miners' League, a new organization claiming to represent the miners of the area, many of whom were Irish, Cornish, Austrian and Italian, had a membership of about 300. A man by the name of Luke Burns, who had had experience with similar associations in Virginia City, was president and L. J. Marks, secretary. They built a large hall costing several thousands of dollars and began to function as a union.

The wages then paid varied from $2.50 a day for above ground to $4.00 for underground workers. The League's intent was to raise them to conform with the wages paid at the Virginia City and Gold Hill mines in Nevada.

Their first big tangle with the mine and mill owners was brought about by the reduction of 25 cents a day on the wages of surface employees at the Consolidated Amador mine, better known as the Old Eureka. After some discussion a general strike was agreed upon, not only affecting the Old Eureka but all mines in the district that did not agree to the proposed rates.

A committee of Miners' League members consisting of some 200 men visited the different mines and ordered them to stop work. It was said that the "committee" carried no arms in sight although according to some reports many of the men packed clubs which they took from the woodpiles at the mines. They would not permit any work to be done, not even allow an engine to be run to keep the water out. In fact, one engineer who stuck by his post after having been served notice to quit, narrowly escaped with his life. Regular peace officers were paralyzed and didn't know how to cope with such a widespread situation. Newspapers of the county printed very little about the strike, fearful that a wrong word would bring about retaliation.

The daily threat to life and the destruction of property so alarmed the citizens with families that they appealed to the governor for aid. General Cozenau and a body of Volunteers from San Francisco were dispatched to Sutter Creek, where they camped on a hill near the old Wolverine Shaft. They brought several artillery pieces with them and they set up a regular military camp* from which guards were sent out to patrol the various mines. Correspondents from the city papers accompanied the troops and soon gave the operation the name "Amador War."

The affair lasted several weeks, but eventually some concessions were made which terminated the siege and the soldiers went home. Ill feeling remained for some time, however, and it was said in subsequent years the memory of this "labor unrest" diverted many thousands of dollars from being invested in Amador County.

Sutter Creek came close to making a name for itself as an automotive center well before the turn of the century when its then dusty streets became a proving ground for one of the first autos to be seen in the Mother Lode. It was a three-wheel contraption built and owned by Mr. Louis Socal.

Making most of the parts by hand, using the forge in his own blacksmith shop, it took two years to build. The carburetor of his own design was made of cast iron and weighed 35 pounds. It was connected to the engine with a piece of one-inch hose three feet long. It worked, too, much to the delight of squealing children and barking dogs, but the one weak point was the ignition system which consumed a set of dry cells every two miles.

*Camp Colton

More practical products were manufactured in Sutter Creek at the famous Knight's Foundry. Established in 1873 by Samuel N. Knight, this concern became a leader in the design and construction of all kinds of mining and milling machinery, hydraulic engines, pumps and various other types of heavy equipment. Among its projects were the hoist and milling machinery for the Argonaut mine.

In 1898 Knight's Foundry successfully outbid competing giants of heavy industry and high up in the Mother Lode country, of all places, was built the machinery for a harbor dredger for the San Francisco Bridge Company. Later, based on the success of the first one, the firm built the dredge San Diego for harbor work at Seattle and in 1902 an even larger one for the Port of Portland.

Knight's Water Wheels, an invention of Mr. Knight, were rivaled only by Pelton and were in use all over the world. Knight died in 1913 and the business was taken over by two former employees. It is still in operation today and remains perhaps the only shop of its kind in the world still run by water power . . . still obtained from the old Amador Canal, now part of the P. G. & E. system.*

Despite all of its activities Sutter Creek is still mainly remembered as a mining center and of all the mines in the area the deepest, most profitable and longest to survive was the Central Eureka.**

Originally located in 1855 as the Summit mine it was abandoned as unprofitable in 1875 at a depth of 550 feet. In 1893 it sold for $6000 and was incorporated the following year as the Central Eureka Mining Company. With the exception of a shutdown of one year, 1907 to 1908, it ran on a paying basis from that date right up until 1942, when gold mining was suspended due to the government's wartime edict.

The Central Eureka's nextdoor neighbor to the south was the South Eureka mine. Developed

*In addition to contributing to the success of such large plants as the Risdon Iron Works and the Union Iron Works of San Francisco, the California gold mines produced notable manufacturers of mining machinery. They were D. C. Demarest's Angels Iron Works at Altaville (near Angels Camp), Knight's Foundry at Sutter Creek and the Miners' Foundry at Nevada City.

**It must be admitted that its success in later years was due to ore from the Old Eureka mine which it acquired.

in 1891 by Jackson Dennis of Sutter Creek the South Eureka was for many years a home-owned enterprise.

Until 1908 production was moderate, coming from small ore bodies in the hanging wall vein. However, in 1908 the footwall vein system was discovered and from that date until the mine closed over 980,000 tons of ore were produced. During the productive years that followed 200 to 250 men were employed full time.

Always known as a progressive operation, the South Eureka was the first mine in Amador County to use electric power exclusively. That was in 1899, while by contrast the Central Eureka was still burning wood in its boilers as late as 1902, when the change was made to crude oil.

Relations between the Central and South Eureka mines were mostly cordial and the two companies cooperated on several joint projects. One was in 1910 when an "agreement for air" paper was signed by both parties which provided for an underground connection at several points for the improvement of ventilation, for the promotion of greater safety and to facilitate operation in case of fire or cave-in.

In 1912 the South and Central Eureka Companies jointly purchased some land suitable for impounding their mill tailings. Also, the South Eureka trammed some of its ore over to the Central Eureka mill, where it leased twenty stamps until it finally brought its own milling capabilities up to a full eighty stamps.

Finally in 1917, after yielding a total production of $5,300,000 from which about $1,000,000 in dividends were paid, the South Eureka closed down. In 1921, after four years of idleness, the Central Eureka Mining Company took an option on the property and began some exploratory work from its own workings. Some of the deeper levels of the Central Eureka were extended into the South Eureka, the deepest being at the 4100-foot level. They also kept the South Eureka workings unwatered and the shaft in repair, but the result of this work was disappointing as no ore of any value was found.

During 1924 the Central Eureka Mining Company purchased the idle Old Eureka mine, which adjoined their property to the north, for $150,000. This purchase of the former Hetty Green property

was deemed advisable from what Mr. Albion S. Howe, then general manager of the Central Eureka, had been able to see underground while visiting the neighboring workings and also as protection against possible litigation over line disputes which had proved to be so expensive to other mines along the Mother Lode. This, plus the fact that the Central Eureka property only ran 1200 feet along the lode line, provided good and valid reasons for acquiring the additional property. When the deal was consummated the addition of the Old Eureka now gave the Central Eureka Mining Company a total unbroken strip of 4400 feet along the best and most productive part of the Mother Lode.

Some work was done in the Old Eureka at the time the mine was taken over, but it was not until 1930 that the lower workings of the Central Eureka were completely abandoned in favor of the ore bodies of the Old Eureka and after 1930 all of the ore produced by the Central Eureka Mining Company came from the Old Eureka.

The consolidation of the two mines gave the operators of the Central Eureka two working shafts, namely the Central Shaft which was 4855 feet deep and the Old Eureka Shaft, 3500 feet in depth. Each was a three-compartment shaft with an average incline of 65 degrees east.

The Old Eureka mine continued past the 3500-foot termination of the main shaft by means of an 11 by 5-foot inclined winze to a total depth of 4150 feet. The ore from this portion of the mine was loaded into mine cars, hand-trammed to transfer chutes and hoisted up the winze to the 3500-foot level, which was also the main haulage way between the two mines.* From this point electric battery locomotives transferred the ore in six-car trains some 3000 feet south to the Central Shaft, where it was hoisted to the surface in three-ton skips. It was then delivered to the forty-stamp mill situated just down the hill a short distance from the headframe. The haulage of men, waste, timber, supplies and the occasional bailing of water was confined to the Old Eureka Shaft.

The modified square set and cut and fill methods of stoping were used with waste and later sand fill from the mill being pumped into the mined-out

*This was true after 1949. Before World War II the main haulage way was the 1200 level.

133

The Central Eureka's 40-stamp mill as seen from the battery floor shows the base of the stamps and the amalgamating plates. The stamp mill was locally made by Knight & Co. *(L. A. Norman, Jr. collection)*

The interior of the Knight & Company foundry at Sutter Creek which has not changed much over the years. Workmen here are putting the finishing touches on a mold from which mortars for a 5-stamp battery will be cast. *(A. "Babe" Garbarini collection)*

areas for disposal. This system had the two-fold advantage of providing out-of-sight storage for tailings combined with furnishing added support to the mine by the filling of abandoned stopes.

Because of the heavy ground the workings would not stay open for long periods of time unless constantly maintained. This was true of all of the Mother Lode mines, and drifts, raises and stopes along the vein or in the slate walls required careful timbering. New levels usually required some retimbering and grade work during the first year, after which they generally required less upkeep. However, if completely abandoned they would gradually close up from the bottom and sides in a period of two to six years. In certain sections of the Old Eureka Shaft the life of timbers was only two years.

In 1934 Mr. Albion S. Howe, who had been general manager for 16 years, decided to quit mining and announced his resignation. In his place the board of directors appointed James Spiers, who had been with the company for six years as superintendent and was well known in Mother Lode mining circles. Mr. Spiers had been superintendent of the Kennedy before joining the Central Eureka and as a young engineer had been responsible for the building of the now famous Kennedy tailing wheels.

Between 1935 and 1939 the Central Eureka ran exploration drifts northward from the 2100 and 2500-foot levels of the Old Eureka, but no commercial ore was located.

The depression which so severely affected other industries produced almost ideal conditions for gold mining. The price of the product was stable, even increased in 1934. The market was assured with one ready customer, the United States Government, and operating costs were down due to low prices for labor and materials.

Even so, the Central Eureka incurred losses during the early 1930s; however, in 1937 the Old Eureka portion of the mine began to produce highly favorable results. Losses were erased, dividends were again paid and a strong cash reserve was accumulated to see the company through periods of difficulty. In fact it was this cash reserve that caused dissention in the ranks of the stockholders and prompted President C. C. Prior to send a letter to all shareholders enlisting their support. In the letter dated April 17, 1940, Prior directed ". . . their attention to a movement seeking to disrupt our organization with the promise of the payment of larger dividends, thus depleting our strong cash position."

Mr. Prior pointed out that the Central Eureka had paid out since 1937 $894,000.00 in dividends while conducting extensive improvements and replacements at the mine in addition to maintaining a large cash reserve. Thus, he concluded ". . . the record speaks for itself. The Central Eureka in the past 2½ years has gained in value from $240,000.00 in 1937 to more than $3,000,-000.00 at this date, according to market quotations plus reserves."

President Prior must have made his point as he and his management group were returned to office when the proxies were counted at the annual meeting.

In 1941 the board of directors, stockholders and employees were grieved to learn of the passing of James Spiers. In the annual report that year the president's message saluted Mr. Spiers as "a man of highest integrity and ability" and pronounced his death as a great shock and loss.

L. A. Norman, Jr.,[*] who had been with the mine since 1936, first as an engineer and later as assistant to Mr. Spiers, was elevated to the position of general superintendent. Unfortunately Norman was not to remain in command for long because on October 8, 1942, the Federal Government's now famous L-208 order closed down all gold mines as nonessential to the War effort.

At the time of the enforced closing the Central Eureka employed 118 men, was solvent and profitable and had a cash reserve of nearly $500,-000. Now, without income of any kind, the mine was placed in the expensive position of trying to maintain the property so that operations could be resumed at the end of the War. Naturally wartime conditions presented many obstacles. Labor, timber and materials were very scarce and, of course, gold mines were without priority of any kind for even the most essential items of maintenance.

The Central Eureka Mining Company even "went to war" by acquiring a lease-option on a

[*]Mr. Norman later became president of Equipment Engineering of Palo Alto, California, a company he founded in conjunction with Richard Krebs, who was metallurgist at the Central Eureka.

strategic copper-zinc development at Battle Mountain, Nevada, which it operated for a time as the "Central Nevada." Unfortunately values were insufficient to warrant continuation.

Finally in June 1946, much to the joy of the town of Sutter Creek, the Central Eureka reopened after being idle for four long years. But there was much to be done before the mine could be considered in first-class condition. There was water in the lower levels and the Old Eureka shaft was badly out of line. There was also some mechanical work to be done at the mill and elsewhere. Postwar conditions were entirely different, too. Everything was expensive. The oldtime miner was no longer available and the new labor was largely indifferent and caused a high degree of turnover. At one time the mine management tried Mexican labor from south of the border, an experiment which resulted in occasional knife fights and a brush with immigration authorities.

Yes, it was an entirely different economic world . . . a costly one which resulted in a net loss of $137,191.00 for 1947, the first full postwar year of operation. In 1948 the figure jumped to an astounding $403,659.00 which, according to the mine management was largely due to the "increased number of employees, higher wages and severe weather which caused some flooding and other damage." It was this bad luck coupled with the costly business of rehabilitating the property that depleted the company's remaining reserve and resulted in a series of assessments against the stockholders amounting to $1,149,000. Dragged down with these demands, enraged shareholders in some cases refused to pay, which caused them to lose their shares at public auction.

It was at this critical point in the affairs of the Central Eureka that Jessie Dean Swift came to the foreground. As a shareholder himself he was one of the many who had become irate at the management of the mine. Establishing what was called the "Stockholders' Protective Committee" Swift, along with three friends and business associates, undertook to unseat the operating officials of the corporation, an unprecedented feat on the San Francisco Stock Exchange.

Swift at the time was 46 years old, a graduate of Stanford University Class of '26, with varied previous business experience. Prior to World War

II he was connected with mining properties in California as well as holding a seat on the San Francisco Curb Exchange.* During the War he held the rank of Lieutenant Commander in the U. S. Navy and after the War he had divided his interests between the MacBride Realty Company in Sacramento and a partnership in the Swift Brothers Oil Company of Tulsa, Oklahoma.

Swift's associates in the venture were Donald D. Smith, Arnold E. Walters and Frank MacBride. Smith was 39, a native of San Francisco and already well known among businessmen of the Bay Area. Prior to World War II he was vice president of the Maywood Glass Container Corporation, a post he left to become a lieutenant in the U. S. Navy. After the war he had become a realtor and builder.

Walters was a resident of San Francisco and president of the Delores Company of California.

MacBride came from Sacramento where he was president of MacBride Homes, Inc.

Collectively they owned 9000 shares of Central Eureka with Swift holding 4000; Walters 3000; Smith 1000 and MacBride 1000. Using this as a base they mounted a vigorous and heated proxy battle which climaxed at the annual stockholders' meeting on April 28, 1949, and resulted in the unseating, by considerable margin, of C. C. Prior, who had been president of the company since 1936.

Swift, who had spearheaded the assault, was, of course, elected president with Arnold E. Walters vice president and Donald D. Smith secretary-treasurer.

The newspapers, obviously impressed with such a dramatic upset, called the new management team a "fountain of youth" and reminded their readers that "dynamic management with progressive ideas can frequently accomplish the impossible."

In his very first statement the new president assured the stockholders that the management ". . . is going to operate at a profit, not a loss." True to his word, six months later, November 1949, the mine showed a net profit of $21,427.00 for the month.

*The San Francisco Curb Exchange was consolidated with the San Francisco Stock Exchange in 1938 which in turn later became the Pacific Coast Stock Exchange.

Not one to lose an advantage, Swift asked the stockholders to approve an increase in the number of shares from 600,000 to 1,500,000. The increased capitalization, he told them, would put the company in a position to finance major development work.

At the annual meeting in April 1950 Mr. Swift was able to report that the Central Eureka had been operating at a profit for the last eight months. Needless to say it was a far happier gathering than the one held the previous year when the stockholders were told their company had lost $403,659.

In May the books showed a profit of $47,000 and by July things were going so well that Swift hosted a group of newspapermen and as they toured the property he told them how the Central Eureka had settled down to a steady profit of $25,000 a month. Optimistic reports also given to the press told of a rich vein of ore about three feet wide which, it was estimated, would produce more than $3,500,000 from the 3900-foot level alone. All of which prompted one reporter to write "The Central Eureka is operating night and day bringing up gold from some 3900 feet below the surface to sell to Uncle Sam, who in turn puts it back in the ground again at Fort Knox."

Another reporter told of making a trip to the 3900 level in the skip, a journey that took him eight minutes to complete. This is entirely possible as the Old Eureka shaft, which was the "man shaft" was not a precision shaft such as the Kennedy which was die straight through hard greenstone. The Old Eureka was always shifting and required constant work. As the result the skips were lowered with care and the ride was a crooked one at best.

At any rate these and other stories carried in the press at the time focused much attention on the Central Eureka. Financial pages frequently carried highly favorable reports on activities at the mine. The stock became so active that trading was extended to the Los Angeles Stock Exchange.

As would be prudent with any growing enterprise the Central Eureka decided to diversify and in 1950 formed the Central Mercantile Company with offices in San Francisco's Russ Building, also the business address of the mining company.

J. D. Swift was president of the new organization and Donald D. Smith manager. Central Mercantile dealt in building materials, industrial rubber goods and lumber.

With Central Mercantile well launched, President Swift predicted in January 1951 earnings for the coming year would come to 50 cents a share and at the same time announced plans for further expansion, this time into copper and molybdenum in Arizona.

At the next meeting in April the shareholders not only approved Swift's excursion into industrial metals but added oil and gas as well.

Not wasting any time Swift announced two months later that the company had secured an option on a copper property in Arizona and was studying the possibilities of investing in producing oil wells in Oklahoma.

Certainly no one could say that the new and revitalized Central Eureka was not an active company with wide and diversified interests, a remarkable accomplishment in that all of this had been brought about in the short space of three years.

Small wonder then that the financial community was surprised when in February 1952 J. D. Swift, hardly fifty, announced his retirement. To fill his place Donald D. Smith, the energetic secretary-treasurer was elected to the presidency.

The surprise generated by Swift's sudden retirement was nothing compared to the shock received on September 2nd of the following year when the former president of the Central Eureka Mining Company was indicted by a Federal Grand Jury on five counts of using deceptive methods to promote the sale of mining stock. Swift, who was now a resident of Tulsa, Oklahoma, was accused of issuing misleading reports indicating a rich new gold vein had been discovered which resulted in raising the value of the corporation's stock. "Manipulating" the sensational rise in the company's stock in 1951, the indictment charged, Swift gave out "misleading information" to the press and public that there had been a "new ore shoot." This caused the stock to jump from $1.10 to $2.00 a share and the rights from 5 cents to 52 cents overnight.

Swift, 52 by this time, was originally scheduled to be tried on an indictment accusing him of fraudulently manipulating the firm's stock. However, at the last minute the U. S. Attorney's Office filed a misdemeanor complaint in the form of a criminal information. Swift pleaded guilty to the lesser charge and was fined $5000 (the maximum fine could have been $10,000) by Judge T. Roche of the U. S. District Court in San Francisco.

In the meantime the Central Eureka Mining Company became party to a historic 100 million dollar suit against the United States in the Court of Claims, Washington, D. C. to decide if the Government had the constitutional right to shut down the gold mines in 1942 without compensating the owners.

Phillip Barnett, San Francisco attorney for the Central Eureka was on the legal staff that represented the three mines claiming damages. They were the Homestake Mine, Lead, South Dakota, the Central Eureka of Sutter Creek and the Idaho-Maryland, Grass Valley, California.

In 1956 Central Eureka attorney Phillip Barnett was highly encouraged with the progress of the case; in fact, he felt that liability had been successfully proven and the only question that remained was whether the mining companies could also recover loss of profit for the shutdown

period. However, it was not to be that easy and although the case was actively fought for a number of years no damages were ever paid to a mining company for that enforced shutdown during World War II.

The Central Eureka Mining Company meanwhile, under the presidency of Donald D. Smith, had changed its name to the Central Eureka Corporation and had transferred its headquarters to San Jose, where it embarked on a further program of diversification, including meat packing, rice mills, ship repair, a tannery, furnace manufacture and film developing.

Finally in August 1958 the unprofitable Central Eureka mine at Sutter Creek was shut down for good and the Central Eureka Corporation, now devoting its time to its other interests, became known as Pacific Industries. Today it still operates under that name as a holding company with interests spread from steel to carbon paper. It is still presided over by Donald D. Smith, who at 59 is yet the dynamic entrepreneur busily involved with mergers and acquisitions.

Many methods of keeping a mine dry have been used including drainage tunnels, bailers and pumps. This set of pumps, electrically driven, operated at the 2,000 foot level of the Eureka mine. Because of the pressure of the water there were similar stations on other levels. (A. "Babe" Garbarini collection)

The Central Eureka mine as it looked shortly after abandonment in 1958. By 1970, twelve years later, nothing remained but the steel headframe, which was being used to support the receiving antennas of a community antenna television company, and the ruins of the mill to the left of this photo and a short distance down the hill. (*Stuart Library of Western Americana*)

Easily seen from Highway 49 as it curves through Amador City, the rusting steel head-frame is one of the few relics of the Keystone mine.

CHAPTER 9

THE KEYSTONE
1851 to 1942
Amador City, Amador County
Incline depth 2,680 feet (52 degrees)
Total production $24,500,000

Just three miles north of Sutter Creek lies Amador City, the home of the famous Keystone mine, once one of the most profitable along the Mother Lode. Today Amador City resembles the main street of a TV western and claims the distinction of being the smallest incorporated city in California, population 202. But time was when this lusty camp boasted 5000 residents and a booming local economy that was fed by the town's main industry — gold mining.

Amador City was named for Jose Maria Amador, a soldier from the San Francisco Presidio, whom history credits as being a valiant Indian fighter.

In 1848 Amador and a group of friendly Indians established a camp on the banks of the creek which bears his name near what is now Amador City. In 1854 the name Amador was applied to the county as well.

During the fall of 1849 Amador City became the home of four ministers whose zeal for the gospel was second only to their zest for gold. However, one must live and it is to their credit that even after the long backbreaking days spent working their claims they devoted their evenings to preaching "soul saving" sermons throughout the surrounding communities.

It was one of these ministers, a Baptist by the name of Davidson, who is credited with the discovery of quartz gold in a gully which thereafter was called Minister's Gulch. That was in 1851 and it was truly a significant find as it marked the original discovery of gold-bearing quartz in Amador

County. Samuel Hill, a resident of Buckeye, was later taken in as backer and the company was organized as the Spring Hill Company. About the same time Thomas Rickey and his son James located a vein on the north side of the creek which later became known as the Original Amador. None of these men had ever seen quartz mining before. In fact, up to that time there was none in the world that could compare with what was soon to become common in the Mother Lode country.

In the enthusiasm to extract gold, the first stamp mill to be used in the area was brought in and set up. It worked with wooden-stemmed stamps about eight feet long actuated by a wooden camshaft. Mr. Hill of the Spring Hill Company went to Sacramento and bought a steam engine to power the mill. It was badly used and ancient in style and was first thought to be a failure as it took enormous quantities of wood to keep up a head of steam in the boiler; however, it was later rebuilt and some of the mistakes were corrected.

The mill on the north side was started about the same time (September 5, 1851) with somewhat better machinery although it was soon found that much of the gold was lost, being too fine to settle into the ordinary riffles.

It was about this time that a German, who had mined in Peru, arrived in the area and since the stamp mill was not the complete success it could have been, he worked out a system of crushing in an arrastra. Although the speed and efficiency of this ancient method leaves much to be desired, by crushing and amalgamating with mercury he

These two views of the Keystone mine were taken at different times, but the dates of neither are available. Bottom photo is a closer view of the mine buildings. Although some changes are apparent in comparing the pictures, the mill and shaft locations remain the same in each. The Keystone had an enclosed headframe at the time, a practice that was later outlawed because of the fire hazard. *(above, Morgan North; lower, California Division of Mines and Geology)*

was able to extract about 74 ounces of gold a week. This was quite enough to establish the Minister's Claim as the first successful quartz mining operation in Amador County.

Even though the early outlook for quartz mining appeared good, expenses multiplied in an unprecedented manner when underground mining was attempted. Heavy swelling ground was encountered and in some cases development proved so costly that the operations were abandoned early in the game. Numerous other troubles, both mechanical and metallurgical, caused the owners of many of the mines to become heavily involved in debt.

That mining was a touch- and-go business is illustrated by the story of the management of the Spring Hill mine. Being a little short of money at the time, they failed to pay for a quantity of hay purchased from a rancher near Campo Seco. After waiting a considerable time for his money the rancher employed the sheriff to watch the mill and take payment in amalgam at clean-up time. However, the superintendent, seeing the lawman in the vicinity, deduced his mission and took the amalgam down into the mine and hid it. The sheriff wasn't one to be outwitted by such an obvious trick and he went below to search for it. Seeing it was now his move, the superintendent stopped the pumps with a view to flooding the workings and saving the gold. The sheriff, however, managed to find the cache before the water had a chance to rise and quickly appeared at the collar of the shaft with the amalgam. The result was a happy farmer, but a light day at the mill.

In 1857 the Spring Hill mine was consolidated with the Granite State and Walnut Hill mines, which had previously been consolidated with the Keystone mine, and the new combination became known as the Consolidated Keystone mine.

As we have seen, the mere ownership of a gold mine, or in this case several gold mines, is not always the key to instant riches. The properties involved in this transaction were heavily in debt. A mortgage on the properties had been foreclosed, but a prior judgment in favor of A. H. Rose and Phillip Crusart took precedence.

Rose, who at that time was State Senator from Amador County, eventually became the sole owner of what then was as unpromising an aggregation of mining properties as could be found on the Mother Lode. It was worked in a desultory manner with the mill earning extra money by running ore for other mines whenever available. Thus, with many vicissitudes, the Keystone mine continued its unhappy existence.

Finally, having had enough of this kind of mining, Senator Rose sold the Keystone Consolidated mine on September 5, 1865, to J. W. Gashweiler,* John Henning and H. N. A. Mason for the sum of $108,000. Although never proven it was commonly said at the time that Rose added in the returns from custom milling to make the mine output look more attractive. At any rate, once having unloaded it, Mr. Rose is reported to have said "No child now living (1865) will ever live to see the Keystone mine a profitable enterprise."

The new owners, sufficiently discouraged, in turn lost no time in locating someone else to take it off their hands. Thus by December of the same year the property was again sold; this time to James McDonald, Andrew B. McCreary and others. The consideration paid at this transaction is not available, but presumably the owners would have been happy to have regained their original investment.

The mine, at the time it was acquired by Messrs. McDonald and McCreary, consisted of the Keystone and Geneva ledges and the Keystone mill, the Geneva being an extension of the aforementioned Spring Hill. The working shaft was only 206 feet deep and ore and water were still hoisted by a horse whim, although it was hoped this would be replaced by steam power.

The superintendent was John J. Faull and under his direction a twenty-stamp steam mill was working on available ore, which by this time was yielding a very respectable $17 a ton from the one vein being worked. Some of the miners conceived the idea that there must be another and perhaps better vein in back of the hanging wall. Accordingly a crosscut was agreed upon which would bear easterly and with the very first round broke into a vein actually bespangled with gold. Now, hardly in their second month of operation, the new owners found themselves in possession of a real bonanza. Within a month after the new discovery

*Also associated with the Empire mine in Nevada County.

143

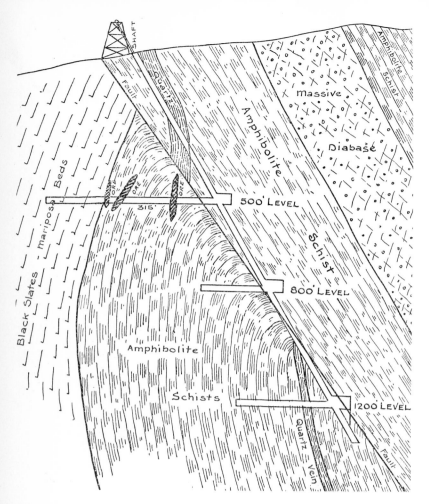

Showing conditions typical of Mother Lode mining is this cross-section to the left. The problems depicted are almost identical with those encountered at the Keystone mine. Here the vein outcrops at the point of discovery and an incline shaft is sunk to follow the vein. After a strong showing for a few hundred feet the vein dips into the footwall. At the 500-foot level a drift is driven off the shaft in an attempt to intercept the vein. However, the vein has faulted and does not continue past this point. Instead a series of ore pockets are encountered. After these are exhausted the shaft is deepened in a further attempt to find the original vein. Crosscuts are again started out from the shaft as probes. The vein, much narrower now, is again encountered at the 900-foot level. It was this type of hide and seek deep inside the earth that made deep mining such an expensive and fascinating proposition.

Below is a later photo of the Keystone Consolidated. At this point the mill appears in the same location as in previous photos, but the headframe enclosure has disappeared leaving the timbers to stand unsheltered. Although similar in appearance and location, this is not the same headframe that was left standing when the mine closed in 1942. *(Morgan North)*

the little Keystone mill had produced over $40,000 in gold and month after month thereafter that rate of return was maintained until the Keystone came to be recognized as one of the most profitable gold mines in the world.

When the Keystone broke into bonanza early in 1866, so soon after A. H. Rose had disposed of the property, it naturally caused him some regret. After brooding over the matter for nearly three years, he finally came up with a remarkable plan by which he hoped to recover the mine for virtually nothing. It is doubtful that a wilder scheme for regaining possession of property legally sold to honest men could have been devised. It's truly remarkable that the Senator could have had the audacity to try such a plan, but apparently nerve was not lacking in Senator Rose's make-up and he lost no time in executing his maneuver, without giving the slightest thought to possible failure or ultimate detection.

The method Rose intended to use consisted of no less a crime than bribing a United States Deputy Mineral Surveyor into returning a falsified survey plat to the land office at San Francisco.

In those days, prior to the official government survey, property owners had no accurate knowledge of their actual boundaries. Both mineral and agricultural land was bought and sold with the understanding that the actual lines would be established when the government survey was completed. Thus it was based on such informal knowledge, that the Keystone Consolidated, the Original Amador and the Bunker Hill mines as well as the Amador City townsite were commonly supposed to be on the west half of Section 36.

Now it also happened that Senator Rose owned a vineyard* just east of Amador City adjoining the Keystone mine. When the official survey was duly made in 1869 and J. G. Mather, government surveyor, filed a plat with the land office in San Francisco, it showed the mines to be situated, just as everyone had supposed, on the west half of Section 36 and the Rose ranch on the east half.

No one thought it strange then, when application for a patent to the east half of Section 36 was presented showing that a Mr. Henry Casey had purchased some property in Section 36 for $400

---

*This is the vineyard often mentioned in histories and guide books as being one of the first in California.

with Senator Rose acting as his agent. However, when the patent was issued by the State Mr. Casey promptly disappeared and Rose came forward to present deeds to the *entire* east half of Section 36 claiming it also included the Keystone Consolidated, the Original Amador and Bunker Hill mines and the entire townsite of Amador City!

Needless to say Rose's demands were promptly refused although there remained great concern on the part of property owners. The resulting confusion necessitated a new land survey which, when made, established beyond all doubt that the mines and townsite were indeed situated in the *east* half of Section 36. It also brought to light the highly interesting fact that Rose's vineyard and other properties were neither on the *east* or *west* half of Section 36, but actually in Section 31 adjoining! But this was no setback for the redoubtable Senator Rose. He insisted that since he had received a patent from the State of California for the east half of Section 36, as originally understood, albeit in error, he should be entitled to it. By this time fraud was clearly apparent, but Rose fought desperately and just as though right was on his side. He even maintained a lobby in Washington at great expense and brought every conceivable pressure, political and otherwise, to bear on the Secretary of the Interior, but without avail. How any man could be so completely exposed and yet continue to pursue his case is truly remarkable. The fact that the various governmental agencies elected to ignore his fraudulent claim is perhaps the only reason he avoided going to jail.*

Rose's bad temper must have grown even worse with each passing year as the fortunes of the Keystone Consolidated continued to prosper. In 1868 the vein varied from 12 inches to 10 feet in width and two shafts, each with its steam hoisting works, kept a steady stream of ore flowing to the twenty-stamp mill. By 1870 the twenty-stamp mill had been increased to forty stamps and the Key-

---

*A. H. Rose was at one time a shareholder in the Hayward mine (Old Eureka) having acquired the interest from the estate of one Charles McNemair who went to the Frazer River in 1857 before the Hayward mine became a paying proposition. Mr. Rose is said to have delayed the settlement of Mr. McNemair's affairs until he was able to contact the heirs in Illinois where he managed to purchase the whole estate, including the share in the mine, for $3000, a mere fraction of its worth.

Modified square set timbering was used to hold the stopes open while following the vein. In another underground view of the Keystone mine we see a heavily-timbered loading station. Chute in the center holds ore broken in the stope above. Ore cars are spotted beneath it and the ore is drawn out as needed. Note passing track to the right. *(both, Morgan North)*

stone was now such a proven producer that its production figures no longer made news. This fact finally prompted the *Mining and Scientific Press* to publish this paragraph in their May 5th issue of 1877: "Notwithstanding that this is undeniably the prince of mines in Amador County it figures but seldom in our mining reports owing to the fact that its yield of bullion month after month shows little variation. It adds close to $40,000 every thirty days to the gold circulation. Disbursements amount to $12,000 monthly, the paying out of this large sum chiefly to miners and other laboring men makes Amador City the liveliest mining town of its size in the State."

And so it went, month after month, year after year, this fantastic enterprise paid off in Midas-like giant jackpots. So great was their fortune during this period of high-grade ore that the owners declared dividends as high as $550 per share per month.

Naturally with such riches known to be available robbery was always a possibility and in the days when gold was freely bought and sold there was little risk in disposing of it. It was somewhere around the late 1870s that a group of Austrians who had been working in the mines were overcome by the temptation to acquire quick wealth. Their plan was not to rob the bullion shipment, that was much too risky, but to rob the Keystone mill. So they waited for the day when a large clean-up had been made. From a distance they watched the amalgam being taken to the brick building near the mill where it was placed in the retort. For several hours the fires were kept vigorously burning while the quicksilver was being vaporized. Finally when the process was completed there was left in the retort a sponge of gold worth over $50,000.

As the retort was still hot and the hour was getting late, the superintendent decided to return in the morning to open the iron container, and left the watchman in charge . . . an ideal situation for the robbers as now they had only to dispose of the watchman. This they attempted to do by boring a small hole in the window frame through which they introduced a quantity of chloroform. As might be expected this had little or no effect on the watchman; so next one of the Austrians boldly entered the retort room, quickly surprised the guard and before he could make any outcry, hit him over the head with a hammer. With the watchman permanently silenced, the would-be thieves, now murderers, turned their attention to the retort, but after opening the iron furnace door found the crucible still too hot to handle. Adding to their difficulties was their lack of knowledge of how to remove the key which would release the heavy cast iron cover to the retort. After fumbling with the problem they became frightened and fled the scene.

The crime was soon discovered and a posse sent out to apprehend the robbers. In a short time several of the culprits were captured while the others were killed during pursuit. One way or another the criminals were all accounted for and received speedy justice western style.

An interesting thumbnail sketch of the Keystone mine as it appeared during its heyday is contained in this write-up that appeared in the *Annual Mining Review and Stock Ledger* published in San Francisco in 1876:

"The Keystone, at Amador City, is unquestionably the leading mine of the county, and ranks among the first in the State. It has maintained its reputation throughout the years. The ore body is immense, some sixty or seventy feet in width, and remarkably uniform in its yield of gold. This is one of the oldest quartz mines in the State, and yet its depth is only between 700 and 800 feet. The ledge being so vast, it requires a greater length of time to sink a foot than in mines where the rock is smaller in quantity. The mine is controlled by a private corporation, and it is consequently difficult to obtain reliable information concerning its gold production. The yield may be set down at $40,000 a month. Month after month the gold approximates to those figures with very little variation. A new shaft is being sunk to the north of the older one, which has struck rich ore. A peculiarity worthy of mention in connection with this shaft is that the hoisting is done by water power by means of Knight's patent reversible water wheel and power gates. The machinery was fitted up by the inventor, (Samuel) Knight, of Knight & Company's Foundry, Sutter Creek, and works to perfection. It is the only instance where water power has been applied for hoisting purposes in mines, but the invention needs only to be

Looking south toward the Keystone we see the large mine dump, buildings and slanting headframe, just barely visible. Headframe and buildings in the left foreground are the neighboring Bunker Hill mine. Lower is a view of Amador City as it looked in 1968. (*above, Donald Segerstrom*)

brought into notice to be extensively adopted. All who have witnessed the hoisting works pronounce them the finest they have ever seen, while the expense is less than one-half of that of steam."

It is interesting to note in the above report the mention of the use of water power for hoisting, which effectively dates its first use for that purpose at least in California. The system later became quite common and for some years water powered hoisting machinery was in use at many locations throughout the California mining belt. However, the shaft mentioned was an auxiliary one north of the main or Patton shaft. As far as is known the Patton hoist ran on steam until 1902 when it was changed over to compressed air. In later years it was, of course, converted to electric power.

During the early 1900s things began to slow down a bit at the Keystone with the mill running on low-grade ore most of the time interspersed with a spectacular strike only now and then.

In 1906 it was rumored that the mine was to be sold to the Bagdad-Chase Mining Company of New York for one million dollars. Bagdad-Chase was at that time operating the Soulsby mine at Soulsbyville in Tuolumne County. The transfer was never made and in 1908 a company of Philadelphia promoters took steps to acquire the mine. Their deal didn't finalize either and in June 1909 James McDonald, who had been the principal owner and operator of the Keystone for 43 years (since 1865) completed a sale to the California Consolidated Mines Company, the company which was at that time operating the Wildman, Lincoln and Mahoney mines at Sutter Creek.

Up to this time the Keystone had produced a total of $17,000,000, mostly during McDonald's ownership. California Consolidated saw no reason why they shouldn't assume there was more where that came from and immediately set about to upgrade the facilities. They installed two new cables on the hoisting drums which would enable the company to sink 600 feet deeper. The work force was increased and the installation of heavier machinery was planned.

Unfortunately the ambitious plans of the California Consolidated Mines Company were thwarted by the performance of the mine itself. The Keystone, which had been a continuous producer for almost sixty years, was now no longer paying its way. Even the latest equipment could not recover gold that wasn't there.

Two years passed while the bills piled up and every blast held the hope of a new bonanza that never came. Finally the miners, who had not been paid for several months, brought suit to recover their wages and the property was soon scheduled to be sold by the sheriff. At the last minute the California Consolidated Mines Company secured a short extension of the time required to redeem the miners' liens on the Keystone as well as their Wildman, Lincoln and Mahoney mines, which apparently were also in trouble.

During this interim Mr. William J. McGee of San Francisco acted as trustee representing the holders of liens on the properties of the California Consolidated Mining Company.

Unfortunately the company was unable to make good its obligations in the time allotted and defaulted. Quickly a new company called The Keystone Mining Company, consisting largely of local and San Francisco creditors, was organized to take over the property.

R. C. Downs, superintendent under McDonald for a number of years before he sold to California Consolidated and had continued with that company, was kept in charge. By April of 1912 the shaft had been unwatered and repaired to the 1400-foot level and a pump installed to further drain the workings preparatory to sinking the shaft still deeper in the hope of locating a downward extension of the vein.

Sink they did! Down and down they went, hitting the 1500-foot level by June. The 1800-foot level was passed in September and by the spring of 1913 the miners had reached the 2600, having sunk the last one·thousand feet in ten months' time.

In August of 1913 the west crosscut on the 2500-foot level cut through a body of well-mineralized quartz. This looked so encouraging that Superintendent Downs gave the order to drift farther west as he believed the main fissures had not yet been opened.

Since so many local people were now concerned with the financial success of the mine, the Keystone Mining Company issued a circular in December of 1913 in which Superintendent Downs

Perhaps the best-preserved relic of the Keystone Consolidated is this handsome brick office building, now over 100 years old. Built in the early days of the mine, it also housed the assay office, melting room and gold storage vault. It now serves as a hotel. (*Stuart Library of Western Americana*)

stated the position of the mine in some detail. The language was miners' talk and fairly technical, but in a mining community that was not inappropriate. Most of the report concerned development and while it sounded as if the miners were busy as bees down in the Keystone, no mention was made of any ore being taken out.

The pamphlet concluded with a statement by the secretary, C. L. Culbert, stating that the receipts, June 10 to December 10, 1913, were $36,-372.00 with cash on hand, as of the latter date, in the amount of $3,829.00. Not a very substantial reserve for a business with some 80 to 100 men on the payroll. Yet the mine kept going and somehow or other managed to pay expenses:

1914 —". . . ore body at 2600 feet developing satisfactorily."

1915 —". . . 40 stamps crushing ore at the Keystone."

1916 —". . . some good ore opened at the 1200 foot level."

1917 —"$1500 profit in July."

But then in 1919 what little luck the Company had left ran out. The mine could no longer carry itself and after the collection of two assessments from the stockholders, operations were suspended.

For eight years, 1911 to 1919, the locally owned Keystone Mining Company had done its level best to make a go of it but the mining business is fickle to say the least and what riches remained locked in the Keystone were not to be theirs.

For a time the owners planned to keep the mine dry with the hope of trying again at some future time; however, this proved to be too great an expense and the workings were allowed to fill with water.

In 1920 the Keystone Mining Company gained control of the South Spring Hill mine which ad-joins the property to the east; however, very little was done until 1933 when the Keystone was reopened by the Keystone Mines Syndicate. After two years of rehabilitation and development work production was under way in 1935 and continued until the fall of 1942, when the Keystone, as all other gold mines, was closed down by government order. During this final seven years of operation about one million dollars in gold was produced.

With the exception of a small amount of work done in 1952 in the neighboring Wonder mine just east of the main shaft nothing has been done at the Keystone since the beginning of World War II.

There are still relics of the Keystone to be seen at Amador City. One of these is the Mine House located on the west side of Highway 49 where gold was weighed and shipped and the corporate affairs of the Company were managed. Now a quaint hotel, this brick structure built over 100 years ago was once the office building of the Keystone Consolidated Mining Company. It contains a number of functional rooms with such imposing names as the Retort Room, the Assay Room, the Grinding Room, the Stores Room, the Bookkeeping Room, the Vault Room, the Directors' Room and the Keystone Room.

Directly across the highway from the Mine House are the foundations of the Keystone Mill and high overhead and red with rust is the headframe of the mine. Engineered to stand at an unusual angle to conform to the 52-degree slant of the Patton shaft it once served it is still a dominant and symbolic structure as it rises above the town, a sizable monument to Amador City's golden era.

Other than that little else remains. The surface works have been junked. The shaft has caved. The famous old Keystone is now just another abandoned mine.

In 1946 when the Plymouth Consolidated mine was reopened by the Argonaut Mining Company, it was worked through the 1,280-foot incline Empire shaft. Its decaying headframe is depicted in this water color.

CHAPTER 10

THE PLYMOUTH

1852 to 1947
Plymouth, Amador County
Depth 4,550 feet (vertical to 1600, continued at 60 degrees)
Total production $13,500,000

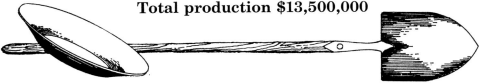

The Plymouth mine, located within the city limits of the town of Plymouth, Amador County, is the most northerly of the major mines along the Mother Lode.* Two other quartz mines, the Amador Star and the Bay State, are located four miles north of Plymouth, but production here was limited and unspectacular.

Very little is known of the early history of the little foothill village of Plymouth other than that at the lower end of the present townsite there was formerly a small settlement called Puckerville or, according to some accounts, Pokerville. Landmarks are totally lacking and very little evidence exists to account for either name although one theory expressed as to the latter has it that during the dry season the miners sat around playing poker while waiting for enough water to resume their operations.

Plymouth proper had its beginning with the advent of quartz mining when it was settled by a man with the unusual name of Green Aden, the Hoopers and other hard-rock miners.

The Hooper mine, originally known as the Phenix (sic) and later the Empire (not to be confused with the famous Empire mine of Grass Val-

*Actually the Mother Lode of California is a mile-wide belt of gold-producing country 120 miles long (162 miles by car along Highway 49 in the western foothills of the Sierra Nevada Mountains roughly from Mariposa on the south to Georgetown on the north). These deposits are not continuous, although popularly conceived to be one main quartz vein. Neither are they confined to quartz veins, for important production has also been obtained from the adjacent rocks.

ley), was eventually worked in conjunction with the Plymouth, but neither the mines nor the town amounted to much until 1873 when the properties were purchased by Alvinza Hayward, Darius O. Mills and Company. With the addition of new development capital and under the superintendency of Charles Green the mine developed into a profitable enterprise and the area began to prosper.

Like all early boom towns Plymouth was plagued by fire and as the result its volunteer fire company was kept in spit and polish condition. But even that gallant company was powerless to cope with the town's most destructive fire which began early in the morning of June 10, 1877.

Starting in a stable it quickly spread to the upper part of town and before it was over, twenty buildings were burned to the ground and the damage was placed at $50,000, a fabulous figure in those days. The early Californian was quick to rebound and before long Plymouth was going full blast again with 22 saloons and a fine race track one-half mile south of town, now the site of the Amador County Fairgrounds.

As Alvinza Hayward was a speculator in many mines (see also Utica and Old Eureka) it was not unusual that he also became a principal owner in both the Empire and the Pacific mines. However, there were other stockholders who held shares in but one. Thus when Empire miners working down an ore chimney ran into Pacific ground the Empire stockholders received benefits that should have gone to Pacific shareholders. This started a damage suit for $250,000 in which Hayward found himself on both sides of the same case. To further complicate matters the Merchants' Exchange Bank of San Francisco, through some other business they had with Hayward, stepped in as an intervener and the lawsuit became a triangular duel with Hayward involved all three ways. This rather unique legal mess brought an army of lawyers and shorthand reporters up from San Francisco and two thousand pages of testimony were taken to be used in the higher courts. The matter ran on for years and was only settled by the consolidation of all properties in 1883 resulting in the formation of the Plymouth Consolidated Mining Company with $5,000,000 in capital stock.

During the year 1883 the gold output of Amador County as compiled from receipts from the U. S. Mint had risen by $1,750,000, a heavy increase from the previous year. Much of this was due to the one million dollars produced by the Plymouth mine* which by then had settled down to an average yield of around $90,000 a month.

On January 9, 1885, the Plymouth Consolidated declared its twentieth monthly dividend by dividing a $50,000 surplus which amounted to fifty cents a share for all stockholders.

By now the operation was running smoothly and profitably. There were some 150 men on the payroll and an eighty-stamp mill was inexpensively operated by water power, the canal being owned by the company and receiving its water from the Cosumnes River. A large portion of the mine's timber and lagging was also delivered by the same canal. Although this method of transportation and power production contained certain obvious advantages it also had some built-in disadvantages such as occasional costly shutdowns during periods of low water.

In September 1887 the Plymouth Consolidated declared and paid its 52nd dividend, making a total of $225,000 for the year and a grand total of $2,800,000 in dividends to date.

But with such good fortune it was only the natural way of things that bad luck stood waiting in the wings. It struck early in 1888 when a fire

broke out in the lower levels of the mine. All of the men were safely evacuated shortly after noon on January 24th, the same day it started.

At first the management predicted only a short delay, but when March came around it became apparent that this was to be one of those stubborn mine timber fires. By April every plan devised for extinguishing the blaze had been tried and proven unsuccessful. The shafts had been covered with dirt in an effort to smother the flames. A chimney over the Empire shaft, intended to create a greater draft and thereby draw the smoke and hot gasses away from the Pacific mine, had been found useless for all practical purposes.

With the fire still out of control in May it was generally agreed that the only effective way to put out the fire would be to flood the mine, something the management was reluctant to do because of the damage that would result. Fire or water — a hard decision to make as both are equally disastrous in a mine, but since the fire had to be put out it was finally decided to flood.

By June the fire was dead, but so was the mine and the town of Plymouth as well. Houses and stores were vacant, something never seen since the town began.

News as to the extent of the damage and the Company's plans to begin work again was vague and unreliable. Everybody had a theory of his own and didn't hesitate to express it, which resulted in a mountainous array of rumors circulating to the great confusion of all. The most substantial one, which was printed by the Amador *Ledger*, placed the starting-up date as October 1st. But when October came and went and the Plymouth appeared as dead as ever everyone knew that the situation was more serious than originally thought.

During the following year some attempt was made to rehabilitate the mine, but when on August 3, 1889, a large cave-in occurred in the Pacific workings of the Plymouth, the mill was immediately shut down and the few remaining employees were laid off.

Now nothing was going on except the feeble gesture of keeping the water from rising. Again rumors flew with reports that the hoisting works had been sold and that the Pacific mill was to be torn down and taken to the Mulatos mine in Mex-

*The Keystone, running second, added $400,000 to the total that year, the balance divided up among the other Amador County mines.

ico, also owned by Alvinza Hayward and Walter Scott Hobart, his partner in the Utica.

All of these rumors had a depressing effect, not only on the town but on the stock market as well, with the result that Plymouth Consolidated shares, once the darling of the mining exchange, now sold for as little as $2 to $3 a share.

Even discounting the rumors, it now became apparent that the restoration of this famous old mine was not warranted under its present condition. It further looked as if Hayward and Hobart were preparing to transfer their attentions to other fields.

Those were the existing facts, but even so the public deserved a more satisfactory explanation, according to the Amador *Ledger* which expressed its opinion in the following editorial comment:

"We certainly think that inactivity calls for an official explanation on behalf of stockholders other than the board of directors. The management has been and still is the subject of severe criticism by the small holders of stock, and it is due to all concerned to determine from disinterested sources whether there are adequate grounds for the dissatisfaction."

The following spring some limited activity resumed at the Plymouth and this brought speculation concerning new development work that was supposed to begin a considerable distance south of the old Pacific mine and this was enlarged to include the possibility of sinking a new shaft. It wasn't until March 1892, four years after the fire, that any attempt was made to dewater the mine.

With 500 feet of water in the shaft it would take at least one to two months of steady pumping and bailing to remove it. The work had begun and with the new activity at the Plymouth it began to look like old times. Men were being hired and a general rejoicing was evident in the town.

But the rejoicing was short-lived for fire and water had dealt a near mortal blow to the Plymouth mine. Expenses proved to be too heavy a load and the resulting financial trouble ended in an attachment for $27,468.73 levied upon the Plymouth Consolidated Mining Company's property by H. G. Stevenson, an action which ended in a sheriff's sale that included all of the land, mines and ditches owned by the Company as of December 27, 1897.

The mine, or what was left of it, remained idle from that date until 1911 when the property was acquired by a firm that did business as the Plymouth Consolidated Mine Company, Ltd. The new owners immediately began to rebuild the works and by April of 1912 were making steady progress toward unwatering the Plymouth shaft with the water level dropping at the rate of eight feet per day. Conditions were not as bad as expected for when the shaft had been recovered to a depth of 800 feet it was found that only 14 sets of timbers had to be replaced. The work was accomplished without pumps and solely by the use of 500-gallon bailers and an electric hoist.

Although shaft repairs interfered somewhat with the bailing, the work on both accounts continued around the clock. The program called for the complete unwatering right to the bottom which at that time was 1700 feet, and when that point was reached it was planned to sink the shaft still farther.

In 1913 reports of important discoveries in the lower levels of the Plymouth were confirmed and the old mine began to develop rapidly. Two new ore shoots were found, the largest 110 feet long and averaging 3½ feet wide. Yielding $5 a ton, they seemed to validate the judgment of the engineers and greatly stimulated interest in mining along the entire Mother Lode.

By November the special funds set aside for development had largely been spent, although with such encouraging results that W. J. Loring went to London to consult with Bewick-Moreing & Company, the famous English firm of worldwide mine managers and financiers now interested in the Plymouth.

The W. J. Loring referred to was William Joseph Loring, born in 1869 at Half Moon Bay, California. As a youngster he worked 12 years underground as a tool boy at the Plymouth and later, after passing through all stages of mining and milling, became assistant general manager at the Utica Gold Mining Company at Angels Camp.

In 1894 he resigned to become manager of the Melones Gold Mining Company at Melones. It was during his management at Melones that he built the sixty-stamp mill and hydroelectric plant. Resigning in 1901 to join the staff of Bewick-Moreing

Galesio Caetani was the dashing Italian prince, mining engineer, statesman and one of the most unusual characters to appear on the California mining scene. Below is the Plymouth mill, which was built by Caetani in 1913 and was the last word in modern design. It introduced, among other features, the first mine-to-mill conveyor system to be seen in California which eliminated costly and inefficient tramming. *(lower, California State Library)*

& Company, he went to western Australia as general manager of the firm's interests in that part of the world with headquarters in Melbourne.

After purchasing Herbert Hoover's interest in the firm in 1908 he was transferred to the Company's home office at 62 London Wall, London, from where he supervised all actual mining operations conducted by Bewick-Moreing & Company throughout the world.

In 1914 Loring returned permanently to the United States where he secured for his Company several profitable mining properties in California; among them the Morgan mine and the Melones Mining Company (which were afterwards consolidated into the Carson Hill Gold Mines), the Pacific Coast Gold Mine, Calaveras Consolidated and the Plymouth Consolidated Gold Mine Company, Ltd., where his career began.

Thus it was that W. J. Loring, now 45 years old and a world-famous mining engineer and manager, was staking his professional reputation on the great possibilities he saw in California gold mining.

While Loring was back in London securing such financing as would lead to the full-scale operation of the Plymouth, things were not standing still at the mine. Before he left he had made arrangements to have a new mill designed and built by an Italian engineer named Galasio Caetani.

With the name Caetani we again delay our narrative of the Plymouth mine to describe this Italian, as unlikely an individual as you'd ever expect to find in the California gold fields.

Galasio Caetani, born in Italy in 1877, was a direct descendant of one of the most illustrious families in his country. Their name and fortune were traceable to the year 1000. The Caetani family produced four popes and had taken an active part in the struggle for the unification of Italy throughout its history. But in spite of his noble background and the wealth of his family, Prince Caetani from the very beginning had longed to make his own way in the world and since his early youth had devoted himself to the study of engineering.

In 1901 he graduated from the Royal University at Rome as a civil engineer and shortly thereafter, on the advice of Mr. Henning Jennings, a well-known American engineer who was at that time an associate of Cecil Rhodes in South Africa, sailed for the United States, where he entered the School of Mines at Columbia University.

After his graduation in 1903 he contacted two of the greatest names in mining at that time, John Hays Hammond and Fred W. Bradley. Mr. Bradley was the first to respond with a job offer at the famous Bunker Hill and Sullivan mines (lead, zinc and silver) at Kellogg, Idaho. Here the young Italian prince began as a simple laborer and gradually working his way up received invaluable practical experience in mining and milling. Displaying great proficiency in his chosen field, young Caetani on several occasions assisted the company president, Mr. Bradley, in examining various mining properties in the United States and Mexico.

For the purpose of gaining new experience Galesio Caetani went to the North Star mine at Grass Valley, California, and later to the Treadwell mine in Alaska. Returning to the Bunker Hill he studied the metallurgical treatment of ores and became manager of the mill, eventually building a plant of his own design. He was also entrusted to carry out similar assignments at mines in Colorado and Mexico.

Having gained a wide experience in both mining and engineering, Caetani then went to San Francisco where he formed a firm of consulting engineers in association with Mr. Albert Burch and Mr. Oscar Hershey and was soon doing business with a number of western mining companies such as the Goldfield Consolidated, Vanadium Corp., the Pacific Coast Gold Mine, the Mountain Copper Company (near Redding) and the Plymouth. Caetani himself designed and supervised the construction of the ore reduction plant for the Mountain Copper Company, and as we have already seen, was commissioned by W. J. Loring to build the new mill at the Plymouth mine.

A respected specialist in metallurgy, Caetani became one of the outstanding contributors to the mining and scientific press and was frequently called upon to deliver learned papers at mining congresses.

The business of the consulting firm was prospering when World War I broke out, but believing that his own country would soon become involved, he hurriedly finished the work on hand and returned to Italy.

Back in his homeland Prince Caetani lost no time in joining the Italian Army where he became a second lieutenant of engineers. As soon as Italy became a party to the hostilities he asked to be sent to the front and was assigned to the Italian-Austrian frontier on a special mission suitable to his training as a mining engineer.

The 10,000-foot snow-covered peak of Col di Loma had become one of the most feared and formidable Alpine strongholds of the Austrian Army. For ten months the Italian Army had tried fruitlessly to conquer this "eye of the Austrian Army," losing over 10,000 of its best men in the attempt. Caetani's job was to mine Col di Loma.

Planning and personally supervising the tunneling beneath the dreaded mountain, Caetani surveyed his objective with such precise tolerance that part of the time his men were blasting through solid rock just 12 feet below the feet of the enemy!

In three months the tunnel system was completed; then high explosives were carefully brought up the mountain and passed hand to hand by the Alpini lying barefoot six feet apart along the passageway. Finally the detonation chamber was packed full and on April 17, 1916, at 11:35 p.m. the order was given to fire.

In a statement made several years after the war was over, Caetani himself vividly described what happened that night:

"I had expected a terrific explosion. I listened and heard only a dull noise and felt a quiver going through the rocks. For a moment it seemed to me the explosion had been a failure and that only one of the lesser mines had exploded. To observers outside it appeared that the earth moved almost slowly out of the crater. But when I came out to the surface, where formerly there had been a white peak with the Austrians clinging to its far slope, now there was only blackness and death."

For this wartime feat Prince Caetani was decorated and made a Captain in the Royal Engineers. He served in other important and dangerous capacities until 1919 when he was hospitalized for a breakdown in health brought about by long hours and the constant driving of himself during the war.

After his recovery he was selected to attend the Paris Peace Conference where he worked with Herbert Hoover, who was at that time heading up the Commission for War Relief.

Owing to conditions in his own country in the postwar period Caetani did not return to the United States but elected to remain in Italy attending to his lands and engaging in local politics. He served as an Alderman in the City of Rome and later as a Member of Parliament. When he finally did return to the United States it was as Italy's Ambassador to Washington, but Galesio Caetani, the Italian prince turned miner, never forgot his years spent in the mines and frequently referred to them in speeches and during press interviews.

But back to our story of the Plymouth mine. It was 1913 and Galesio Caetani, then a successful engineer of 36, was busily designing for the Plymouth the most modern and highly efficient ore processing plant ever seen on the Mother Lode, introducing to California gold miners, among other features, the first conveyor system of ore delivery from mine to mill. In 1914, although Caetani had left for the war by this time, his new mill at Plymouth was regularly returning a profit to the company. In fact, things looked so good that year that the Plymouth Consolidated announced that it was building a hospital for miners and would retain a resident physician.

Departing from a policy of secrecy usually practiced by gold mining companies of this era, the Plymouth people in what today would be called good public relations, issued a regular statement on production to the news media. No doubt in an attempt to encourage other mines to do the same the *Mining and Scientific Press* complimented the Plymouth management in the following editorial comment:

". . . this is a concise and interesting way in which to publish monthly returns and it would be of widespread value to mining men of the country if other Mother Lode companies would follow suit. No harm is done in such publicity while interest in the industry is increased."

These regular releases to the press reported good earnings with occasionally spectacular finds of gold all through 1916, 1917, 1918, 1919 and throughout the 1920s. W. J. Loring's group still owned the mine with Mr. Loring in active man-

At right is the steel headframe over the 4450 foot Pacific Shaft of the Plymouth mine. Ore skip can be seen in the center just slightly above ground level and close inspection reveals men standing near the shaft. The tall narrow box-like object near the left leg of the headframe is a water bailer which has been set aside until needed. The hoist was a Nordberg and was later sold to the Cresson mine, the largest producer at Cripple Creek, Colorado. Lower photo shows a side view of the headframe and the covered conveyor system that transported the ore from shafthead to mill. *(California State Library)*

agement, employing about 100 men. In 1925, it was sold to the Argonaut Mining Company, owners of the big Argonaut mine at Jackson.*

Very little work was done by the Argonaut people between 1928 and 1939 although a small amount of exploration was conducted in the upper levels of the Empire shaft. Most of the effort was directed toward the operation of a combined flotation and cyanide plant which the new owners had erected to treat the tailings. This activity was affected by World War II and by 1943 the mine was completely shut down.

In 1946 the Empire workings of the Plymouth were reopened by the Argonaut Mining Company

———

*Loring continued his active mining career until he was well into his seventies serving as Vice President and General Manager of the Hammon Copper Company, Ltd., Korkland, Arizona.

and they resumed the prospecting interrupted by the war. A small amount of pocket ore was encountered on the 400-foot level where an old drift was extended northward for about 700 feet, but the showing was not sufficient to warrant further exploration and the work was stopped early in 1947.

Nineteen hundred and forty-seven was the end of the line; not only for the Plymouth but for its parent company, the Argonaut Mining Company, for it was then that the board of directors recommended not only a shutdown of mining operations, but the complete dissolution of the company and the disposal of all its property.

Thus it was that the old Plymouth Consolidated along with the big Argonaut mine at Jackson was sold to B. Monte Verda and E. C. Taylor for real estate and salvage and not as two of the most famous gold mines in California.

Although the mines are gone, the Mother Lode town of Plymouth remains as a living reminder of a golden era.

Tiny and crude when compared to the big Nordberg used at the Pacific Shaft, this hoisting works serviced the Empire shaft where the last work was performed in 1947. This rusting machinery and a rotting wooden headframe are the last visible remains of the Plymouth mine (1969).

The Idaho-Maryland mill, once capable of handling 700 tons of ore every 24 hours, silently rests in ruin beside a logging pond. This mill not only processed the ore from the nearby Idaho shaft, but did a lively business in custom milling for independent mines in the surrounding counties.

CHAPTER 11

THE IDAHO-MARYLAND
1851 to 1956
Grass Valley, Nevada County
Vertical depth 2,200 feet
Total production $64,240,543

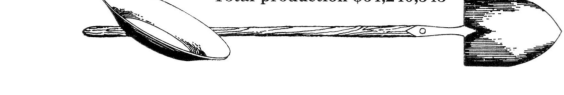

One of the most famous and productive gold mining districts of California lies some distance north of the Mother Lode. We refer to that area as the Northern Mines, or more specifically as the twin cities of Grass Valley and Nevada City. These picturesque mountain towns, both proud with accomplishment, are in many ways as dissimilar as they are alike (for instance Grass Valley voted Democratic while Nevada City was traditionally Republican).

Nevada City will have you know it was not named for the State, and actually it was the other way around. The "blue-black stuff" (silver ore) brought from Utah Territory and assayed at Nevada City caused a rush of its citizens to leave for the Washoe mines where they were called Nevadans. Others believe the name of the Silver State was a shortened form of the name of the mountain range.

Previously Nevada City had been known as Deer Creek Dry Diggings, and later Caldwell's Upper Store. The "City" was added in 1851 to distinguish it from the newly formed California County of Nevada.

Nevada City was in every way a mining town and many sizable and profitable mines operated nearby; however its fame was soon eclipsed by Grass Valley, its neighbor two miles to the south. For here was the site of three of the larger and richer mines in the United States: the Idaho-Maryland, the North Star and the Empire. These huge operations, virtually industrial giants of their day, made the Grass Valley of a century ago the eighth largest town in California, larger than Oakland, San Diego or Los Angeles.

During the Great Depression of the 1930s when the rest of the country was suffering from severe financial doldrums Grass Valley was a veritable boom town. The mines were at their best; unemployment was unknown and business in general was brisk. The lobby of the leading hotel was usually crowded with men in khaki, business suits and even an occasional dinner jacket. Many were with their ladies who appeared in equally varied attire. In fact so busy was this area during those dark depression years that traveling men passed the word that Grass Valley was the only town in America where one needed to make hotel reservations in advance.

The fame of Grass Valley was such that mining men from all over the world came to visit or work in the mines in order to observe and study the latest techniques in the science of deep mining and efficient and profitable recovery. That Grass Valley was the Mecca of the mining world is shown in this anecdote from far off South Africa, where a young and inexperienced mining engineer had gone to seek employment. After several turndowns he was heard to remark that he was going to the United States to spend one night in Grass Valley so that he, too, could add that magic name to his references.

It's little wonder then that many famous names dot the pages of Nevada County's colorful past. Among them would be George Hearst, father of William Randolph Hearst, who lived, mined and

163

sowed the seeds of the vast Hearst fortune at the Lecompton mine near Nevada City; William M. Stewart, the greatest mining lawyer of his time, now known as the father of mining law; Judge James Walsh, the man who later led the historic rush to the Comstock; A. A. Sargent, for a time the editor of Nevada City's pioneer newspaper, who became a United States Senator and later Minister to Berlin; Benjamin P. Avery, who became Minister to China; and former President Herbert Hoover who, with his newly won engineer's degree from Stanford, obtained his first mining experience at the Reward, Mayflower and Champion mines. These and many others, including John Hays Hammond and the Bradley brothers, were all graduates of Grass Valley's practical school of mines.

But mining men and politicos were not the only celebrities produced by those flamboyant cities of the Northern Mines. Actress Lotta Crabtree is said to have made her first public appearance as a small child by dancing on the anvil in front of a local blacksmith shop. Lotta, who went on to become famous in the entertainment world, was the protégée of the internationally notorious Lola Montez. Miss Montez had also been attracted by the widespread fame of Grass Valley and had come from Europe, where she was known as the Countess of Landsfeldt.

There is little doubt that Lola's presence added a certain Bohemian flavor to the Grass Valley social scene, although her reputation may have been a bit too much for the more respectable element of the town. It was common knowledge that the Countess was a well-known adventuress who had risen from a music hall dancer to become confidante, bedpartner and power behind Louis I of Bavaria. The resultant scandal and unrest was the cause of the revolution in Bavaria in 1848 forcing Louis to leave the throne and Lola the country.

Arriving in Grass Valley in 1853 with a pet bear on a silver chain, a hamper of champagne and trunks full of low-cut velvet and satin gowns Lola and her new husband, Patrick Purdy Hull, bought a home on Mill Street, which may be seen today.

Although Lola busied herself in domestic life, she is chiefly remembered for her Bohemian soirées to which she invited the young and spirited element, much to the dismay and perhaps envy of her neighbors.

One day, for reasons not recorded, Hull shot Lola's pet bear for which he was promptly evicted from the household and sent on his way. Lola soon tired of living alone and left Grass Valley in the summer of 1855 for a dance tour of Australia. She returned once more, but only briefly; this time to sell the only house she ever owned and move on. She died virtually penniless in New York in 1861.

No narrative on California gold mining and Grass Valley in particular would be complete without some mention of the Cornish miners who largely dominated the labor scene. These "Cousin Jacks" as they came to be called throughout the mining districts came into the picture when California mining entered the era of hard rock. This was a lot tougher than washing the gold from creek beds for now there was rock to blast, caving ground to be timbered and water to be pumped. The California miner was not knowledgeable in these matters. According to some writers it was General John C. Fremont, himself a mine owner, who hit upon the idea while buying mining supplies in London. At first he imported just a few Cornish miners picked for their experience with deep mining in the tin mines of Cornwall. They in turn, no doubt, wrote for their relatives and friends, who soon brought not only their mining technique but their customs . . . their odd speech, their songs, their saffron buns and, of course, the traditional pasty.* But most important of all they brought their centuries of underground experience which enabled them to get the gold "inside rocks" as the placer miners characterized the new mining. The Cornishmen in turn thought of the placer miners as "farmers rather than miners" as they went about showing them how it should be done.

Their skill combined with a strong national pride often caused other nationalities to consider the Cornishman clanish and it is true that he was so loyal to his countrymen that every time he obtained employment he would ask: " 'ave 'e got a job for my cousin Jack?", which dubbed him "Cousin Jack" forever after.

---

*A triangular dough casing shaped like a large apple turnover containing a meat pie-type filling that is equally tasty served cold from a miner's lunch box or heated as the main dish at dinner.

The whimsical side of the Cornish personality is demonstrated by their firm belief in Tommyknockers, those legendary elf-like characters who, according to Cornish superstition, protected the mine from cave-ins. These creatures derived their name from their habit of tapping on the timbers in the mine as a means of warning of impending disaster. The Cornish miner held a great respect for the Tommyknockers and a belief that was almost religious in its conviction, but the best definition of a Tommyknocker was given by an old Cornishman who described them as "little fellows who 'ave the miner's best interest at 'eart. We brought 'em 'ere from Cornwall. They make the mines safe when we go 'ome. They are a cross between a gnome and a brownie with a dash of Leprechaun among them."

One of the most pleasant of all Cornish customs is the singing of the traditional Christmas carols on Christmas Eve. This they have done ever since their arrival in the 1850s. Their fame so spread that for years they have been invited to sing in San Francisco and other cities. In 1940 the choir broadcast over a national radio network from the 2000-foot level of the Idaho-Maryland mine. The broadcast received such enthusiastic response from all over the world that it was repeated in 1951 and again in 1952.

The Grass Valley Cornish Carol Choir originated with the early Cornish miners imported from England to work the extensive underground quartz mines, and their singing has been a tradition in Grass Valley ever since. For many years the choir sang in San Francisco and other California cities. Here the group is shown singing from the 2000 level of the Idaho-Maryland mine on a nationwide broadcast on Christmas Day, 1940. The rock walls deadened the sound and the tonal quality of the broadcast did not do justice to the voices. Since the closing of the mines the group contents itself with singing on the steps of the Grass Valley *Union* on Christmas Eve. Their recordings have sold around the world. *(photo courtesy Grass Valley Union)*

Perhaps other than the presence of the Cornish miners themselves their one most important contribution was the Cornish pump. Without this cumbersome but highly effective device deep mining would have been utterly impossible.

The Cornish pump was simply a huge timber pump rod running to the bottom of the mine and operated with an up and down motion by a steam engine at the surface. The rod itself was then connected to individual pumps throughout the mine which would pump water from one level to the next until it had been lifted clear out of the mine. A. B. Foote, superintendent of the North Star mine in Grass Valley, acknowledged the importance of these pumps with this statement: "They were the most reliable and efficient means of keeping deep mines unwatered. A Cornish pump is a vertical shaft and is simple enough, but the idea of taking a wooden beam down the long and crooked shafts characteristic of this district, following the ups and down of the vein, would seem to be practically impossible. Think of a mass of wood and iron strung out for a distance of a half mile, weighing altogether over 135,000 pounds, moving back and forth, six feet at a stroke, four times a minute and doing this night and day for forty years!"

As we have already pointed out the Northern Mines are not to be considered in any way a part of California's Mother Lode district. Even the geology of the Northern Mines differs from that of the Mother Lode area. For instance, very little faulting has occurred in the Grass Valley district. Mariposa slate, so typical of Mother Lode mining, is largely absent and the Calaveras rocks do not usually contain gold. The ores of Grass Valley occur in veins caused by fissures in the rocks being filled with quartz and mineral-bearing solutions which have been shot up from the depths of the earth. The larger veins dip on an average of 35 degrees whereas the Mother Lode veins are usually steeply dipping. There are other differences too technical to go into, but one last interesting characteristic is the thinness of the veins, many averaging only 18 inches thick. Their small size, however, is offset by the greater values they contained and the fact that they ran for several miles and extended to unknown depths. Thus following these veins created a vast and complicated tunnel system which has been tabulated as follows: the

Empire-North Star group had an interconnecting complex 300 miles long; the Idaho-Maryland 90 miles, while the various independent mines contributed an additional 200 miles, thereby making a combined multi-tiered underground world with some 600 miles of passages . . . virtually all under the streets of Grass Valley.

Aside from the early explorations of the Spanish Californians, Grass Valley was first visited by French emigrants in 1846. Then some gold miners from Oregon spent considerable time there in 1848. Soon it became a welcome resting place for the wagon trains from the east that had just crossed that final barrier, the Sierra Nevadas. Both humans and livestock found it to their advantage to rest a bit in the grassy meadow around Greenhorn Creek. In 1849 some of the newcomers decided to settle permanently and built crude cabins for protection. Soon a company of men from Boston were panning gold along Wolf Creek and the spot became known as Boston Ravine.

Grass Valley was about as good a placer mining area as you would find in those early days of gold mining, but the real discovery came in October of 1850 when one George McKnight stubbed his boot (while chasing his cow some accounts claim) against an outcrop jutting from the hillside and exposed a glittering piece of quartz. After crushing it with a hammer he soon washed out a dollar's worth of gold.

That gold could be imbedded in solid rock seemed impossible to the placer-oriented miners. In fact it was against all of their uneducated theories of mining. But it didn't take them long to learn and soon the miners were leaving the streams and gravel beds to look for the new gold. One man ground up a rock as large as his head and recovered $500 worth of gold. That was enough to bring men running from miles around. Soon every hammer and anvil within twenty miles were being used to break rocks.

An unknown Mexican who had, no doubt, seen hard-rock mining in his own country, built an arrastra which he operated by mule power.

Judge Walsh and Collins, his partner, had just completed a steam sawmill and are given the credit for starting the first steam-driven quartz mill. Another authority, however, gives the honor to two Germans who in the employ of J. Wright,

Jr. built a "first" quartz mill on Wolf Creek in January 1851. It was powered by water and the stamps were logs shod with iron. While it may have been a first, unfortunately it was a failure as were most of the early stamp mills.

Many and varied were the theories advanced as to how the gold could be extracted from the quartz. Many experiments were conducted, some imaginative and others childish, such as the "smelter" promoted by one Doctor Rodgers. This particular project sounded good in theory and the miners rushed to buy stock in the enterprise. The smelter was duly built and with great ceremony filled with quartz ore and firewood. A terrific fire was maintained for two days and nights and then the entire countryside gathered to witness the results. When the furnace had cooled sufficiently to be approached the quartz was raked out and examined. It was smoked and chipped, but otherwise appeared intact. The wood ashes were then collected and carefully washed. The result was precisely nothing!

The mines that eventually were to be consolidated into the big three of Grass Valley started out with modest promise in the 1850s and 1860s when quartz mining was being introduced and pioneered in California. After many discoveries and closures and a variety of owners these mines eventually became the Empire, the North Star and the subject of this chapter, the Idaho-Maryland.

It is rather difficult to set a date as to the inception of the Idaho-Maryland mine as, like the others, it was a consolidation of a number of claims and smaller mines, the main components being the Brunswick, the Maryland, the Idaho and the Eureka. For the purpose of this narrative we will consider the earliest discovery date of the aforementioned mines, which was 1851, as the beginning date.

The Eureka was first located on February 7, 1851, and after an unspectacular period of development under several owners was acquired by William Watt in 1865 for $400,000. Within two years of acquisition the mine produced some $2,000,000 of which $500,000 was clear profit. Continuing to be profitable under Watt's ownership the Eureka produced and sold as bullion $4,480,633.12 with almost half of that amount paid out in dividends, at the same time making William

Watt the richest man in Grass Valley. In 1873 the rich vein was worked out and the mine was closed in 1877. The Grass Valley *Union's* obituary for the Eureka mine was the lead story for Saturday, June 23, 1877, and in its salute to the mine claimed that ". . . in its last month the mine was still financially solvent." According to the *Union* it paid its regular monthly dividend of $40,000, produced from ore already blocked out. Very little was done with the property from 1877 until the 1930s when the Eureka was acquired by the Idaho-Maryland.

The Brunswick mine was discovered in 1851, and was first known as the East Eureka, then the O'Connor, the Brunswick and finally the Brunswick Consolidated Mining Company. In its original location it was situated just east of the Maryland mine, but in later years a new shaft was sunk 2½ miles east of Grass Valley on the Colfax Road. Although the steel headframe erected in 1940 has long been scrapped, the concrete silo-like ore bin and part of the hoist house still stand near the intersection of Brunswick and Union Hill Roads. The Brunswick was never a very large producer during its early days and didn't come into its own until after its consolidation with the Idaho-Maryland group in the thirties.

The Maryland mine stemmed from an original 600 by 2000-foot claim which was probably filed about the same time as that of its neighbor, the Idaho. Samuel P. Dorsey, the express agent at Grass Valley, had secured the claim on the strength of his studies as an amateur botanist. He claimed he could follow the course of the lode by observing the surface growth and with very little more than this theory formed the Maryland Mining Company, with himself as president.

In 1880 the company drove a 675-foot tunnel into the ledge and built a hoist for further development. It was not until the neighboring Idaho closed down in 1891 that the Maryland began to show much promise. In May, 1893, the Maryland management had the opportunity to purchase at satisfactory prices the property, stamp mill, hoisting works and other hardware from the Idaho, which was believed to be worked out, and thus was born the Idaho-Maryland Mining Company. With the newly acquired equipment and perhaps some change of luck, the Maryland began to prosper. In January 1894 a fire destroyed the hoisting

167

This lithograph shows the layout of the Idaho mine as it looked around 1880. Railroad in the foreground is the long abandoned Nevada County Narrow Gauge. Components are mill, steam hoisting works and enclosed headframe. In January 1894, fire destroyed the hoisting works and adjoining headframe suspending operations for a time. Lower photo was taken during the reconstruction, possibly late 1894 or 1895. (lithograph from Thompson & West's History of Nevada County, Howell-North 1970; lower photo, Bancroft Library)

works and operations were suspended until the surface plant could be rebuilt and the underground works unwatered. Fate again intervened when Victor Dorsey, a son of the owner, who had taken up mining, was accidently killed in the workings. Samuel P. Dorsey, by now quite elderly, never again entered his mine and after several years of limited operations the great mine was allowed to fill with water and the surface plant became the habitat of bats.

The Idaho claim was patented in May 1863 by a rather large group of Nevada City and Grass Valley citizens, many of whom became prominent in the affairs of the county. The president of the group was M. P. O'Connor with William Young serving as vice president. Two months later a shaft was begun. After a year's exploration the mine only turned up a vein so small that the owners didn't even bother to work it and promptly shut the mine down. In September 1867 the Coleman brothers, John and Edward, previously the owners of the North Star, sold that mine and bought out the Idaho group, organizing at that time the Idaho Quartz Mining Company with John C. Coleman as the first president (he was later succeeded by his brother Edward) and William Young and M. P. O'Connor of the old crowd as vice president and secretary respectively.

The Coleman brothers constituted a unique business team with John C. keeping an eye on financial matters and Edward efficiently managing the works and the men. As they prospered they became leaders in the civic, political and religious life of the community. Although they saw eye to eye on most matters they differed greatly on national politics. One was a Democrat and the other a Republican and each tried to outdo the other in promoting fund-raising excursions, torchlight parades and other party events.

The new company under the Colemans proved that the tiny showing of quartz did indeed lead to something better by producing a rich bonanza in a matter of weeks. The news of the new strike soon spread and the Idaho became famous as one of the great gold producers of its time. There were only 3100 shares of $100 par value stock outstanding in the Idaho and by 1875 these shares were selling on the San Francisco Mining Exchange at $750 a share with monthly dividends ranging from $5 to $25.

In 1880 the Idaho mine suffered a bad fire underground. This in itself was not an unusual occurrence. What makes it worthy of comment are the methods used to combat the fire. In an era before oxygen breathing equipment two brave men known only as Page and Tucker attempted to invade the fiery depths of the mine wearing the cumbersome rubber suit and brass helmet used by deep sea divers! Here is the full story of this attempt at mine rescue as reported in the *Mining and Scientific Press* for June 15, 1880:

"The attempt of the men in divers' armor to extinguish the fire in the Idaho mine was unsuccessful. They went down the shaft twice. At the 900-foot level the candle went out and the electric light showed a thick smoke, but they found no difficulty in breathing, the supply of air through the hose and into the helmets being good. Near the 1000-foot level the cage was stopped. The heat was great and the helmets became very hot. The rubber around the wrists softened. The signal to hoist was given and the men were taken to the surface.

"Several reasons are assigned by the men for their failure to accomplish anything. The pump which supplied them with fresh air was, unfortunately, situated at the mouth of the 700-foot level, and consequently the air was vitiated and impure to such a degree as to be absolutely poisonous. Again, the provisions made in a diver's submarine suit for disposing of the air after it has been deprived of its life-sustaining properties are altogether regulated by the pressure of the water upon the rubber suit. As the surplus air expands the rubber, the water pressure releases a spring, which opens a valve and allows the foul air to escape without admitting any water. In the Idaho mine the clothing of both Page and Tucker became bulged out with the impure air, the atmospheric pressure being inadequate to release the spring, and consequently both men were compelled to open the valve themselves and take chances on the poisonous gases surrounding them effecting an entrance. Some idea of the heat experienced may be formed when it is known that one of the eyeglasses of Page's helmet was cracked. Had it broken, his life would have been forfeit. They are

Aerial view of the Idaho-Maryland mine's main operating area at Grass Valley, plainly showing (1) the steel headframe and the Idaho shaft, (2) the hoist house, (3) the old 20-stamp mill and (4) the new mill and cyanide plant. The flat area to the right (5) of the new mill was the tailings disposal area. (W. H. French)

satisfied that their experiment will be of value, as it will cause scientists to endeavor to discover some material from which diving suits for mine fires may be manufactured."*

The article then continues with this curious entry: "As far as possible air has been excluded from the lower levels. The stove plan for burning charcoal and generating carbonic gas has been abandoned and a furnace for the same purpose has been built. This comprises an iron shell six feet in diameter and lined with brick eight inches deep. At least a week will be required for surcharging the mine with carbonic gas. Then the gas will have to be expelled before workmen can go down into the depths. If bad caves have occurred, many weeks will elapse before the 200 employees will again be at work." Although further details are lacking apparently the reference to charcoal stoves and carbonic gas indicated a plan to fill the mine with inert gases thus cutting off the oxygen supply and smothering the fire.

The Idaho Quartz Mining Company continued as a highly profitable enterprise until 1891 when the available ore was exhausted. Its record of production up to the time of closing came to something like $12,500,000 of which $6,000,000 was paid out in dividends. In 1893 it was sold to the Maryland Mining Company.

After disposing of the mine the Colemans moved to San Francisco where they continued to be interested in many large projects throughout California.

That John C. Coleman was merely "interested" in California affairs would be a gross understatement. In addition to his mining investments in Grass Valley, John Coleman was one of the organizers and the first president of the Nevada County Narrow Gauge railroad which ran from Colfax to Nevada City from 1876 to 1943. He was president of the Mohawk and Sierra Lumber Co., 1870-1905; Nevada County State Senator, 1878-1879; Director, North Pacific Coast Railroad, 1892-1902; Vice President, North Pacific Coast Railroad, 1901-1902; Director North Shore Railroad, 1902-1905;

Director, California Gas & Electric Co., 1901-1905; Vice President, California Street Cable Railway, San Francisco; Director, Merchants Exchange Bank, San Francisco; Director, Fireman's Fund Insurance Co., San Francisco; Director, San Francisco Drydock Co., San Francisco; Director, Union Traction Co., San Francisco; Director Contra Costa Gas Co.; Director, Philippine Telephone & Telegraph Co.; and Vice President, Philippine Plantation Co.

Born in England in 1823, miner John C. Coleman concluded his full and active life in San Francisco on March 23, 1919, at the age of 96.

In 1915 the Great Idaho-Maryland Mines Corporation had its beginning when another mining man by the name of Errol Mac Boyle began consolidating a number of mines and claims into one company.

Mac Boyle was slim and aristocratic in appearance, a one-time tennis champion and a graduate of Columbia University and the University of California School of Mines. Although a man of culture, he had started at the very bottom of the mining business. Now he wanted to combine the Idaho-Maryland, Brunswick, Union Hill and several smaller properties. This was no ordinary risk Mac Boyle proposed. The Idaho-Maryland mine had been idle since 1900 and the production records of the other mines involved were by this time only fair. Nevertheless Mac Boyle and a group of associates, including Edwin L. Oliver and F. W. McNear, took over the limping properties and began to consolidate them into one company.

In 1919 the proposition began to look attractive to eastern capital and the entire group was optioned to the Metals Exploration Company, a syndicate financed by Harry Payne Whitney.* Work was begun on the Idaho-Maryland by unwatering the shaft which was 1000 feet deep at the time and many of the old workings were reclaimed and ex-

---

*More conventional use of diving equipment was made some years later at the Rainer mine near Angels Camp when a deep sea diver was brought up from San Francisco to free a skip jammed at the bottom of a flooded shaft.

*Harry Payne Whitney, born New York City, April 29, 1872, financier, sportsman. Educated Yale and Columbia. In 1902 acted as guide to Daniel Guggenheim through the silver, lead and copper districts of the Western United States and Mexico. He was later a director of the Guggenheim Exploration Company and other large corporations. In 1921-22 he provided funds for the Whitney South Sea Expedition sent by the American Museum of Natural History to collect birds of Polynesia. Died October 26, 1930.

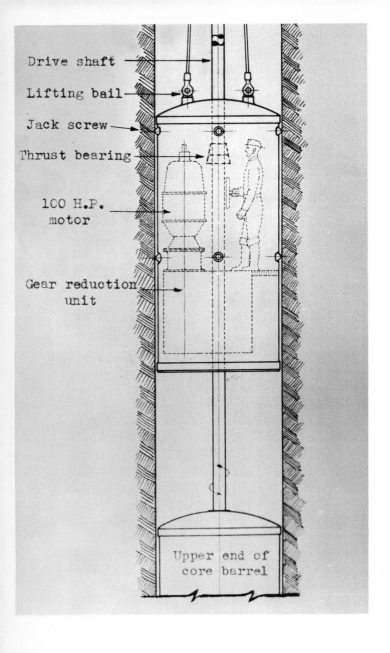

Drive shaft

Lifting bail

Jack screw

Thrust bearing

100 H.P.
motor

Gear reduction
unit

Upper end of
core barrel

During the 1930s the Idaho-Maryland Mines Corporation successfully drilled the first shaft using machinery that was designed and built in its own shops. The diagram shows the general cross-section of the drill unit used to bore the 5 foot diameter Idaho No. 2 shaft. Power was transmitted from electric motor to drive shaft via a noiseless link belt and a reduction gear. Lower left, the entire machine, including operator, was lowered and raised with this hoisting gear. Lower right shows one of the cores brought up from the shaft. The wall of the shaft was just as smooth as the polished surface of this core. After the shaft was completed (upper right) a special cage was used to carry men in and out of the 1,125 foot hole. Capacity was 10 men per deck. *(upper left and right and lower left, California Division of Mines and Geology)*

tended. The Eureka workings were also examined as it was said that a considerable amount of $10 ore had been left there; however, none was found. The twenty-stamp mill at the Union Hill mine was moved to the Idaho-Maryland and about $300,000 was produced. In 1924 and 1925 the company recovered $260,000 before abandoning the project at a loss. The total amount invested had been $2,000,000.

Errol Mac Boyle, who had originally acquired the mines, had some theories of his own regarding the fault structure in these properties, but his advice had been ignored by the eastern "experts." So in 1925 when Mac Boyle and his small group of associates had the opportunity to take back the mines from the discouraged purchasers they began a modest development program conducted along the lines Mac Boyle had indicated. Starting first with a crew of leasers, the nature of development was soon encouraging enough to warrant operations on company account entirely. At that time the holding company was known as Idaho Maryland Consolidated Mines, Inc., while the Idaho-Maryland Mines Company was the operating company.

In 1935 the holding company and the operating company were consolidated into one corporation known as the Idaho-Maryland Mines, Inc., bringing all of the holdings under one operating unit. Edwin Oliver was president, Errol Mac Boyle, executive vice president and Albert Crease the general manager.

It was at this time that the entire group of mines, which up to now could only be averaged out as marginal, suddenly came into their own and in spite of their late start blossomed into the great Idaho-Maryland Mines Corporation which in just fifteen years of operation produced $26,767,000 to become one of the all-time success stories of the mining world.

Mac Boyle and his statuesque wife Gwendolym, "Glen" as she was called, began to enjoy the fruits of their great wealth, spending more of their time in San Francisco, where they occupied a large, extravagantly decorated apartment at Two Thousand Washington Street. It boasted gold leaf ceilings with fine furniture and antique Irish Waterford glass which the Mac Boyles had purchased from the William B. Bourn estate (major owner of

It was upon the theories of mining engineer Errol Mac Boyle that the success of the Idaho-Maryland Mines Corporation was based. *(W. H. French)*

the Empire mine). All of this was a far cry from the corrugated iron-roofed shack of meager comfort the Mac Boyles occupied when Glen first married her young mining engineer. Now the couple entertained lavishly, both in town and at the historic Fountain Grove Vineyard located on the edge of Santa Rosa which they acquired in 1937.

During the 1930s the eyes of the entire mining world watched Idaho-Maryland engineers as they experimented with a revolutionary new method of shaft sinking. Perhaps in theory the method wasn't so revolutionary but the equipment certainly was, for it consisted of a huge core drill called the Newsom Drilling Machine developed in the mine's own shops. The shaft it drilled was known as the Idaho No. 2 and was some 7000 feet from the main Idaho-Maryland shaft. This was the first shaft of this size ever sunk by the drilling method. It was a single compartment five feet in diameter and was

The Idaho-Maryland mine just east of Grass Valley is seen when it was in operation. At left is the steel headframe over the Idaho shaft, and the large building at the opposite side of the photo is the old 20-stamp mill. Building top center is the new mill which was capable of handling 700 tons every 24 hours. The Idaho No. 2 shaft was to the left of the main Idaho headframe and the Brunswick mine was top right and over the hill about a mile. Below is the Brunswick shaft and 20-stamp mill. This mill was used to process ore from the Idaho until the mine made enough money to build the big new mill.

more than 1000 feet in depth. The shaft had several advantages over conventional sinking. First, it was cheaper to sink, secondly no explosives were used and as the result the walls were smooth and unbroken, thus eliminating the need for timbering, and third, it was stronger because of equal stress. It is a well-known fact that a round hole will hold its shape more easily than a square one.

Many other machines and tools were made at the well-equipped machine shops of the Idaho-Maryland including the 120-volt DC trolley locomotives used in the mine. These efficient little traction motors could be turned out in the 1930s at a cost of $300 each.

The years prior to World War II were highly profitable. This was a period of good production and high development work. The payroll had carried the names of a thousand men for over 15 years and the various shafts regularly sent over a thousand tons of ore a day to the mill. When the twenty stamps at the Idaho mill could no longer handle the load, additional capacity was added by the construction of a new mill near the main Idaho shaft capable of handling 700 tons every 24 hours. Capacity of the New Brunswick mill was also increased to slightly more than 600 tons in 24 hours.

By the end of 1940 steel was on the ground for the erection of a new 135-foot headframe at the New Brunswick shaft. An Ottumwa double drum hoist powered by a 1000 hp electric motor was installed capable of operating six-ton skips to a depth of 4800 feet vertically. This, along with a 600 hp 8-foot single drum Nordberg man and material hoist, was to make the shaft the most modern in the area. The New Brunswick shaft was sunk from 1400 feet to nearly the 3300-foot level with plans to go still deeper.

As was the case with the other gold mines the Idaho-Maryland was closed during World War II. At the cessation of hostilities it was reopened, but strangely enough without its former success. Perhaps it was only coincidental that Errol Mac Boyle, the man who knew the mine so well, was also ailing and died in 1947. His company tried to carry on, but, faced with the inflexible price of gold and the old story of increased costs, the once famous Idaho-Maryland Mines Corporation which Mac Boyle had put together almost singlehanded was now in deep trouble.

Finally in 1956 the company suspended operations for good. The machinery and other assets were sold and the once famous Idaho-Maryland mine of Grass Valley passed into history.

Unlike the neighboring Empire-Star group and some of the big mines of Amador County there were no ore reserves known to exist at the time of closing; for gold at any price the Idaho-Maryland was worked out.

But that's what they told Errol Mac Boyle back in 1915.

One of the few remaining relics of the famous North Star mine is the stone powerhouse on Wolf Creek just south of Grass Valley. Built in 1895 to furnish compressed air for the mine it first housed a Pelton water wheel 18 feet, 6 inches in diameter. This was augmented in 1898 with a wheel 30 feet in diameter which then became without question the world's largest Pelton wheel. In 1961 the wheel and the entire powerhouse were turned over to the City of Grass Valley as a historical site and mining museum.

CHAPTER 12

THE NORTH STAR

1851 to 1956*
Grass Valley, Nevada County
Vertical depth 4,200 feet**
Total production $33,267,734

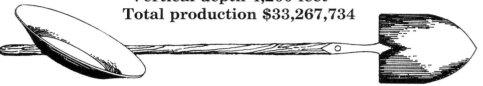

The North Star vein, known first as the Lafayette or French Lead, was discovered in 1851 west of Wolf Creek on the edge of Lafayette Hill about a mile and a half south of Grass Valley on the Allison Ranch Road. It was not worked until 1854 when it was operated in a small way as the Helvetia & Lafayette mine. In 1860 two brothers, Edward and John C. Coleman, arrived in Grass Valley, purchased a large interest in the mine for $15,000 and changed the name to the North Star.

John Coleman, who seems to have been the dominant brother at this point, was born in England in 1823, arriving in the United States in 1854 and in Grass Valley in 1860 at the age of 37. With him he brought considerable knowledge of hardrock mining and soon assumed charge of the mine, appointing his brother Edward the superintendent.

The North Star became a good producer under their management and was successfully operated for seven years, during which time $500,000 in dividends were paid. In 1867 the Colemans and their partners sold out to a San Francisco group for $450,000 and with their share John and Ed-

ward Coleman bought into the Idaho mine, which was to make them both immensely wealthy (see Chapter 11).

For a time, however, it seemed that the full amount would never be paid, as soon after purchase the new owners hit a barren zone in the vein. They persevered with the shaft sinking and in October, 1868, penetrated the barren zone, which once again made the North Star a paying proposition.

In 1875, after a few profitable years, the mine was believed worked out at a depth of 1200 feet and it was allowed to remain idle for almost ten years.

In 1884, W. B. Bourn, encouraged by his successful reopening of the Empire mine (Chapter 13), became interested in the possibilities of the North Star and with a group of associates, including some local businessmen, purchased the property from W. E. Dean, Thomas Bell, J. A. Faull and others, for $16,000.

The new company began with a working capital of $40,000, which was promptly added to by an assessment of $20,000, enabling the owners to thoroughly rehabilitate and equip the mine, making it by 1886 the most modern mining plant in California. The successful reopening of the Empire already mentioned, plus the results achieved at the North Star, gave the then sagging quartz mining industry a new impetus.

In 1887 Mr. Bourn and his partners sold control of the mine to James D. Hague and associates of New York.

---

*In 1929 the North Star was purchased by the Newmont Mining Corporation which was also acquiring the Empire Mines Company and was operated in conjunction with that group until 1956. The total production figure shown here is for the North Star only up to the end of 1928. From 1929 on the North Star figures are included with those of the Empire.

**The Central shaft penetrated the earth to 4000 feet vertically. Actually the mine was worked to lower levels through an incline winze which made total depth approximately 4200 feet from the surface.

This early photo shows the surface works of the North Star mine. In the lower photo, taken deep underground, miners are sinking the incline shaft still further. The style of drills and the fact that the men are using candles rather than carbide lamps dates this picture sometime around 1900. *(upper, California Division of Mines and Geology; lower, Arthur B. Foote)*

The North Star remained a profitable operation until well below the 2100-foot level, where once again the vein narrowed to almost nothing.

In a wise move to diversify their holdings, the North Star management acquired in 1884 the Massachusetts Hill and Stockbridge properties. Immediate steps were taken to pump out the Stockbridge shaft as the initial move toward working this additional area. This increased activity called for some source of dependable power to run the pumps and other necessary machinery. This was a rather serious requirement, and was brought before the executive committee of the Board of Directors in New York, which considered the matter vital enough to hold their meeting on the day before Christmas 1894.

At the meeting James D. Hague, the president, was authorized to ". . . make such arrangements with the Original Empire Mill and Mining Company and with the Grass Valley Water Company as may be necessary and desirable for the establishment upon the premises of the Empire Company of an electric generating plant and for the supply of water for such purposes on the said premises."

It had been Hague's idea to install a hydroelectric plant and he immediately hired Arthur deWint Foote, a civil engineer, and brought him to Grass Valley to design and construct the facility. After visiting generating plants at Lake Superior and other places and studying electrical installations in general, Foote concluded that he could not recommend electricity as either safe or dependable for underground use at that time. Instead he decided upon a bold system using compressed air entirely.

Foote's plan called for water powered air compressors with the water to be obtained from a pipeline connecting with the Grass Valley Water Company's 22-inch line, which at that time terminated at the Empire mine. The new extension would be 20 inches in diameter and 7070 feet long. The right of way between the two mines followed Empire Street to Whiting and from there directly to the proposed powerhouse on Wolf Creek.

The winter of 1884 was spent in designing and drawing plans for the plant and by spring (May 4, 1895) a contract was signed with the Risdon Iron and Locomotive Works of San Francisco covering the manufacture and installation of a riveted steel pipeline; the arrangement being that the North Star Mining Company would themselves purchase the sheet steel (perhaps to retain quality control) and the Risdon Iron Works would fabricate the pipe and install it. The contract carried further elaborate specifications such as a ninety-day time limit and rigid inspection clauses. The steel plates for the pipe were from the Pennsylvania Steel Company and the Central Mills of Harrisburg rolled the slabs to such perfection that only seven sheets of the entire lot were rejected by the inspector.

Signed on the same date as the Risdon contract, the Fulton Engineering and Shipbuilding Works of San Francisco was commissioned to build and install a water wheel and compressor. This contract called for either a Knight or a Pelton water wheel, but left the final choice open.

The studies of A. D. Foote, E. F. Cobb and E. A. Rix indicated that a large sized wheel would be the most efficient for this particular job. In fact, Foote calculated that a wheel thirty feet in diameter would be ideal. The Pelton people hesitated to build a wheel larger than 15 feet in diameter and Foote could not convince them that the larger wheel could be safely operated. They did compromise, however, on a wheel 18 feet 6 inches in diameter, which was built. Its total weight was approximately 10,000 pounds and was operated continuously at 110 revolutions per minute while delivering 226 horsepower and for a time had the distinction of being the largest Pelton wheel in the world.

The Pelton Company had guaranteed an efficiency of 85% at full load and at the same time agreed to govern the speed of the wheel so that it should not exceed 120 revolutions per minute nor raise the air pressure above 105 pounds per square inch. This they apparently did and repeated tests by Mr. Foote showed the efficiency of the wheel to be a trifle over 90%.

But the wheel was not the only problem to be solved. There were no compressors of the required size on the market either; so E. A. Rix of San Francisco designed the great machine in cooperation with Mr. Foote and Mr. Cobb. When completed it consisted of horizontally mounted cylinders, the low pressure one 18 inches in diameter and the

This is a very early picture of a group of miners about to go to work in the North Star mine. They are sitting in a special open skip used for transporting men and supplies. As soon as the hoisting engineer got the signal from below that the opposing skip was clear and could be moved, these men would start down while others would be coming up in the other compartment. The two pictures below give some idea what it is like to be underground. The enclosed ore skip must be more than halfway down as there is no cable showing between the other set of tracks. The other picture of the shaft shows the utility compartment which contained the compressed air pipes, water lines and the electrical cables. In the earlier days this compartment also carried the rod for the Cornish pump. (Arthur B. Foote)

This panoramic view of the North Star works at the location of the old main shaft shows the park-like terrain of the Grass Valley countryside. The building at the extreme right of the picture is the mill with a tramway connecting it with the shaft installations. Below is a closeup of the mill just below the shaft shown above. The mill was built directly over the county road which passed under the building through the tunnel-like opening seen just behind the pine tree in this photo. The rock walls still stand on either side of the Old Auburn Road indicating the site. *(Arthur B. Foote)*

At the upper left is the first North Star Pelton water wheel, which was built in 1895. Its diameter was 18 feet, 6 inches. The horizontal compressor cylinders it drove were 18 inches in diameter for the low pressure (right) and 10 inches for the high pressure one to the left. Each had a stroke of 10 inches. The man in shirtsleeves is Arthur D. Foote, the North Star superintendent. When the Central shaft was started in 1897 additional demands were made for compressed air. To meet these requirements a new 30 foot wheel (right) was designed and installed the following year, along with a larger compressor. The new compressor consisted of four cylinders mounted as an inverted "V" with two low-pressure cylinders 30 inches in diameter and two high pressure ones 18 inches. Stroke was 30 inches. Below is the powerhouse on Wolf Creek where the wheels and compressors operated for many years. The 30 foot wheel was higher than the building and the cupola was built to accommodate it. (*Arthur B. Foote*)

high pressure 10 inches, each with a stroke of 24 inches. When operating, the compressor delivered 1412 cubic feet of free compressed air at ninety pounds per square inch.

Leaving the powerhouse the compressed air was conducted through 600 feet of six-inch pipe to the Stockbridge shaft on Massachusetts Hill, where it was used to drive a 100-horsepower Corliss hoisting engine, pumps, a blacksmith forge, drills and other mining tools.

The pipeline conveying the water to drive the compressor came down from its connection at the Empire mine as planned and was carried across Wolf Creek on a four-arch rock and concrete aqueduct 135 feet long, known locally as the Chinese Wall. The pipe was enclosed in the four-foot section of solid masonry at the top. The piers were carried down to bedrock some eight to ten feet below the level of the creek and with the exception of the lower portion of the center pier which is concrete, the entire bridge is made of rough stone hauled from the Stockbridge dump and painstakingly laid in the same style as the powerhouse itself. The rock and sand in those days each cost 75 cents a yard and the masons were paid $4.00 a day.

Perhaps of interest to some would be the construction costs of the entire project in 1894. For this, as well as some of the other facts, we are indebted to the Nevada County Historical Society who carefully gathered them from the writings of A. D. Foote:

Final cost of pipeline in place $27,000
Total cost of Pelton wheel and compressor   7,410
Aqueduct over Wolf Creek   1,435
Masonry and brick powerhouse   7,330
Total $43,175

Although Foote felt that electricity was not suitable for mine power, he recognized the advantages of electric light and installed as part of the design of the powerhouse a small Pelton wheel which drove a Westinghouse generator of ancient design. This small 110-volt unit, used only for lighting, was purchased in August 1895 from the Electrical Engineer Company of 34 Main Street, San Francisco. The machine was installed by mine employees and adjusted to operating condition by an electrician representing the vendor.

Other equipment at the powerhouse included a motor-driven 1200-cubic-foot auxiliary compressor installed at the extreme western end of the building and, added in later years, a motor generator which furnished direct current for the two-foot gauge Baldwin-Westinghouse locomotive which operated on the surface and connected the Central shaft and the old North Star shaft with the mill and the dumps. Since this generator required the attendance of an operator at the powerhouse it was moved about 1948 to the Central shaft hoist house where the surface motorman could more conveniently attend to it.

At the Board of Directors meeting July 22, 1896, President Hague reported the resignation of R. R. Roberts, who had been superintendent of the North Star mine. He also announced that he was recommending the appointment of A. D. Foote, the able engineer who had built the Wolf Creek power plant, to the post at a salary of $300 a month. The action of the president was enthusiastically endorsed.

As the Massachusetts Hill property became active and more machinery was added to the line, it became apparent that a greater supply of compressed air was needed than could be provided at the powerhouse. When the Central shaft was begun in 1897 the need became critical.

The situation was submitted to the Board of Directors on May 18, 1898, and it was "resolved: that the president is hereby authorized to take such steps for the enlargement of the power plant at Wolf Creek and for the provision of such additional machinery there as he may deem advisable."

Once again Foote, Cobb and Rix set about to design a new water wheel and compressor combination. The experience gained with the 18-foot wheel had confirmed Foote's original theory that a thirty-foot wheel could be successfully operated and the new Pelton was constructed to that diameter. It then became without any doubt the largest in the world and completely dwarfed the little 18-footer.

The new wheel was built entirely of steel, except for the hub which was of cast iron and had patented Risdon buckets made of solid bronze. Even then the buckets must have been quite costly so it isn't surprising that later replacements were produced locally from cast iron.

At the Massachusetts Hill mine, the building on the extreme left with the smokestack contained the preheaters which heated the compressed air for the air-operated hoist. The hoist was located in the raised section to the right of this, while the headframe was enclosed in the large building adjacent. The trestle leading out to the right is a tramway for ore cars brought up from the mine. At a later date the trestle was extended to the North Star mine where the ore was milled. The stone building to the right contained the blacksmith shop and change house for the miners. The lower photo shows the "indoor" headframe and hoist. The name on the cylinder reads: "Rix compound pneumatic hoist built by Union Iron Works, San Francisco 1896." In order to maintain the greatest efficiency with the compressed air and to keep it from freezing the machine, due to sudden expansion, the air had to be preheated and the pipes wrapped in asbestos. *(photos courtesy Empire-Star Mines Company)*

The wheel was assembled in San Francisco and shipped in sections by rail. At Colfax it was transshipped to the tiny flat cars of the Nevada County Narrow Gauge* for the trip into Grass Valley; however the huge semicircles failed to clear the You Bet tunnel and had to be taken off the train at the south portal of the tunnel, dragged through on the ties and reloaded at the other end. When finally installed and with water hissing through three 1¾-inch nozzles at 335 pounds per square inch, the new wheel developed 1000 horsepower at 65 revolutions per minute and had an enormous flywheel effect.

Mr. Rix's compressor was also radically new in design. It consisted of four cylinders mounted on an inverted "V", rather than horizontal, and attached to the large double A frame which supported the wheel bearings. Technically it was described as a duplex compound, single-acting machine having two low-pressure cylinders thirty inches in diameter and two high-pressure of 18 inches each with a thirty-inch stroke.

Superintendent Foote, who had been so disdainful of electric power, was the first to see its advantages as equipment improved. Therefore he added to the new water power installation a large Stanley electric motor so that the compressor could be driven by either water or electricity, thus assuring uninterrupted operation.

In 1900 the North Star began a 28-year period of high profits which were augmented by a number of other mines acquired by the company over a period of time. Some of these mines which had been incorporated into the North Star group included the original Gold Hill mine, the Lone Jack, New York Hill, Rocky Bar and Sebastopol.

In 1915 the wooden headframe at the Central shaft was replaced by a steel structure and the celebrated Nordberg air-driven hoist was installed. This pneumatic hoisting engine was one of the finest of its kind and being air-driven it ran like clockwork with hardly any noise to be heard inside the building. On the outside, where the exhaust air was released, it sounded exactly like a steam locomotive pulling a long heavy train. This huge machine had drums nine feet in diameter with six-foot faces and it raised and lowered skips

to an incline depth of 7300 feet. The rope speed was 1200 feet per minute and the load capacity was four tons of ore in addition to the 5000 pounds of skip and cable weight. When water power became too expensive it was found to be more economical to switch to electric power and it was replaced in 1933 by a 500-horsepower electric motor.

A smaller hoist in the same building remained air operated until the mine closed. It handled a single counterbalanced cage that was used for lowering hay for the mules, timber, tools, blasting powder as well as for men who needed to go in and out of the mine during the shift. Thus the main hoist could devote full time to hauling ore and waste out of the mine throughout the working period. At the end of the shift the ore skips in the main compartment would be uncoupled and double-decked cages put on to transport the full crew coming out of the mine.

The veins of the North Star were generally so flat that the ore would not run. As shoveling was slow and expensive the levels in later years were run 300 feet apart and scrapers were used to drag the ore from the face of the drift to a point where it could be dropped to the level below and into the waiting ore cars.

Little timbering was ever required in the North Star with the exception of shafts, sets and in what was called the "X" vein. Generally speaking the walls were hard and the ground firm and stable.

Around 1925 the huge water-driven Cornish pump that had operated in the old North Star incline shaft since the 1880s to drain the upper 2400 feet of workings was replaced by electrically driven turbines.

Over the years A. D. Foote, the one-time $300-a-month superintendent, acquired an interest in the North Star and as the resident manager lived comfortably with his family at North Star House, a huge 22-room mansion surrounded by acres of grounds, both natural and landscaped.

As Foote benefited from the success of his career at North Star he was able to invest in other mining properties (see Chapter 14) and he became another famous figure in California mining. Long before this his wife Mary had developed a reputation as a novelist and artist. In fact, her regular contributions to the publications of the day helped add to the meager income of the young engineer

*Nevada County Narrow Gauge opened for business April 17, 1876 and was abandoned October 1943.

Below the steel headframe of the Central shaft is the electric tramway, built in 1905. It hauled ore to the old North Star mill and the new Central mill which had been built the previous year near the Central shaft. Later the North Star shaft and mill were closed and most of the shops, offices and other installations were clustered around the Central shaft as shown in the general view below. In this photo, taken around 1920, the Central headframe can be seen rising above the pines. The building at its base is the hoist house and the large tiered building below it is the mill; smaller building in right foreground is the cyanide plant. (Arthur B. Foote)

during the early years of their marriage. Many of her drawings and stories were inspired by the hardships and experiences the couple encountered during their travels throughout the West. Her novels still have a captivating charm and because of their vivid descriptions of the era in which she lived are valuable period pieces. Many of Mrs. Foote's books are to be found at the Grass Valley Public Library along with a number of her drawings.

Mary Hallock Foote was born on November 19, 1847, at Milton, New York. In 1876 she married Arthur deWint Foote and from then on spent her life in the mining communities of Colorado, Idaho and California. During most of her years at Grass Valley she lived at North Star House, and continued to reside there after her son Arthur B. Foote had succeeded his father as superintendent of the mine. In the late 1920s she moved to Hingham, Massachusetts, where she died on June 25, 1938.

Many of Mary Foote's unpublished short stories were bound by "Granddaddy's Press" as the author's husband called his hobby room at North Star House. There he bound separate booklets for each branch of the family. One of these was titled "How the Pump Stopped at the Morning Watch." The pump referred to is, of course, the big Cornish pump of the incline shaft. Some day it is hoped that this and other unpublished works of Mary Hallock Foote will be available in more lasting form.

On May 1, 1929, the North Star mine was sold to the Newmont Mining Corporation of New York which also acquired at that time the famous Empire group. This consolidation, operating as the Empire-Star Mines Company, Limited, produced one of the world's largest gold mining conglomerates and encompassed a number of producing gold mines in addition to the giant Empire and North Star. Its holdings ran into several thousands of acres owned outright as well as the mineral rights to many more.

As the years passed the mine management found it convenient to install independent electrically driven air compressors at the various shafts closer to where the air was being used, and by 1933 the big Pelton wheel at the Wolf Creek plant was no longer operating.

World War II saw the shutdown of the North Star along with the Empire and all of the other gold mines of the country. When operations were again permitted the North Star resumed its role as an integral part of the Empire workings.

During the early 1950s postwar Nevada County experienced a power shortage and Grass Valley industrial users were instructed to immediately reduce their power requirements by twenty per cent. Some of the mines then operating purchased Diesel generating plants to make up for the loss in commercial power delivery. Someone then remembered the old stone powerhouse on Wolf Creek and an attempt was made to get it back in operation. Once again water was turned into the pipeline but as the pressure was increased its old joints spurted numerous leaks. Time had taken its toll and the ancient steel could not stand the pressure produced by the 735-foot head. Even if this had not been the case it is doubtful that the revival of the Pelton wheel would have lasted long for the 344% increase in the cost of water made these historic machines impractical to operate.

In 1956 when the North Star shut down for good an attempt was made to preserve the old Pelton wheel, but little was accomplished at the time. Both vandals and curious neighborhood small fry kept breaking into the boarded-up plant, doing damage and sometimes setting it afire. In September of 1959 arrangements were completed which called for the salvage of all mine machinery of the Empire-Star Mines, including the old powerhouse equipment.

With the cutting torches getting ever closer Mrs. Phoebe Cartwright, who lived near Grass Valley, became alarmed at the thought of losing forever this historic Pelton wheel. After an appeal was made in the Grass Valley *Union*, an anonymous donor contributed $2,000 and with numerous smaller donations the wheel was purchased from the salvage operators on the very last day. This dramatic rescue of such a sizable relic from the golden past influenced the Board of Directors of the New Verde Mines Company (the liquidating company) to donate the old powerhouse building containing the wheel and the 1.168 acres on which it stands to the City of Grass Valley for a mining museum.

Beautifully situated on acres of sloping lawns amid the California pines, North Star House served as the mine manager's residence and guest house for the mine. It was designed by famous California architect Julia Morgan, who also created William Randolph Hearst's San Simeon castle. The house was built in 1905 for the then extravagant sum of $23,000. Below, interior of North Star House. (*Arthur B. Foote*)

The gift was made on July 9, 1961, and since that time plans for the development of the property have been in the hands of the Nevada County Historical Society with the first order of business the construction of a roof over a large part of the building so that space can be provided for indoor displays. At the same time other equipment has been acquired and is being assembled at the site.

When the controversial freeway bisected Grass Valley and Nevada City with its wave of destruction, it completely obliterated the Golden Center mine which for years had been a curious landmark right in the heart of Grass Valley. Fortunately the museum site was ready to receive the old stamp mill, pumps and various other examples of heavy mining machinery.

After total restoration has been made, the old powerhouse will be an attractive landmark as well as a shelter for a valuable collection of mining relics. Today, even though incomplete, many visitors stop to visit these heavy machines to reflect on the men who built and operated them and to ponder on the part they played during the golden era of California mining.

Interior view of the Wolf Creek powerhouse as it looked in 1899 just after the second Pelton wheel and compressors were installed. The wooden structure in the center of the photo houses the 30-foot water wheel. The compressors are located on either side. The two low pressure cylinders are closest to the camera while the two high pressure cylinders are behind. The electric motor operated the compressors if water was not available. *(Bancroft Library)*

189

NORTH STAR ALBUM

Arthur B. Foote, for many years manager of the North Star Mines, was also an avid and able photographer who took pictures of all the major events that took place during his regime. He methodically collected the work of other photographers to augment the record. The following pages contain a selection of these pictures which were made available to the author by Mrs. Ray Conway of Grass Valley, daughter of Arthur B. Foote.

An active man, Mr. Foote was involved in many mining ventures in addition to the North Star. He also visited other mines in the Mother Lode and Alleghany districts which resulted in filling in many gaps in the photo history of these areas. In addition to the pictures, Mr. Foote kept a record of the problems of the mines and how they were solved, the people involved and the results obtained. This record enabled the accurate captioning of many of the pictures and gave them more meaning.

In contrast to the many western mining camps which were peopled with transient and rather rough characters, the Grass Valley-Nevada City area was unique in that its well-educated engineers and businessmen led very gracious and full lives. Their large and well-appointed homes had tennis courts, swimming pools and stables for their riding horses.

Perhaps because gold mining was not a competitive business, they found they could enjoy those in the area who were also engaged in mining. This fact led to the formation of a society that enjoyed many pleasant social activities such as picnics and fishing parties. These often involved a chuck wagon to carry the ice, beverages and food. Banquets and dances were frequent occurrences, as were horseback riding and wagon trips.

This social life continued right up to 1941 when the mines shut down because of the war. After the war many of the mines failed to reopen and of those that did, only one was able to last more than ten years. The "old-timers" were all fairly alike in age and by 1950 death had started to claim them. Now, there are none left and the fine life they led went with them.

James D. Hague, pictured at left above, was a New York financier and the principal owner and president of the North Star Mines Company. At right is Arthur deWint Foote, civil engineer and later superintendent of the mine, who was originally retained by Hague to build the Wolf Creek powerhouse. The lower photo shows the engineering office at the North Star. The man at the right concentrating on his drawings is Arthur B. Foote, son of A. D. Foote, who succeeded his father as manager. (*Arthur B. Foote collection*)

An early mining method was the single jacking; that is, each man held a drill and hit it repeatedly with a hammer to make a hole in the rock. Blasting powder was then inserted in the hole and set off. Needless to say progress was slow by this method. This picture (top, left) is also interesting in that it shows the width and slope of the vein. Below, great improvement came with the introduction of the compressed air drill. This early model was big and unwieldy. A. B. Foote states in his notes that after the Central shaft was begun in 1896 it took nearly five years to sink it 1600 feet with the equipment then available; in 1926 with "modern equipment," the same shaft was deepened 2000 feet in 22 months.

The above picture shows a skip being lowered down a winze. This is an auxiliary shaft within the mine which does not surface and is used to work an isolated segment of the vein at some distance from the main shaft. There were many of these in all the larger mines. The adjoining photo shows a bulkhead of rock built up to hold up the back of a stope. These walls were built with waste rock. This was easier than hoisting it to the surface. *(Arthur B. Foote)*

193

Chutes such as these were built under the stopes so the ore could be drawn off by gravity into the cars. Where the stopes were at a distance from the main shaft, several cars would be chained together and hauled by mules. The mules were used up to fairly recent times but when small battery powered locomotives were built, the mules were gradually phased out. *(above, Arthur B. Foote collection; below, California State Bureau of Mines)*

194

At first glance the picture above looks like an act in a rodeo. The cages used in the mines were too small to accommodate a mule on all fours. This necessitated preparing him to go down in a vertical position. This fairly apprehensive group are doing the rough job of tying his feet under him and placing a sling around him to carry the weight of his body. Lest any reader think the final position (right) inhumane, remember that if his head were allowed to move around in its normal position, he would undoubtedly arrive down on the station below without it. Barns were carved out of the rock on the main working levels for the mules to live in. Unless a mule became ill, he lived his adult life without coming up. The miners made friends with their four-legged helpers and the life was not bad for them. Many were quite intelligent and knew enough when they came to a switch that was set in the wrong direction to right it with a kick of the hoof. *(Arthur B. Foote collection)*

Behind the safety chains at this shaft station can be seen the inclined North Star shaft with its double track as it continues downward to other stations at greater depths. Below, at another station, is a skip used to transport men and materials into the mine. The block and tackle and rail were used to remove the timbers and other heavy objects from the skip and to set them aside for use in the mine. *(Arthur B. Foote collection)*

196

Miners waiting for the skip at the collar of the North Star incline. The two arrangements that look like wagon shafts are rails that can be put down on the shaft rails to change skips. Men and materials are handled in low sided open skips while ore and waste are carried in fully enclosed models. Below is a section of a drift showing the large low pressure pipe for blowing in fresh air to distant working places. At the right is an underground powder magazine. (Arthur B. Foote collection)

In this mill the pulp can be seen flowing over the amalgam plates which have previously been treated with mercury to collect the gold. The man at left is working up amalgam balls (combination of mercury and gold) after cleanup and before retorting. *(Arthur B. Foote)*

198

The amalgam balls are then placed in a retort and the mercury vaporized. What remains is gold and is called a "sponge." At right, the sponges are weighed. After sufficient sponges have accumulated they are melted and poured into gold bars. Below, veteran North Star employee Thomas Marshall pours molten gold into a bullion mold. He would then take them in his Model T Ford down to the post office and mail them to the U. S. Mint. It is estimated that he must have taken over $30,000,000 in gold into town for shipment. (*Arthur B. Foote*)

Above is the wooden headframe which served the Central shaft from 1896 to 1916. Below, is one of the skips which operated in the Central shaft. It had wheels on both top and bottom because the shaft made a sharp upward turn below the 4,000-foot level. *(Arthur B. Foote)*

200

The "dolly" or auxiliary hoist (top) was used in the Central shaft to raise men and materials without tying up the main hoist. The Rix air hoist (below) installed at the Central shaft in 1900 was originally designed for 2500 feet of rope, but by early 1915 was winding over 4,000 feet. The wedging action of so many layers of cable was continually breaking the flanges off the drum. The mine had outgrown its equipment and it was time for replacement. (*Arthur B. Foote*)

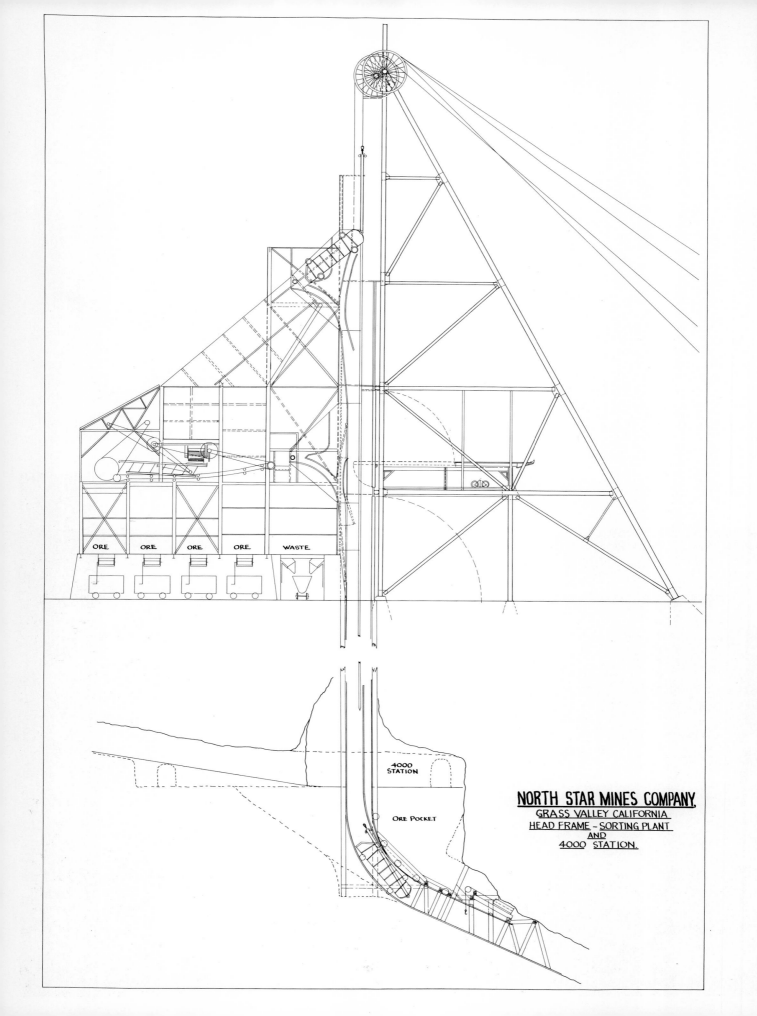

ORE ORE ORE ORE WASTE

4000
STATION

ORE POCKET

NORTH STAR MINES COMPANY,
GRASS VALLEY CALIFORNIA
HEAD FRAME – SORTING PLANT
AND
4000 STATION.

The drawing at left shows a section of the Central shaft and is a profile of the new steel headframe built in 1915. The shaft curves below the 4,000 station, necessitating wheels at top and bottom of the skip. Guide rails and idlers for the cable were required when the side of the shaft suddenly became the roof. The 4000 station was a point on the vein which was 4000 feet from the collar of the North Star shaft. The Central Shaft intersected this point 1600 feet vertically from the surface and then continued at an angle of about 40 degrees for another 2500 feet along the vein. At this point another vein of the same slope but in the opposite direction cut off the North Star vein. This vein had good ore in it and was followed until it went back under the vertical portion of the Central shaft. In 1925 the Central was sunk vertically from the 4000 station a distance of 2000 feet at which point it picked up the elusive vein again. This made a straight lift of 3600 feet against a slower haul of 6600 feet when the vein was followed.

Following the shaft upward to the headframe the skip encounters its first vertical switch at the waste level. At this point in the headframe the skip can be sidetracked to the left and its contents dumped into the waste bin. If the skip contains ore it is then hoisted all the way to the top where it encounters another vertical switch that permits the contents to be dumped into the ore bins. In the dumping procedure (refer to drawing) the wheels on the top of the skip take the turn-off to the left while the wheels at the bottom continue upward via another set of rails. Thus the skip is now in a bottoms-up position that allows its load to be dumped.

The hoisting bail is attached to and pivoted at the bottom of the skip thus allowing for the tumbling action and the subsequent righting for the return trip. The enclosed area at the left of the headframe, in addition to the waste and ore bins, contained the primary crusher and conveyor belts for sorting the ore which achieved a richer ore mix and provided greater efficiency at the mill.

There were other switching off points (see right side of headframe) and storage areas for skips and crew cages and the two were interchangeable in the shaft. During the shifts the man cages would be sidetracked and stored and the big ore skips substituted. When it was time to change shifts the man cages would be put into service and the ore skips sidetracked.

The installation of the big Nordberg air hoist in 1915 necessitated an increase in the supply of compressed air; so along with the new hoist, headframe and other construction an extension was made to the Wolf Creek powerhouse to accommodate a new compressor. The flywheel can be seen through the framework. This compressor was powered by an electric motor so in the event the water pipe broke, which it frequently did at inconvenient times, the hoist could be moved and the men brought out of the mine. (*Arthur B. Foote*)

By 1914 the North Star mine had completely outgrown its hoisting equipment and serious consideration had to be given as to whether enough ore remained in the mine to warrant expensive rebuilding. William Hague, son of James D. Hague who had died in 1908, displayed the same courage and foresight that his father had in 1895 and advised building the new plant that was needed to further develop the mine. Since most of the ore was coming from the Central shaft it was decided at that time to rebuild the Central hoisting works and to move office, milling operations, shops and all from the old North Star shaft to the Central shaft area. It was also decided to continue using compressed air for power and a huge new Nordberg air hoist was ordered. When the contract was signed it was noted that some of the pieces were to weigh as much as 11 tons. However, when the machinery arrived at Colfax via the Southern Pacific it was discovered that the crank shaft, the largest single piece, weighed 23 tons! There then began the monumental task of getting the huge load delivered to the mine. The shaft made the initial part of its journey from Colfax to the mine aboard a special train of the Nevada County Narrow Gauge Railroad using two flat cars, breaking the back of one of the cars by the sheer weight of the steel. (top) At the Narrow Gauge freight yard the shaft was loaded onto two heavy duty wagons. Three eight-horse teams were hired, which could have pulled it nicely but the horses were not used to working together and the team with the fastest gait would try to pull the whole load and finding it impossible would quit. It took two days to haul the 23 ton crank shaft two miles. It must have been quite a sight for Grass Valley residents as the great load came through town (center).

Below, the final lap, up the hill to the Central shaft. At left the gleaming steel crank shaft rests on its bearing pedestals at the construction site. (Arthur B. Foote)

The Central shaft construction site was a busy place in 1915. The steel headframe had just been completed, but the original wooden frame can still be seen in the background, and it was used right up until the changeover was made. The cylinders of the big Nordberg air engine are mounted in place on concrete blocks and the cable winding drums are being assembled by halves. On the opposite page is the interior of the hoisting works after completion in 1916. Upper photo shows the cylinders of the hoisting engine. The hoisting engineer operated from the glass-enclosed booth. The lower picture, taken from the opposite end of the room, shows the huge winding drums. The machine in front of the drums is the dolly hoist. (*Arthur B. Foote*)

206

The double-decked cage below was used to transport men in and out of the mine during shift changing time. Although two stops had to be made at each station the added capacity cut down on hoisting time in the long run. At right is the cage and skip transfer area. Cable can be seen coming from the compartment to the left and is attached to the top of a cage which is either being taken out of or being returned to service. At the lower right is one of the big ore skips with wheels at top and bottom. The cages did not go below the 4000 station at this time so needed no wheels. *(Arthur B. Foote)*

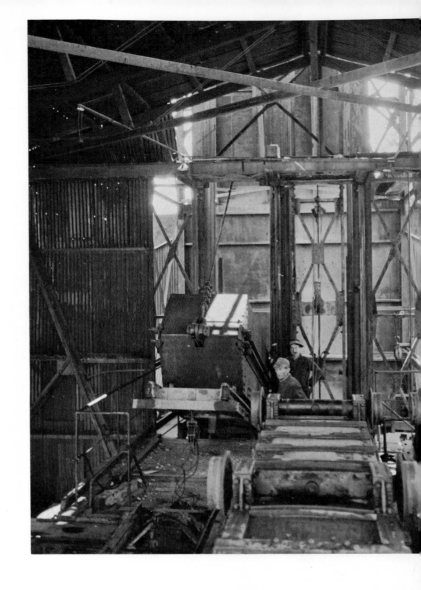

This fine detail photograph of the Central shaft headframe was taken after completion in 1916. The upper guides of the three compartments and the cable sheaves are plainly visible. The enclosed portion contains the ore and waste bins, primary crusher and sorting belts. *(Arthur B. Foote)*

Miners with their drills and supply of sharp steel are shown here sinking the Central shaft in 1926. This job was driving the 2000-foot connection between the 4000 station and the vein which had wandered back under it. The men in this picture were obviously placed by the photographer because if they were actually drilling this close together one of them at least would have a hole drilled in his foot within minutes. While drilling is in progress water is fed to the drills which avoids dust and forms a sludge of the cuttings. The driller must blow this sludge out of the hole frequently so had actual work been in process the boss' Sunday suit would have been a wreck in a matter of seconds. *(Downey Clinch collection)*

Miners, lunch pails in hand, entering the cages on the way to work in the depths of the North Star mine. Lower photo shows that the safety doors have been closed and the cager (man responsible for the loading and unloading of the cages) is about to signal the hoist house. The cage in the left compartment is at the bottom of the mine and all will have to be in readiness there before the hoist can be moved. (*Arthur B. Foote*)

This interesting building of local stone at Grass Valley was the mine office. Affixed to the wall is a bronze plaque which reads in commemoration, "Empire Mines, 1850-1957."

CHAPTER 13

THE EMPIRE MINE
1850 to 1956
Grass Valley, Nevada County
Inclined depth 11,007 feet
Total production $70,000,000*

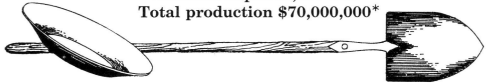

Today many visitors drive up Empire Street in Grass Valley past the dumps of the Pennsylvania mine, through the park-like forest of pines, past the iron gates of the big stone mansion and as they peer over the stone wall at the remaining mine buildings they sense that something very big must have gone on here. Perhaps it is the stone buildings more than any one thing that gives the scene a rather strange and un-California-like appearance . . . like pictures we have seen of the mining empires of Wales or Cornwall. But it is California and it was an empire, even to its name, for this is the famous Empire mine, the great granddaddy of all the Grass Valley mines . . . of

---

*There is an historical plaque on the outside wall of the Empire mine office in Grass Valley that claims a total production of $120,000,000; however, the author is unable to document this figure. W. D. Johnson, Jr., in "The Gold Quartz Veins of Grass Valley, California," U.S.G.S. Professional Paper 194, U. S. Government Printing Office, Washington, D. C., 1940, records total production from the years 1884 to 1928 at $35,048,752.51. Doris Foley and Jim Morley in "Gold Cities," Howell-North Books, Berkeley, California, 1965, accept that figure and suggest that ". . . in all probability this amount has been doubled since." Thus, after a great deal of nonproductive research the figure of $70,000,000 has been used here.

Actual production figures for the Empire mine are next to impossible to acquire as during the period of heavy production 90% of the Empire was owned and controlled by W. B. Bourn, followed by his son, W. B. Bourn, Jr. Very little was required in the way of reports and public statements and a policy of strict secrecy made it difficult to obtain accurate information on yield and profitability. The Newmont Mining Corp., owners of the mine since 1928 have been equally reluctant to make this information available.

all the hard-rock mines in California for that matter.

Not only was the Empire mine one of the oldest, it was indisputably the largest, and this fabulous complex of buildings, machines and underground workings was responsible for much of the gold credited to Nevada County. At the time of its closing the Empire held the enviable record of being the oldest continuously worked gold mine in the United States . . . 105 years! Through it all the Empire continued to pioneer and perfect the principles of deep mining, proving to the world that quartz mining, properly conducted and managed, could be a legitimate enterprise to which business concepts apply. In fact, it was because of the Empire's steadying influence that Grass Valley became an attractive little city of permanent homes instead of disappearing from the map during the misfortunes common to mining towns.

What was to become known as the Empire mine was a consolidation of literally hundreds of mines and claims into one ownership and management. Some of the individual components to make up this mining empire were the Ophir, Rush and Laton, Keefe and Judd, Magenta, Osborne Hill, Pennsylvania, Gold Hill, Granite Hill, Heuston Hill, Golden Treasure, Biggs and Simms (Sultana), Bowery, Cassidy, Central North Star, Coe, Crown Point, Daisy Hill, Hermosa, Homeward Bound, Hudson Bay, New York Hill and the W. Y. O. D. to name a few.

The last mentioned, the W. Y. O. D., with its initials standing for "Work Your Own Diggings," was the unique brainchild of an imaginative young miner by the names of Charles A. Brockington. It was his idea to gather together a group of miners who would contribute their labor and skills in return for moderate wages, stock and dividends. Beginning with Brockington's two brothers, Tom and Abe, plus four friends, it wasn't long before some twenty-five or thirty others joined the company. Financial details were handled by the banking firm of Weisbein Brothers and the W. Y. O. D. ore shoot did its part by producing handsomely. In fact, this experiment in cooperative mining operated successfully for many years. It was only after the members of the Work Your Own Diggings Association began dying off that it was sold to become a part of the Empire group.

The nucleus of the great Empire amalgamation was, of course, the original Empire mine which in turn had its beginning from a gold-bearing ledge known as Ophir Hill and was discovered one mile southeast of Grass Valley in October of 1850 by George D. Roberts. Some reports have it that it began with Robert's tiny thirty by forty-foot claim but there is also evidence to indicate that Mr. Roberts may have originally purchased the property for its stand of timber. At any rate he presumably worked his newly discovered mine for several months before becoming discouraged with the difficulty of separating the gold from the quartz.

In 1851 the claim was sold to Woodbury, Park and others who, although the ledge yielded liberally, failed in 1852 because of mismanagement. A short time later the mine was placed on the auction block to be sold for its debts. John P. Rush bid in a half interest and the other half was picked up by the Empire Company, an existing firm which had been operating a mill on Wolf Creek. Two years later, in 1854, Rush sold his half for $12,000 to the Empire Company which then incorporated as the Empire Mining Company, consisting of C. K. Hotaling, James O'Neill, B. B. Laton, Fred Jones, Silas Lent, James H. Wilcox, Thomas Barnstead, W. W. Wright, James Beauchamp, Richard Groat and John E. Southwick.

During the period 1852 to 1854 the mine yielded over $900,000. In July 1864 Captain S. W. Lee and A. H. Houston, who had bought up the stock in the corporation, came into full possession

of the mine. The new company acquired additional property and after spending about two months pumping water from the mine began operating on a systematic basis as of September 1864. By 1865 a perpendicular depth of 201 feet had been reached in the mine and the ore was yielding an average of $58.50 a ton at the mill. The outlook was so encouraging that nearly $200,000 was invested in new machinery, a drain tunnel and a new thirty-stamp mill which was to be the subject of considerable comment. Here was felt the influence of the mine's principal owner, Capt. S. W. Lee. A former ship's captain, Lee still clung to many of his marine ideas. The interior of the mill, for instance, was ceiled and painted and surprisingly neat . . . not at all like the rough structures usually associated with mines. Because of this and the peculiar design of the superstructure it came to be known as the "steamboat mill." Raymond Rossiter, writing in his *Mineral Resources of the States and Territories West of the Rockies,* described the steamboat mill as: ". . . considered the most magnificent in the State." The Mill's stamps weighed 800 pounds and dropped 58 to 65 times a minute. It had a daily capacity of forty tons when a Blake crusher was used ahead of the stamps to do the heavy work.

After 1867 there began a general decline in the fortunes of Grass Valley mining and the entire camp was presumed to have petered out. Even the Empire suffered from reverses at this time, causing Captain Lee and his partner to dispose of a fifty per cent interest in the mine for $125,000. The new money was put up by Lake, Cronise, Horner and other partners in San Francisco.*

On September 20, 1870, a disastrous fire swept through the surface works of the Empire mine, destroying the pumping and hoisting plant, all the winter supplies and the steamboat mill. Total damages amounted to $140,000.

Earlier that year the mine is reported to have changed hands when a Mr. Nesmith became the

*Throughout the long history of the Empire mine there are found many names associated with the property that are famous in mining circles and a few that are familiar in California even today. Among them are J. W. Gashwiler, John Hays Hammond, M. V. Clement, David Watt, David McKay, Cooper Thurston, William D. Hague, Captain Thomas Mein and William Clift, whose fortune built San Francisco's Clift Hotel.

new superintendent. A new ledge was discovered that yielded $35 to $40 a ton and Mr. Nesmith began to introduce many changes at the Empire; the first order of business was a new mill to replace the previous thirty-stamp mill destroyed in the fire. Early in 1871 a new $40,000 twenty-stamp mill was completed which not only had the capacity for doing the work previously performed by the thirty-stamp mill but consumed one and a half cords of wood less per day and required two men less to operate it than did the once highly acclaimed steamboat mill. The new mill, also steam powered, had a capacity of forty tons in 24 hours with 900-pound stamps dropping nine inches 72 times a minute.

It was some time around here that a major interest in the property was acquired by William Bowen Bourn. Mr. Bourn was a native of Somerset, Massachusetts, where he was reared and educated. At the age of 35 he came to California and was identified with various commercial, shipping and mining endeavors, becoming one of the prominent and influential capitalists of San Francisco.

The Empire Mining Company had been producing $100,000 to $250,000 a year, but by 1878 the famous Ophir vein appeared to have been exhausted and in November of that year the 1200-foot Ophir inclined shaft was allowed to fill with water as the company turned its attention to its Rich Hill vein. It was also at this time that almost everyone was beginning to have doubts about the future of quartz mining in Grass Valley, and by 1879, out of all the mines in Grass Valley, only the Empire, the Idaho and the New York Hill were operating. The New York Hill was soon to close.

To verify their fears the Empire management called in three well-known experts to examine the mine, which at that time was controlled by the W. B. Bourn estate, the elder Bourn having died in 1874. It was the considered opinion of these authorities that the Empire was too deep for profitable operation and to all intents and purposes must be considered worked out.

Plans to abandon the property were under way when W. B. Bourn, Jr. returned from an extended visit to Europe. Upon hearing of the sad state of affairs at the mine he quickly moved to take over the management of the Empire. This he did by forming a new company which he incorporated in

1879 as the Original Empire Mill and Mining Company.

It was not the usual corporate takeover Bourn planned but a desperate attempt to save his late father's mine. All of the shareholders were invited to join him in the new company and all declined with the exception of J. B. Fargo, who had been a stockholder in the Empire since 1856.*

The reorganized company took possession in 1879, lost no time in pumping out the shaft and as soon as practical resumed sinking. Bourn was a determined fighter, but it wasn't to be an easy victory for this was a time when belief in California quartz mining was at a low ebb. Difficulties, financial and otherwise, haunted the operations for four long years. Finally Bourn's faith and energy triumphed and the old Empire broke through into a new era of prosperity. It was also an era of new ideas, new money, new equipment and increased exploration.

Two years after W. B. Bourn, the younger, took over the mine he brought into the business, in a minor capacity, George W. Starr. Starr, a young kinsman of Bourn's, had previously tried out at West Point but decided that an army career was not to his liking; so after serving an apprenticeship of six years George W. Starr was made the mine's superintendent in 1887.**

In 1884 water power was brought to the Empire at a cost of $100,000, the surface plant reconstructed and improved and in 1886 the twenty-stamp mill was increased to forty stamps. The main shaft had reached a depth of 1700 feet on the incline that year (750 feet vertical) and the big Cornish pump operating in the shaft was raising 18,000 gallons of water every hour. The hoisting works was also powered by water which it received through a 22-inch pipeline from the company's reservoir 1300 feet away. The Empire was now employing between 120 and 160 men in the mine at $3.00 per day with eight men assigned to surface work.

---

*Mr. Fargo and his heirs retained their interest in the Empire for most of the life of the mine and were amply rewarded. There is no traceable relationship between Mr. J. B. Fargo and the Fargo of the Wells Fargo Company.

**In later years after a highly successful mining career George Starr gave much of the credit for his mining know-how to the Cornish miners he worked with in the Empire.

In this old photo miners are cutting a station off the incline Empire shaft. Single jacking was slow, hard work. During the period from 1892 to 1898 the Empire shaft was sunk only 110 feet. During 1899 it was sunk 205 feet and twice that the following year. The average cost for driving a 5 x 7 foot drift in 1899 was $5.76 a foot while shaft sinking amounted to $16.87 a foot. (*California Division of Mines and Geology*)

It was this same year, 1884, that W. B. Bourn, Jr., encouraged with the successful comeback of the Empire, purchased the North Star (see Chapter 12) and once again Grass Valley became the mining capital of California.

Mr. Bourn's association with the North Star was short-lived for in 1887 he sold the mine and in 1888 he also sold control of the Empire. No doubt pleased with the revival of both mines he was content to retire from active management.

With the dawn of the "gay nineties" the Empire mine was ringing with activity. The working shaft was down 1900 feet on the incline with mining going on in 19 levels. Two ledges were being worked simultaneously, the Ophir and the Rich Hill. The ore shoot of the latter was 650 feet long while the Ophir ledge was 1800 feet long. Both had an average width of 15 inches.

In 1893 Mr. George W. Starr, who had now been superintendent of the Empire for seven years, tendered his resignation in order to accept a highly attractive offer from the noted Barnarto Brothers as manager of their South African mines. Before leaving Starr expressed his faith in the Empire and cautioned the management not to be discouraged over the splitting up of the Ophir ledge, which at that time had branched out into several stringers at the 1700-foot level.

Following Starr's advice some exploration work was carried on during 1893, '94 and '95, but the mine did not pay expenses. By 1896 the situation was becoming critical and W. B. Bourn, Jr., who had once before saved the mine, came out of retirement, repurchased his interest and assumed command.

Bourn was an aggressive miner and knew only one way to go . . . that being to get through the barren ground as quickly as possible. Money was made available and shaft sinking was begun in earnest. The 1800, 2000 and 2100-foot levels were extended in search of either the elusive Ophir ledge or a new lead entirely.

In 1895, bronzed from five years in South Africa, George Starr returned to California and was considering joining the Alaskan gold rush when he was offered his old job as superintendent of the Empire. Mr. Starr's answer was not immediately forthcoming. Instead he undertook a thorough ex-amination of the property and carefully studied the work that had been done during his absence. What he found is best expressed in his own words:

"I found that by extending the drifts my former theory of the split in the Ophir vein had been proved true and that as soon as the ledge horse had been driven through, the vein was as strong as ever. The 2100 North drift I found had penetrated a rich ore body which then had cut 540 feet of good ore. Good ore was in the face of the drift and the ground above was virgin to the surface, this drift being farther to the north than any of the old levels. Very large areas of north and south ground were unexplored. A probably valuable reserve was in a parallel vein known as the Rich Hill which hadn't been worked since 1880, in other parallel veins and in extra lateral rights. Lack of sufficient development was the cause of all under-

Quartz mining at the Empire was not a volume operation. The gold was not obtained from the general rock, but from strictly defined veins. These were followed wherever they led. This picture shows the width and angle of descent of the Empire vein at this point in the mine.

The Empire "cottage," in reality a mansion situated on the mine grounds, was the Grass Valley home of the mine's principal owner W. B. Bourne, Jr. It had been designed by well-known architect Willis Polk. Mr. Bourne also had a mansion in San Francisco as well as the famous "Filoli" estate in Woodside on the San Francisco Peninsula. Filoli was a word coined by using the first syllables of the three words Fidelity, Love and Life. After the death of Mrs. Bourne in 1936 the "Filoli" estate was purchased by Mr. and Mrs. William P. Roth, who changed the name to the "Why Worry Farm." Below, is a room of the Empire cottage. *(lower, California Division of Mines and Geology)*

ground troubles. The surface conditions were deplorable . . . the mine had outgrown the plant."

With these facts in mind Mr. Starr made his proposal. As a condition of acceptance he asked for a fund of $200,000 to properly equip and open up the property. That would be the actual amount needed, but Starr explained he might be able to get by on less if the old hoist and pumping plant would live long enough to permit mining and milling to continue.

The Executive Committee was not too keen on risking such a large sum and felt that the ore in sight didn't justify such an expenditure. Starr's answer to this was that he would admit that there was no large quantity of ore in sight, but they controlled a property with a record of 47 years' continuous working with only a very limited area of its holdings exploited. They had produced more than seven million dollars with but a small percentage profit all because of lack of development and a plant not suited for economical or expeditious operation. Starr felt strongly that the mine's future prospects warranted the expenditure. That was his proposition. Take it or leave it.

In due time he received the following letter:

San Francisco
May 9, 1898

Mr. George W. Starr, Esq.
Empire Mine
Grass Valley
Dear Sir:

I have the pleasure to inform you that the Executive Committee have accepted your ideas and that you are this day appointed managing director by the Board of Directors. You will be given a free hand in the equipment and development of our property with the understanding that if necessary to carry out your plans the sum of $200,000 will be furnished you and that on completion of the plant the necessary expenditure for 600 feet per month of development, consisting of shaft sinking and drives, will be allowed.

We sincerely trust that including the cost of the above development you will succeed in bringing all costs down to $7 per ton.

Yours very truly,

W. B. Bourn, President

Thus George Starr received his mandate. The Board of Directors had called his hand and now his job was to deliver to them a profitable mine. With this responsibility firmly in mind Starr first set out to force the underground development

with all possible speed. The 2100 drift was rushed ahead with results that far exceeded his expectations and the raises above the 2000 level showed even more encouraging results. Shaft sinking was continued although not without difficulties.

In the meantime plans and estimates were prepared for a new surface plant and on July 6, 1898, the work of pulling down the old and constructing the new was begun. This reconstruction took exactly one year and in spite of the extensiveness of the overhaul the work of the mine was not interrupted. The mill was completely rebuilt without hanging up more than ten stamps at a time while the lightweight rail in the shaft and headframe was relaid with 30-lb. rail in a 42-hour period, during which time the stamps never missed a beat.

In spite of these major improvements Starr had no occasion to call on the Company for additional funds but managed to finance the reconstruction out of earnings with enough left over to declare a dividend for the stockholders. What's more, just as Starr had predicted there began an era of increased production which showed a steady climb during the next 29 years resulting in a total of $10,000,000 in dividends paid to shareholders between 1899 and 1928.

The Empire mine of 1900 was the show place of all the California mines. Cottages had been attractively scattered throughout the pines for the mine officials and W. B. Bourn, Jr. had during the 1890s completed his magnificent stone "cottage," actually a mansion of impressive proportions, designed by the well-known architect Willis Polk. The surrounding 13 acres of lawn, grounds, pools and an artificial lake gave the property more the appearance of an immaculately maintained park than the headquarters of a vast mining complex.

Technically the Empire was also a show place and engineers from all over the world came to Grass Valley to see this famous gold mine operate with all the precision of a fine Swiss watch.

In 1900 the main shaft of the Empire reached an inclined depth of 3080 feet and in 1912 the Empire Mines and Investment Company, as it was now called, acquired the nearby Pennsylvania mine. By 1914 the combined yield of the Pennsylvania and the Empire was a dependable $1,200,-000 a year.

W. B. Bourne, Jr. (center with pole), and party were photographed on a fishing trip. The sporty looking gentleman below is George W. Starr, the well-known manager of the Empire. The car, a 1909 Ford, belonged to Arthur Foote, manager of the North Star mine. The two men, lifelong friends, crossed the Sierra in the dead of winter in this car. It took them several weeks to go from Grass Valley to Truckee. *(Arthur B. Foote)*

With the Empire's forty-stamp mill crushing 54,000 tons and the twenty-stamp mill at the Pennsylvania running 26,000 tons, the total was 80,000 tons of ore handled each year. At that time the ore coming out of the mine was valued at $15 per ton. The cost of operation in 1914 was $4.50 to $5.00 per ton resulting in a clear profit of $10.00 for every ton processed or a net profit of $800,000 per year.

In 1914 the Company installed a new Wellman-Seaver-Morgan hoist powered by a 500-horsepower Westinghouse electric motor. This installation now permitted the operation of new skips fourteen feet long by three feet wide and two feet deep capable of handling a load capacity of four tons each from an inclined depth of 7500 feet. The old water-driven hoist was left intact and ready to provide emergency standby service just in case of power failure.

Nineteen hundred and eighteen was a busy year for the Empire. The earlier forty-stamp mill had now been completely replaced with a huge sixty-stamp mill with each stamp weighing 1575 pounds, dropping a distance of seven inches at the rate of 102 times per minute. Once again the Empire was proclaimed the most modern in the State. The Company's holdings in 1916 had been 430 acres, but by 1918 the Empire had expanded its domain to 600 acres.

It was also in 1918 that the Empire began to have trouble with the North Star mine whose surface plant was located on Wolf Creek a mile or so to the west. The North Star Mining Company brought a $15,000 damage suit against the Empire Mines and Investment Company for allegedly working a vein that passed under lands owned by the North Star. The case was settled out of court by drawing a vertical boundary line which both sides agreed to honor.

The boom years following World War I were not especially good years for the mining industry due to the great increase in the cost of labor and materials. The total mining and milling cost had risen in 1918 to $7.00 a ton. The Empire along with other gold mines had to find ways to reduce operating costs. One such move for the Empire was to close the Pennsylvania mill and transport the ore from the Pennsylvania mine in electric trains to the Empire mill which then ran to full capacity treating all the ore from both the Pennsylvania and Empire shafts. Two small Baldwin mine locomotives provided the traction.

Although exact costs and production figures are not known for this period, it would appear that due to these and other efficiencies plus continued good ore the total production of both the Pennsylvania and the Empire for 1918 would be in the nature of $1,500,000, which would represent an annual net profit of over $1,000,000.

During 1923 and 1924 declining silver prices brought greater attention to gold mining which resulted in increased activity in the Grass Valley area, causing the California State Mineralogist to report in 1924 ". . . many of the Nevada companies have moved their activities to the Grass Valley district and in the past months that city has taken on some aspects of a boom camp."

Although many old mines were being acquired and worked by outside companies the year 1924 saw the same ownership and the same steady progress at the Empire. The inclined depth of the Empire shaft was now 6200 feet or 390 feet below sea level. This was also the year that the Empire and Pennsylvania, up to now operated as separate mines, were connected at the 2600-foot level of the Empire and the 2400-foot level of the Pennsylvania. The nearby Sultana mine was taken over by the Empire and that same year saw 1000 men employed in the Grass Valley mines with 400 of them working for the Empire.

In 1928 the Empire Mines and Investment Company embarked on a reorganization program allegedly to broaden the already wide coverage of the company. It emerged, devoid of the usual high sounding "consolidateds," "amalgamateds" or "incorporateds," with the simple and dignified name of Empire Mines.

In the meantime Newmont Mining Corp.,* a New York-based company with world-wide interests, had been diligently examining all of the working Grass Valley mines. Their findings proved sat-

---

*The president of Newmont was Fred Searls, Jr., member of a prominent Nevada County family. Searls, once one of the owners of the Tightner mine in Alleghany, was thoroughly familiar with gold mining in the Northern mines. It was on his recommendation that Newmont embarked on this acquisition.

Social occasions were a necessary part of country living. In the above picture, the riders seem prepared for an outing. The man with the white hat at the right is George W. Starr, manager of the Empire. The gentleman closest to the gate is Arthur B. Foote, manager of the neighboring North Star. Below, a lively day on the tennis courts which were a part of the Bourne estate. The building served as a clubhouse and bowling alley. *(Arthur B. Foote)*

isfactory and on May 1, 1929, the greatest consolidation in western mining history took place with the union of the Empire mines and the North Star group. This new company, now called the Empire-Star Mines Company, Ltd., placed 3700 mineral acres under one ownership, making this the giant of all the western gold mines.

Empire-Star was incorporated in Delaware in April of 1929. It was capitalized for the sum of $2,000,000 with shares at $10 par value. Forty-nine per cent of its stock was given to the shareholders of the North Star mine who exchanged their North Star stock for shares in the new company.

The combined operation of these properties made for greater efficiencies; for instance, the North Star mill was shut down and an overhead tram 6000 feet long was built to transport the North Star ore across town to the Empire mill. The clanging of skips and the rumble of the mill became a constant sound. Ore trains scooted about the grounds and between the mines in a constant flurry of activity, while beneath the stone office building the melting rooms poured molten gold into the bullion molds and stored the precious metal until it could be shipped to the mint.

In 1929 George Starr, the famous superintendent of the Empire, retired and was replaced by F. W. Nobs. Nobs, a veteran mining engineer who had been with Herbert Hoover's consulting firm in Mexico and Central America, had spent his last 14 years at the Empire and was to add still another 25 years under Newmont.

By 1930 greater milling capacity was indicated and the mill was increased to eighty stamps each weighing 1780 pounds.

During the depression years of the 1930s California produced more gold than any state in the Union and the Empire-Star Mines Company was the largest of all the gold producers in California. During this period the Empire and Pennsylvania veins were actively mined by the company while the North Star was operated by lessees.

Truly gold mining was the only depression-proof business and by the end of 1931 the Empire management acquired the Murchie mine about five miles from Grass Valley. Further expansion included the Sultana group consisting of 27 claims occupying 188 acres contiguous to the Empire mine. Arrangements were also made that year for the joint operation of the Zeibright mine at Bear Valley 25 miles east of Grass Valley.

Not only was the mine paying a good return to the shareholders, it was also responsible for the prosperity of the town through its sizable payroll and purchases, while at the same time being the largest single taxpayer in Nevada County as well as operating the Pennsylvania and Dannebrog mines at Browns Valley in Yuba County.

This prosperity continued right up to 1942, when World War II conditions closed down all of the Grass Valley mines. At the time of closing the local mining industry employed about 2500 men with an annual payroll of $4,500,000. The Empire-Star mines suspended operations late in October of 1942, retaining a crew of 100 men for maintenance purposes only.

Although regular mining was suspended for the duration, a substantial quantity of gold was recovered during the mill cleanup operation in 1943. That same year the New Verde Mines Company, a subsidiary of the Newmont Mining Corporation, was granted a special permit by the War Production Board to operate part of the North Star because of the tungsten content of its ores, and in March of 1944 the Empire-Star Mines Company received a special grant to operate the Empire-Star mines until December 31st with a ceiling of 175 men.

Finally on July 1, 1945, the War Production Board lifted its Order L-208. The restrictions on the purchase of new machinery were eased somewhat. But the damage had been done. Nineteen hundred and forty-six, the first full year of postwar gold mining, found a totally different economic climate for that industry. Heavy start-up costs consisting of expensive labor, difficulty in obtaining experienced miners, high prices of machinery and materials all crowded the fixed price of gold and many of the California gold mines dropped from the picture at this point.

After a year of unprofitable operations, the Empire-Star Mines Company suspended work at the Empire, Pennsylvania and North Star mines at Grass Valley on July 1, 1946. The mill, however, remained open to treat concentrates from neighboring mines as well as those from the Company's holdings in Yuba County.

In 1947 the Company reopened its Grass Valley mines mainly on a block leasing basis. This system involved the leasing of sections of the mine to experienced miners who then paid a percentage to the company. Thus the mines operated through 1948, '49 and well into the '50s.

For ten years, 1946 to 1956, the Empire operation was conducted at a loss with the hope that the value of gold might be adjusted to the level of the postwar economy and the chance that the courts might rule in favor of the mines in the suits, then pending, to recover the unnecessary costs of their enforced shutdown years. Neither of these conditions was to be fulfilled and when in 1956 the mines were hit by demands for increased wages and a prolonged strike called by the Mine Workers Protective League, there was no alternative but to surrender.

Ironically this was one of the few strikes to be called at the Empire since the original Grass Val-ley Miners' Union No. 90* went out in January 1907, the principal issue then being the eight-hour day.

At the time of shutdown in 1956 the company employed 400 men and was California's last major gold mining company. During 1957 and 1958 cleanup and salvage operations were conducted at the mines and dumps and finally in 1958 the machinery and equipment of the Empire-Star Mines Company, Limited, were sold at public auction.

As of 1969 the Newmont Mining Corporation still retains the main property of the Empire mine. The park-like grounds and the vine-covered Bourn mansion are still the show places of Grass Valley, but how long they can remain in their present form and for what purpose the property will eventually be used only time can tell.

———

*Organized in 1894 during the struggle for better working conditions.

Cleanup at the mill. Many of the ores nearer the surface contained substantial quantities of free gold. Since gold is ductile, it would not break down sufficiently to go through the screens and was trapped with mercury within the mortar. Every so often the stamps would be hung up five at a time and the amalgam that had become packed around the dies in the bottom of the mortar would be chiseled out. Some of this amalgam can be seen in the pan on the table. (*California Division of Mines and Geology*)

The view on the opposite page of the office buildings and yard was taken from the top of the 94-foot Empire headframe, probably around 1931. The enclosed walkway enabled the staff to visit the mill unobserved, which acted as a deterrent in case any millmen got sticky fingered. (*W. D. Johnston, Jr., U. S. Geological Survey*)

The Norwalk air compressors at the Empire mine were driven by water power through a rope drive which can be clearly seen in the picture. To maintain tension one strand of the rope was led outside of the building via pulleys where it made one turn around a floating counterweighted idler wheel before returning to complete the loop. Below is the Empire headframe circa 1900. Although undoubtedly rebuilt and strengthened the headframe remained similar in appearance to this until 1969 when it was destroyed by dynamite for reasons of safety. *(upper photo courtesy of Empire-Star Mines; lower, California Division of Mines and Geology)*

At the top of the opposite page is the Empire hoisting works. Hoist drums were 6 feet in diameter with 8-foot friction bands which are in turn driven by two friction wheels made of compressed paper. Power is derived from two 10-foot Pelton water wheels (one for each direction). When this picture was taken around 1900, the capacity of the hoist was 750 tons in 24 hours. It was capable of hoisting from a depth of 5,000 feet at a speed of 1,000 feet a minute. In 1914 a new electric hoist was installed, but the old water-powered equipment was left intact for standby service. At lower right is the 2100 foot station showing the old telephones, signal bells and antique wiring methods. Drills and tools are piled on the floor of the station. *(California Division of Mines and Geology)*

This is the way the Empire looked around the turn of the century. The large building at the right was the mill which contained 40 stamps of 1000 lbs. each. Later these were supplanted with 1800-lb. stamps and 40 more were added. From the standpoint of tons-per-day capacity, this was the largest stamp mill in California. *(Nevada County Historical Society)*

Below is one of the 500 H.P. Byron-Jackson pumps which could pump 1000 gallons per minute against a head of 1600 feet. Of course this was not enough head to get the water to the surface and several similar pumping stations were located at points along both the shaft and the winze.

The bottom of the Empire main shaft was reached at an incline depth of 4600 feet. The ore at this point had raked away from the shaft and long drifts had to be run at each level to reach it. A main haulage drift was run from the bottom of the shaft out to an area closer to the ore and a winze was sunk on the vein. This winze eventually reached an incline depth of 11,000 feet from the surface.

At right is the 10,000 station. This was taken after the shutdown in 1956 and shows how rapidly deterioration takes place once maintenance ceases.

Below is a picture of the 4600 winze hoisting station. The large Nordberg hoist was brought down in sections not over four feet at the smallest measurement. Its ability to wind over 6400 feet of cable was probably unmatched in the country.

The middle picture is of the hoist from the operator's side. The dials at the top center show the position of the skips in each compartment. (*Empire-Star Mines*)

Surrounded by forest and perched precariously on a steep mountainside overlooking the deep canyon of Kanaka Creek, the Sixteen to One mine boasts a million dollar view and an envious production record.

CHAPTER 14

THE ORIGINAL SIXTEEN TO ONE MINE
1896 to 1965
Alleghany, Sierra County
Inclined depth 3,000 feet
Total production $35,000,000

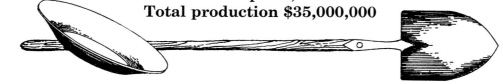

A good story, like gold, is where you find it and this one began in the classified section of the San Francisco newspapers in June 1965 with an ad which read:

> "To be sold. 25 beautiful irreplaceable quartz and gold specimens suitable for museum or private display."

A simple ad, but behind it ran a pathetic story of the decline in the fortunes of one of California's most famous gold mines, the "Original Sixteen to One Mine" of Alleghany. It is a story so typical of the plight of the California gold mining industry that it could be used as a textbook example. Faced with increasing operating costs the owners decided to sacrifice the collection of choice showpiece nuggets saved from fifty years of mining.

The collection was actually worth around $6000 if figured at the legal price of $35 an ounce, but because of unusual size and shape it was hoped it would bring much more on the collectors' market. The offering was displayed at the Wells Fargo Museum in San Francisco and June 11th was set as the auction date. The high bidder was William Ghiclotti of Nevada City, a former Pacific Gas & Electric Company truck driver who had made his money in timber and real estate, but knew the fascination of gold. His bid was $24,000.

With this money and the prospect that the mine's 268 shareholders would go for a 30 cents-a-share assessment, the management had hoped to extend the life of the mine a while longer. But the wait for a rise in the price of gold had been a long and discouraging one already and the stockholders

did not favor the assessment, and so on December 31, 1965, the last of California's fabulous Sierra Nevada gold mines closed down. George Jansen, the mine's attorney, neatly summed up the situation when he said "You cannot produce gold at a cost of $50 an ounce and sell it for $35 an ounce and stay in business indefinitely."

The little town of Alleghany, the home of the famous Sixteen to One mine, is situated on the west flank of the Sierra Nevada mountains about twenty miles from the summit. It is in the southern section of Sierra County at an elevation of 4500 feet. By road it is 40 miles from Nevada City and 13 miles from Downieville, the county seat. The name Alleghany was first applied to a drift being driven by a group of miners who hailed from Allegheny County, Pennsylvania. By 1855 a settlement had sprung up and the name was taken to include the town as well.

The Alleghany district has been a consistent producer of gold since the spring of 1851 when a group of Hawaiian sailors discovered coarse nuggets in the bed of what came to be called Kanaka Creek. A short time later the Big Blue Lead, that prehistoric river channel that caused much of the hydraulic excitement in California, was discovered just west of the present town of Alleghany.*

---

*From California historian Theodore H. Hittel: "The largest dead river is known as the Big Blue Lead, and has been traced from the Little Grizzly, in Sierra County, across Nevada County to Forest Hill, in Placer County, a distance of 65 miles. The course is southeast, the position about 30 miles west of and parallel to the crest of the Sierras. The elevation is 5000 feet above the sea at the Little Grizzly and 2800 feet at Forest Hill, showing an average fall of 33 feet per mile."

Original Tightner mine buildings at the Knickerbocker tunnel portal as they appeared in 1907. (*H. L. Johnson collection, California Division of Mines and Geology*)

The diagram below shows the underground workings of the Sixteen to One mine. (*California Division of Mines and Geology*)

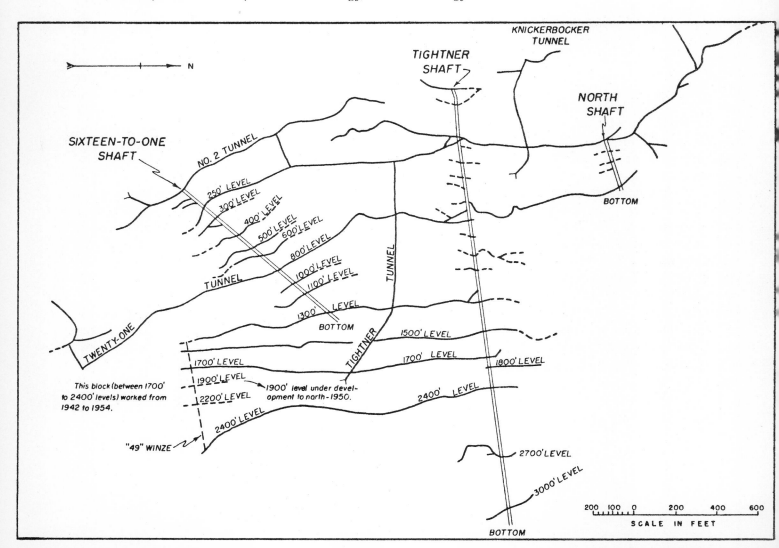

KNICKERBOCKER TUNNEL

TIGHTNER SHAFT

NORTH SHAFT

SIXTEEN-TO-ONE SHAFT

N

NO. 2 TUNNEL

250' LEVEL

300' LEVEL

400' LEVEL

500' LEVEL

600' LEVEL

TUNNEL

800' LEVEL

1000' LEVEL

1100' LEVEL

1300' LEVEL

BOTTOM

TWENTY-ONE

TUNNEL

TIGHTNER

BOTTOM

1500' LEVEL

1700' LEVEL

1800' LEVEL

This block (between 1700' to 2400' levels) worked from 1942 to 1954.

1700' LEVEL

1900' LEVEL

1900' level under development to north-1950.

2200' LEVEL

2400' LEVEL

2400' LEVEL

"49" WINZE

2700' LEVEL

3000' LEVEL

BOTTOM

200 100 0   200   400   600
SCALE IN FEET

In the beginning, as with most of the other California gold camps, the production came from the streams and gravel beds. The famous Rainbow mine, which had its own stamp mill working in the 1850s, once produced $60,000 in a single day. In fact, during the driving of drifts on the Alleghany and Knickerbocker claims in 1853 a bedrock vein was encountered but little attention was paid to it at that time. However, when the placer deposits became worked out in the mid-60s, miners, out of necessity, began to seek other sources of gold with the result that all of the later activity came from lode deposits.

Quartz mining in the Alleghany-Downieville area differs from other California gold-quartz districts in that nearly all of the production was obtained from small shoots of high-grade ore which could yield several thousand to the ton and very little was obtained from the steady milling of lower grade ores. For instance, the Oriental mine once dug $734,000 from an area 14 by 22 feet and as late as 1912 the old Red Star produced $80,000 from a single pocket of high grade.

To trace the origin of this pocket phenomenon we must go back millions of years to the time when the vein was being formed. At that time during some prehistoric upheaval of the earth the quartz was crushed and the free gold was deposited in the fractures. Because of this scattering, mining in the Alleghany district takes on the aspects of a gigantic underground Easter egg hunt. Nevertheless the area is known as the richest pocket belt in the world. This makes for pretty exciting mining as well as a feast or famine proposition and the mine must always have enough capital on hand to carry it through a borasca period until another pocket or "jewelry shop" is reached. An example of this "hit or miss" type of mining is contained in the story of a teamster who grew cold and restless while waiting at the Sixteen to One mine for his load. He walked into the tunnel, found a pick and more to keep warm than anything else started swinging. To his surprise he uncovered a slab of gold so huge he couldn't pry it out without help. It was worth $24,000.

Actually the Sixteen to One mine of recent years is a consolidation of three mining properties known individually as the Sixteen to One, the Twenty-One and the Tightner.

The Twenty-One was the first of the three to be developed and was in operation prior to 1868 (Browne, J. R. *Mineral Resources of the States and Territories West of the Rocky Mountains for 1868*, p. 139, 1869), but never made any notable production. About 1914 it was reopened by Hunt, the cannery man, who found high-grade ore in a new vein. What looked like good prospects were soon dashed to bits when a crew from the Sixteen to One suddenly broke into the Twenty-One workings, clearly showing, to the embarrassment of all, that both mines had been working on the same vein. The Sixteen to One brought suit for trespass against the Twenty-One in Federal Court in San Francisco which in 1919 resulted in a judgment for $93,000 against the Twenty-One. The owners found it simpler to dispose of the property and the mine was purchased by the Sixteen to One for $60,000. The Twenty-One tunnel now forms part of the 800-foot level of the Sixteen to One.

In the 1870s and 80s when several rich finds were made, one pocket at the North Fork contained more than $70,000 while another at the Rainbow mine yielded $116,000. One slab of quartz from the Rainbow contained $20,648 in gold and was taken to San Francisco for exhibition in 1882.

Spurred by such successes a three-way partnership was formed in 1891 by Jack Binning, G. W. Hildebrande and Charles Currieux, motivated by an oldtimer by the name of Jim McCormick. McCormick had remembered the bedrock vein that had been uncovered and ignored in the Knickerbocker tunnel nearly forty years before. Fired with enthusiasm and guided by McCormick's memory, the partners soon located the Contract and Contract Extension lodes which ran north and south of McCormick's remembered vein. After driving farther north a small winze was sunk but the vein tightened, causing the mine to be dubbed the "Tight'ner" by the townspeople.

In 1903 Henderson L. Johnson took a lease and bond on the Tightner mine. Johnson, a native of Ohio, had been a former schoolteacher and had mined in Colorado and New Mexico. He had also been foreman at the Gaston mine near Graniteville in Nevada County and had been associated with mines in the Alleghany area since 1890. Now in charge of his own mine, Johnson decided

During the winter when the roads were closed Ted Fraser hauled bullion from the Tightner mine on skis. Wild west fans will be disappointed to learn that California gold seldom traveled with armed escorts, but was simply addressed to the U. S. Mint in San Francisco and sent via registered mail. Lower, Alpha Hardware trucks from Grass Valley-Nevada City returning from a freight haul to the mines at Alleghany via the Foote Grade. This hair raising mountain road clings to the steep walls of the Yuba Canyon with only the help of well-fitted masonry. Not shown in the picture is the thousand foot drop to the South Fork of the Yuba River. Picture was taken by a passing motorist in 1923. *(upper, Arthur B. Foote; lower, Courtesy W. P. Fuller, Jr.)*

to drift south toward the Alleghany tunnel instead of continuing north on the vein as the previous partners had done. Although no gold had been found in the direction Johnson proposed, the vein was stronger. Whether through judgment or luck his first blast dislodged $20 worth of gold and it was soon apparent there was more where that came from. This discovery firmly established quartz mining at Alleghany as the town's chief (and only) industry for over sixty years and "H. L.," as he was known, with Jack Binning, one of the original owners, as superintendent was to recover nearly $470,-000 from his Tightner mine.

At one time Johnson sold a three-fourths interest in the mine to Senator Jones, once prominent in Virginia City. Jones returned the property at the end of the option period saying that the mine was too "pockety" for the price asked. However, "H. L." continued to have great faith in the mine and operations continued with the result that more high-grade ore was found in the winze off the south Knickerbocker drift.

Later a property known as the Eclipse mine, situated north of Kanaka Creek, was purchased and the present Tightner Tunnel was run. This tunnel cut the vein at about 400 feet vertical depth below the old Knickerbocker Tunnel and later was cut through to connect with the Sixteen to One mine at the 250-foot level.

In 1908 Johnson added a number of other properties, including the Rainbow, Red Star and Eldorado. In 1911 Johnson received patent on the Contract and Contract Extension claims over the objection of the Dead River Mining Company; his rights being upheld by the U. S. Forest Service, based on the proven record and long operation of the Tightner.

That same year (1911) Johnson sold out to O'Brien, Foote and associates of Grass Valley for $550,000 and retired to Berkeley. Although "H. L." had become wealthy from the Tightner mine, he didn't live long to enjoy the fruits of his labors. He died in 1918 from tuberculosis, no doubt complicated by silicosis, the dreaded miners' disease.

The new Tightner Mines Company continued to be a profitable operation under the direction of J. M. O'Brien and A. D. Foote. Foote was the well-known superintendent of the famous North Star mine at Grass Valley. A. B. "Cap" Hall was placed in charge of the Tightner and was later succeeded by George Scarfe.

During 1913-14 the Tightner Mines Company and Sierra County jointly embarked on a spectacular all-season road. Named the Foote Grade for engineer Foote the road still clings tenaciously to the precipitous sides of Kanaka Canyon and the even steeper gorges of the Middle Yuba River as it makes its tortuous way to North Columbia. Of special interest are the rock retaining walls which keep the roadway from slipping off the face of the cliff and plunging into the canyon a thousand feet below. These bulkheads were built by Italian laborers who carefully fitted together the irregularly shaped rocks without the use of mortar.

Foote and O'Brien operated the Tightner mine and its twenty-stamp mill until 1918, producing a total of $3,000,000 from which $500,000 was paid out in dividends.

In 1919 the Tightner mine was reopened by the Alleghany Mining Company, an organization put together by Fred Searls, Jr., the mining engineer son of a well-known Nevada County family, who later became president of the world-wide Newmont Mining Corporation.* Searls attracted a top-flight management team consisting of A. F. Duggelby, superintendent, and W. H. J. Goldsworthy, engineer. Under their direction the Tightner produced some $600,000 in gold during the next four years. Unfortunately for the Tightner people it was soon to become apparent that the Tightner and Sixteen to One veins were one and the same. Costly litigation was avoided when an agreement was reached between the two parties and both companies cooperated in running a raise appropriately known as the Compromise. The Tightner retained the Red Star property adjoining to the north and continued development work down to the 1000-foot level. The ground ceded to the Sixteen to One Mine proved exceedingly rich and it soon became apparent that the richest part of the mountain did not belong to the Tightner Company and when their expensive development in the depths of the mine did not prove satisfactory the entire mine was sold in 1924 to the Sixteen to One.

*See Chapter 13, The Empire Mine.

235

The Sixteen to One mill. (*California Division of Mines and Geology*)

Below is a general view of the Sixteen to One mine and the town of Alleghany taken from the opposite side of the canyon. The Number 2 adit enters the mountain at the top of the mill (right). The long enclosed structure leading to the left side of the photo is a snowshed providing cover-ing for a tramway. Stations along the tramway are black-smith shop, warehouse and electric shop. The building at the far end of the line is the powder magazine, situated away from the main mine buildings for obvious reasons. (*Richard Brooks*)

For a mine that was destined to produce millions the Sixteen to One mine had a rather inauspicious beginning. The property was originally owned by the Rainbow mine but was never deemed worthy of development. The portion later to be known as the Sixteen to One was located by Thomas Bradbury from an outcropping in his own back yard. That was in 1896, the same year William Jennings Bryan, as a delegate to the National Democratic Convention wrote the "Silver Plank" in the platform which advocated that coins be minted with 16 parts of silver to one part of gold. His oratory at the convention on this and other subjects resulted in his being nominated for President of the United States. Although he was not elected there is no doubt that Bryan's flamboyant personality and imaginative politics created excitement in those times and his "Sixteen to One" slogan must have seemed an appropriate name for a new mining enterprise.

In 1907-08 Tom Bradbury, assisted only by his brother "Cap" (Theodore Bradbury) and Yeates Lawson, drove a new lower crosscut into the vein and drifted south. This tunnel became the No. 2 tunnel of the Sixteen to One and served as the main adit for 58 years.

In this section of the mine, the vein is not very well defined and it was some time before Bradbury's persistence was rewarded by the discovery of small bunches of high-grade ore. A shortage of funds kept Bradbury from developing his mine further, but on the basis of some success the mine was optioned to a partnership of promoters named Wilson and Vander Beugle.

The new operators drifted north and hit an ore body so rich that it was sacked and taken directly to the Citizens Bank in Nevada City where it weighed in at $100,000. Wilson is then said to have double-crossed his partner by pocketing the proceeds and leaving town, thus terminating the partnership and forcing the mine into bankruptcy.

In 1911 the Bradbury brothers and Yeates Lawson, who still held title to the mine, made an agreement with J. G. Jury and W. I. Smart to lease the property with an option to buy. Jury and Smart with the addition of H. K. Montgomery organized that same year as the Original Sixteen to One Mine, Inc., consisting of 200,000 shares, par value $1, of which 164,000 shares were outstanding. It was this company that operated the mine for 54 years, right down to its final days.

Smart was the first superintendent but soon left and H. J. Langton, one of the directors, took charge. About this time H. U. Maxfield, a new stockholder, began to take an active part in the management of the company. Maxfield was a native of Arkansas who was now a highly successful financier in Oakland. In 1915 he persuaded his associates to appoint Mark Sullivan, a more experienced mining man than Langton, as superintendent. This they did; however Langton hadn't done badly and his development work was paying off well and the mine was already in production.

Mark Sullivan retired in 1923 because of ill health and "Cap" Bradbury succeeded him, only to die the following year. Then foreman Tom Bradbury, the original discoverer of the mine, was promoted to superintendent. It was Tom Bradbury who hired his nephew, C. A. "Dick" Bennett, as mill foreman in 1926. Bennett, who came from a pioneer Alleghany family, had helped Bradbury lay out the No. 2 tunnel nearly twenty years before while still an engineering student. Bennett became superintendent in 1929 when Bradbury retired and continued to run the mine until it closed in 1965. H. U. Maxfield, who became president of the company shortly after it was incorporated, held that post until his death in 1951 at the age of 87.

During its heyday it was not uncommon for a pound of ore to yield $50 in gold and single shoots would produce anywhere from $200,000 to a million! One eighty-pound piece of quartz yielded $5,000 and another chunk weighing 160 pounds netted $28,000 and in the mid-1930s a "bunch" was uncovered that contained about $750,000. The mine was exceptionally profitable during the 1920s and 1930s and reported dividends totaling $1,238,-501 had been paid to 1924. In 1934 alone bullion receipts were $578,000 with dividends of $287,000. In 1936 $246,000 was paid to the stockholders from a production of $514,000.

In 1942, when C. A. Bennett was superintendent and F. A. Austin engineer, the total cost of mining, milling and development work ran $6.50 to $7.00 a ton. This left a healthy profit margin. At that time the mine was running with a year-

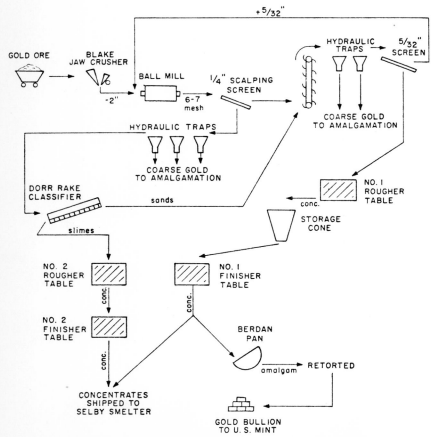

Richard Brooks, the last man on the Sixteen to One payroll, inspects the cams of the old ten-stamp mill. In the later years of operation a ball mill was used exclusively. At left is the flow sheet of the Sixteen to One mill. (*California Division of Mines and Geology*)

GOLD ORE → BLAKE JAW CRUSHER

-2"

BALL MILL

+5/32"

6-7 mesh

1/4" SCALPING SCREEN

HYDRAULIC TRAPS

5/32" SCREEN

HYDRAULIC TRAPS

COARSE GOLD TO AMALGAMATION

COARSE GOLD TO AMALGAMATION

DORR RAKE CLASSIFIER

sands

NO. I ROUGHER TABLE

conc.

STORAGE CONE

slimes

NO. 2 ROUGHER TABLE

conc.

NO. I FINISHER TABLE

conc.

NO. 2 FINISHER TABLE

conc.

BERDAN PAN

amalgam → RETORTED

CONCENTRATES SHIPPED TO SELBY SMELTER

GOLD BULLION TO U. S. MINT

round crew of 95 of which some 65 were employed underground.

Someone with a statistical bent once figured that for each foot of development, including shafts and principal raises, but excluding development raises, there was a production of about $230 and the average yield of material mined over the years came to over $20 per ton.

As the mill buildings were built at the mouth of the No. 2 tunnel it was a simple all-year tram from the entrance of the mine to the bunkers. In later years the old ten-stamp mill was abandoned and the crushing done in a ball mill. The daily capacity of the mill was 120 tons, producing twenty tons of concentrate a month. The Alleghany district was a pocket area, nevertheless it was the mine's policy never to put quartz on the dump. All broken quartz was milled, but in spite of such efficiency the entire return of the mill amounted to but one-third of the total production of the property. The other two-thirds came from high-grade ore which was amalgamated in two Berdan pans and shipped out via the U. S. Mails as pure metal.

The actual working depths of the mine were reached by two shafts. These shafts, actually winzes, were begun inside the mountain and both men and materials entered and exited through the original No. 2 tunnel. Some 300 feet in the tunnel was the head of the Sixteen to One shaft and associated hoisting equipment. This shaft was in the vein and descended at an incline to the 1300-foot level. At this level a connection was made with the other main shaft, the Tightner, and another connection was made at the 800-foot level with the old Twenty-One tunnel, which, being at the level of Kanaka Creek, acted as the main drainage tunnel. The Tightner shaft, which was at one time the main working shaft, continued down to the 3000-foot level in exploration work although the lowest working level of the mine was the 2400-foot level. Actually half the tonnage for the mill came from the Tightner shaft at levels above 1800 feet. This ore was then trammed to the Sixteen to One shaft and was hoisted the last 250 feet to the surface. The other half of the mill tonnage came from the Sixteen to One shaft at the 1300-foot level. There was one other called the 49 Winze that extended down to the 2400-foot level and was

the scene of most of the activity since World War II. This new winze was 1500 feet south of the Tightner shaft and ran parallel to it. It was equipped with a 100-horsepower single-drum hoist and a 1½-ton skip that traveled at a speed of 500 feet per minute. The Sixteen to One shaft had a 75-horsepower single-drum hoist that handled one and one-third tons of live load at a speed of 450 per minute. The main Tightner shaft was equipped with a double-drum hoist and 2½-ton skips which ran at 600 feet per minute as far as the 2100-foot level.

In the summer of 1930 exploration work ran the Tightner down to the 3000-foot level and for this work a fifty-horsepower single-drum hoist was used. Perhaps the Sixteen to One hoist will be salvaged, but inaccessibility and rising water have doomed the rest of the mine machinery to spend eternity deep in the heart of the mountain.

Like most of the California gold mines the Sixteen to One used mules to pull the underground ore cars. Thus it was, until replaced by air or electric locomotives, that a sizable mule population spent their entire lives deep in the California gold mines. But aside from this rather confining existence the mules were not cruelly treated. On the contrary, they became the pets and mascots of the miners and woe to any misguided newcomer caught mistreating a mule! Undoubtedly the most famous of the Sixteen to One mules was a big white animal assigned to the Tightner workings. She had a big rear end and a slow, lazy gait that earned her the name Mae West. She spent most of her life underground and when she was replaced by electric locomotives in the late 1930s or early 1940s she was brought to the surface for retirement. She became the pride of Alleghany and was allowed to roam the streets at her pleasure. She would call at people's homes and wander in and out of stores where she would be given apples or carrots. She lived in happy retirement in this fashion and finally died a very elderly mule.

Other inhabitants of the Sixteen to One, seldom spoken of to outsiders, were the ghosts within its depths. The following accounts are related on the authority of John Finn, a chemist and consulting engineer, who periodically made inspections and measurements regarding the purity of the air underground. Finn is still remembered

Underground at the Sixteen to One. Upper left, men are working with a slusher hoist (a form of mucking machine). Right, removing the muck from the face of the drift by the use of one of the deep, narrow ore cars used at the mine. Below, underground hoisting station. *(upper photos courtesy John Finn; lower, Wells Fargo Bank History Room)*

throughout the California gold country and recalls much of its color. Here we have his account of a singular ghost.

"The Man from Five-Forty-Two" was the name given to an apparition frequently seen in the Sixteen to One. The name came from the simple fact that he exclusively haunted the 542-foot level of the mine. He was never seen on any other level. They say he appeared just as he must have looked the day he was laid away . . . black suit, white shirt and a black bow tie. He never made any noise. In fact he was a very solemn ghost, which is why the miners didn't think he was a mining man. They had him figured more for a former storekeeper, clerk, or maybe a schoolteacher. He had no apparent business in the mine . . . just wandered around as if he were curious or perhaps looking for something. Sometimes they didn't see him for weeks; other times he would show up every day. He did have one peculiarity in that he appeared without a head — although sometimes he was seen carrying it. He didn't cause any harm but just walked the drift. However, miners refused to work in the 542-foot level except in pairs.

An older and infinitely more evil spirit of the Sixteen to One was the "Ghost of Twenty-Six-Hundred." During the last quarter of a century that the mine operated this ghost terrorized the 2600-foot level and is believed to have caused the death of three men. One, he (or it) pushed down a shaft. He toppled a boulder on another, and the third he frightened to death, at least that's what the miners believed when they found the body of the victim sprawled face down on the tunnel floor with a look of terror frozen on his face. There was no other reason, either apparent or medical, for the cause of death. Unlike "The Man from Five-Forty-Two" the ghost of the 2600 level was never seen, but a ghost doesn't always have to be seen to be felt.

Were there really ghosts in the Sixteen to One? Ask John Finn and he will smile and say, "You have to believe in ghosts before you can see one."

Although the product of a stormy and complicated beginning the Sixteen to One mine settled down to a smoothly running corporate life. It was operated on a continuous basis by the same ownership and virtually the same personnel since its corporate inception in 1911, and as it was the main

reason for the existence of the town of Alleghany it became a real hometown operation. The business of the mine was the business of the town and almost every employable male worked at the mine. Even father and son teams were not uncommon on a Sixteen to One shift.

While operations were curtailed during World War II, the Sixteen to One fared better than most gold mines and was allowed a small crew for maintenance purposes . . . and even was permitted to mill 200 tons of ore for each six-month period. Certainly not a great amount, but because of the high-grade nature of Sixteen to One ore it was enough to show a profit all during the war years.

In 1945 normal mining operations were permitted but because of higher costs it was not possible to resume the prewar scale of operations. The crew at the mine now averaged about 45 men.

A bad fire in 1954 on the 250-foot level near the main Tightner shaft collar seriously damaged the shaft and hampered operations in that portion of the mine thereafter.

During the postwar years the Rainbow and Sixteen to One Extension mines were purchased. Also acquired was the Tightner Mines Company which still controlled the Red Star property.

The Sixteen to One now owned the most promising group of mining properties in the Alleghany district, but unfortunately continually rising costs and the gradual exhaustion of the developed portions of the mine resulted in depletion of working capital.

During the last year or so of operations the mine payroll had been reduced to 12 to 15 men and the work had been more or less exploratory rather than producing. The management sought that one long chance of finding ore of a high enough grade to warrant continued operation in the face of the terrifying costs.

The end finally came at the December 9, 1965, meeting in San Francisco of the mine's board of directors. With President Walter Stinson presiding, the directors reluctantly voted to close the mine.

Mr. C. A. (Dick) Bennett of Nevada City, who served as superintendent and engineer in charge of operations during its heyday remained in an advisory and consulting capacity the last year. Wilford Hart of Alleghany followed as manager

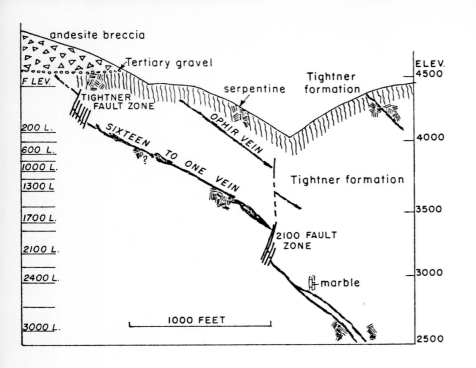

andesite breccia

Tertiary gravel

serpentine

Tightner formation

F LEV.

TIGHTNER FAULT ZONE

SIXTEEN TO ONE VEIN

?

OPHIR VEIN

Tightner formation

ELEV. 4500

4000

3500

2100 FAULT ZONE

marble

3000

2500

200 L.

600 L.

1000 L.

1300 L.

1700 L.

2100 L.

2400 L.

3000 L.

1000 FEET

Diagram at the left shows a cross section of the Sixteen to One and Tightner mines. At the top left are the placer gravel beds under which the original discovery was made. From this it is easy to see how the top of the Sixteen to One vein was exposed by the old drift miners. The drawing also shows that for all practical purposes the Sixteen to One and the Tightner were all one vein. Lower photo, taken in a Sixteen to One stope, shows where the vein has been removed. *(diagram: California Division of Mines and Geology; lower, John Finn)*

for the next six months until he accepted a position with the Industrial Safety Division of the State and moved to Southern California. Tom Hogan followed Hart and remained during the gloomy duty of closing the mine. After the actual closing Richard L. Brooks, a long-time employee of the Sixteen to One and now resident deputy of the township of Alleghany remained as agent for the company, keeping an eye on the property until the equipment could be disposed of.

It was Dick Brooks who made the final cleanup at the mill, who carefully sewed up the canvas bag and sent it sealed in a registered mail pouch by stage to the U. S. Mint "down below." What may have been the last "pill" of bullion from the famous Sixteen to One mine weighed 44 pounds, 14 ounces. It cost $41.60 postage and paid the owners of the Sixteen to One $19,001.

The same economic forces which closed Sierra County's Brush Creek mine in 1964 and all the other California gold mines before that, also caused the demise of the famous old Sixteen as of December 31, 1965. Barring an increase in the price of gold or some other economic miracle (or catastrophe) future historians must surely agree that the Sixteen to One mine was truly the last producing gold quartz mine in California, the once golden state.

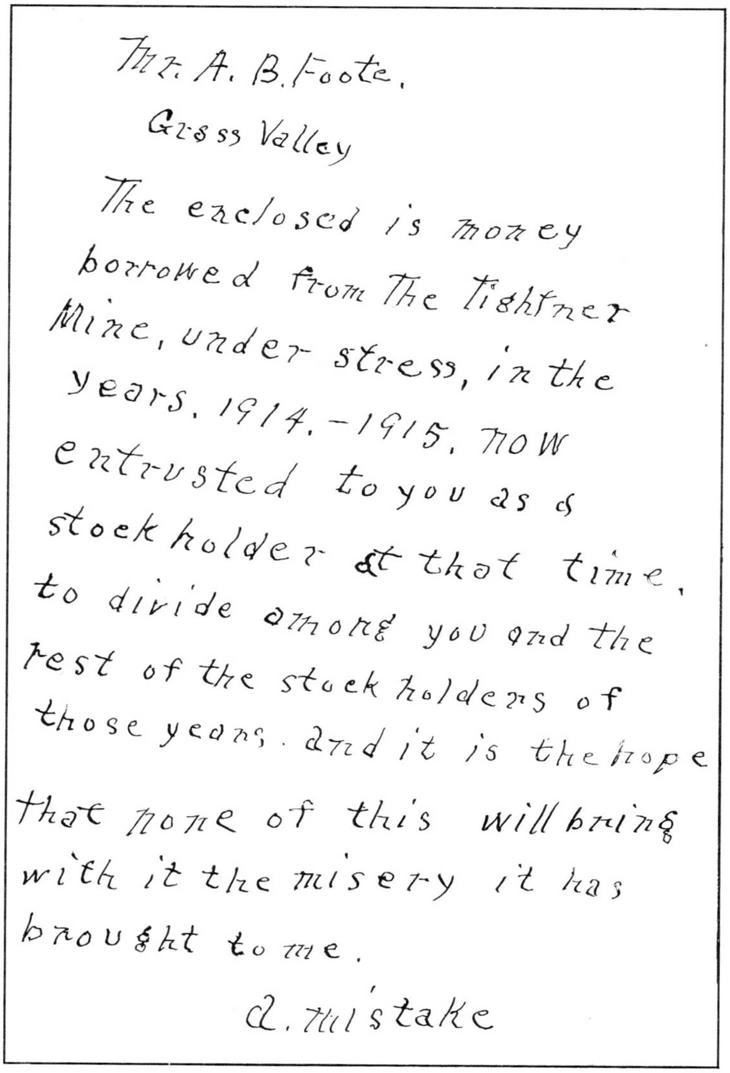

From 1911 to 1918 Arthur B. Foote, Manager of the North Star mine in Grass Valley, and J. M. O'Brien operated the Tightner mine in Alleghany. It was during that period that one of their employees high-graded some gold from either the mine or mill. In 1931, some 30 years later, Mr. Foote received a registered letter bearing the return address of simply "A. Man, Sacramento." The envelope contained $2700 in bills and this letter (right). The mine had since been sold and Mr. Foote had quite a problem making proper restitution at that late date. Nevertheless it is hoped that such a display of belated honesty did not go unrewarded if only in the easing of the conscience of some aging and anonymous miner. (*Arthur B. Foote*)

Mr. A. B. Foote,

Grass Valley

The enclosed is money borrowed from the Tightner Mine, under stress, in the years. 1914.–1915. Now entrusted to you as a stock holder at that time, to divide among you and the rest of the stock holders of those years. And it is the hope that none of this will bring with it the misery it has brought to me.

A. Mistake

243

ADIT at a small Mother Lode gold mine.

ARRASTRA. Often these were driven by waterpower when available.

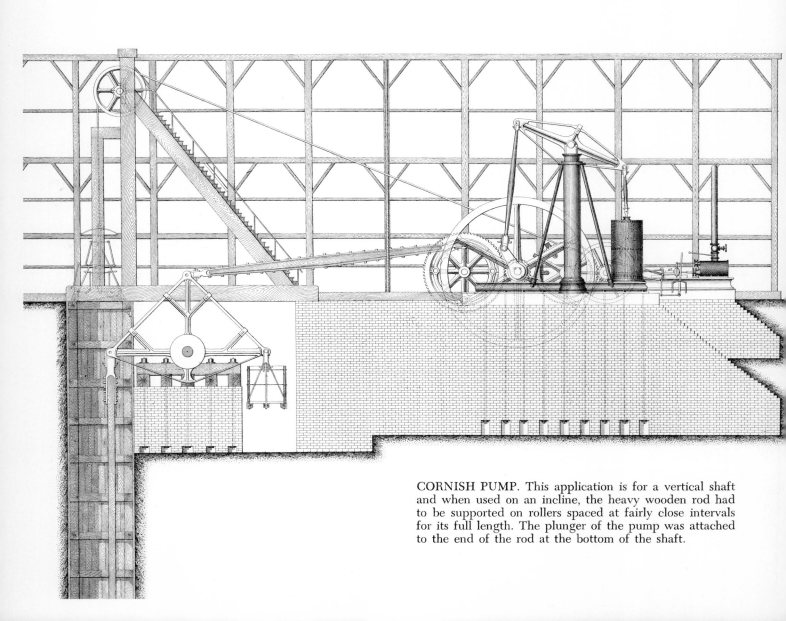

CORNISH PUMP. This application is for a vertical shaft and when used on an incline, the heavy wooden rod had to be supported on rollers spaced at fairly close intervals for its full length. The plunger of the pump was attached to the end of the rod at the bottom of the shaft.

GLOSSARY
OF MINING TERMS

ADIT. A passage driven into a mine from the side of a hill.

AGGREGATE. Uncrushed or crushed gravel; crushed stone, rock or sand.

ALLUVIAL. Minerals found associated with deposits made by flowing water.

AMALGAM. An alloy of mercury with one or more other metals.

AMALGAMATION. The process by which mercury is alloyed with gold and silver from pulverized ores.

APEX. The end, edge, or crest of a mineral vein nearest the surface.

ARRASTRA. A circular rock-lined pit in which broken ore is pulverized by stones dragged around the pit. These are attached to horizontal poles fastened in a central pillar.

ASSAY. A means of ascertaining the commercial value of ore.

AURIFEROUS. Containing gold.

BACKS. The ore above any horizontal opening, such as a tunnel or drift.

BALL MILL. A rotating horizontal cylinder with a diameter almost equal to the length supported by a frame or shaft in which materials are ground using grinding media such as iron or steel balls.

BASE METAL. Any of the nonprecious metals.

BLOCK CAVING. A method of caving in which a thick block of ore is partly cut off from surrounding blocks by a series of drifts, one above the other, or by boundary shrinkage stopes; it is then undercut by removing a slice of ore or a series of slices separated by small pillars underneath the block. The isolated, unsupported block of ore breaks and caves under its own weight. The broken ore is drawn off from below, and as the caved mass moves downward, due to continued drawing of broken ore from below, it is broken further by pressure and attrition.

BONANZA. In miners' phrase, a body of rich ore.

BOOMING. The accumulation and sudden discharge of a quantity of water. In California, the contrivances for collecting and discharging water are termed "self-shooters".

BORRASCA. In mining, barren rock or non-paying ore. An unproductive mine. Opposite of Bonanza.

CALAVERAS ROCK. Certain metamorphic rock in the Sierra foothills. Usually associated with the Mother Lode.

CHIMNEY. An ore shoot.

CHLORINATION. The process of dissolving gold ores, after crushing and roasting, by the use of chlorine gas.

CLAIM. A parcel of land legally held for mining purposes, the location of which is recorded and marked by monuments.

CLAIM-JUMPING. Taking over mining property after it has been staked by someone else, usually before the claim is recorded.

CONCENTRATE. The product of concentration.

CONCENTATION. Separation and accumulation of economic minerals from gangue.

CONCENTRATOR. A plant where ore is separated into values and rejects.

CORE DRILLING. Process of obtaining cylindrical rock samples by means of annular-shaped rock-cutting bits rotated by a borehole-drilling machine.

CORNISH PUMP. A single-acting engine in which the power for pumping operations was transmitted through the action of a cumbersome beam.

COUNTRY ROCK. The rock in which a mineral deposit or an intrusion is enclosed. The common rock of a region.

COUSIN JACK. A Cornish miner. Derived from his habit, whenever offered a job, of asking if there was also one for his "Cousin Jack".

CRADLE. A wooden box, longer than wide, provided with a movable slide and hopper, and mounted on two rockers. It is used for washing gold-bearing earths.

CROSSCUT. A horizontal opening driven across the course of a vein or in general across the direction of the main workings. A connection from a shaft to a vein.

CYANIDE PROCESS. A process for the extraction of gold from finely crushed ores, concentrates and tailings by means of cyanide of potassium. The gold is dissolved by the solution and subsequently deposited upon metallic zinc or by other means.

DRIFT MINING. The face here is compacted gravel and the roof is hard lava. Where the roof was soft massive amounts of timber had to be used so the gravel had to be pretty high grade to be mined by this method.

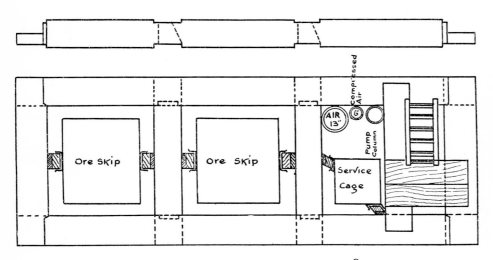

SHAFT. This is a cross section of a typical California shaft showing the compartments and the method of timbering used. Since all hoists were capable of failure, ladderways were a must as well as ventilating air, compressed air and water pipes.

DETRITUS. Sediments produced by the erosion of rocks through the various geologic agencies.

DIP. The angle at which a bed, stratum, or vein is inclined from the horizontal.

DREDGE. A large raft or barge on which are mounted either a chain of buckets or suction pumps and other appliances, to elevate and wash alluvial deposits and gravel for gold, tin, platinum, diamonds, etc.

DRIFT. A horizontal passage underground. A drift follows the vein, as distinguished from a crosscut, which intersects it.

DRIFT MINING. A term applied to working alluvial deposits by underground methods of mining. The paystreak, varying from 2 to 8 feet, sometimes greater, is reached through an adit or a shallow shaft. Drift mining is more expensive than sluicing or hydraulicking; consequently, it is used only in rich ground.

DRIVE. To excavate horizontally, or at an inclination, as in a drift, adit, or entry. Distinguished from sinking and raising.

DUMP. A pile or heap of waste rock material or other nonore refuse near a mine.

FACE. The solid surface of the unbroken portion at the advancing end of the working place.

FAULT. A break in the continuity of a body of rock. It is accompanied by a movement on one side of the break or the other so that what were once parts of one continuous rock stratum or vein are now separated. The amount of displacement of the parts may range from a few inches to thousands of feet.

FLOAT. The term float or float rock means bunches, blotches, pieces, or boulders of quartz or rock lying detached from, or resting upon the earth's surface without any walls.

FLOATATION. The method of mineral separation in which a froth created in water by a variety of reagents floats some finely crushed minerals, whereas other minerals sink.

FLOATATION CELL. Appliance in which froth floatation of ores is performed.

FOOTWALL. The wall or rock under a vein.

GALLOWS FRAME. The frame supporting a pulley, over which the hoisting rope passes.

GANGUE. Undesired minerals associated with ore, mostly nonmetallic.

GIANT. The nozzle of a pipe used to convey water for hydraulic mining.

GLORY HOLE. A funnel-shaped excavation the bottom of which is connected to a raise driven from an underground haulage level.

GREENSTONE. An old name for those compact, igneous rocks that have developed enough chlorite in alteration to give them a green cast. They are mostly diabases and diorites.

HANGING WALL. The wall or rock on the upper side of an inclined vein.

HARD ROCK. A term used to distinguish between material which can be excavated without blasting and rock having a strong bonded structure.

HARD-ROCK MINE. A mine in hard rock; especially one difficult to drill, blast, and square up.

HEADFRAME. The steel or timber frame at the top of a shaft, which carries the sheave or pulley for the hoisting rope, and serves various other purposes.

HIGH-GRADE. A rich ore.

HIGH-GRADING. Theft of valuable pieces of ore.

HORSE. Waste inclusions within ore deposits.

HYDRAULIC MINING. The process by which a bank of gold-bearing earth and rock is excavated by a jet of water, discharged through the converging nozzle of a pipe under a great pressure.

JEWELRY ROCK. Rich ore.

LAGGING. Heavy planks or timbers used to support the roof of a mine, or for floors of working places and for the accumulation of rock and earth in a stope.

LEACHING. The removal in solution of the more soluble minerals by percolating waters.

LEAD. Commonly used as a synonym for ledge or lode.

LEDGE. A mass of rock that constitutes a valuable mineral deposit.

LENS. A body of ore or of rock thick in the middle and thin at the edges.

LEVEL. Mines are customarily worked from shafts through horizontal passages or drifts called levels. These are commonly spaced at regular intervals in depth and are either numbered from the surface in regular order or designated by their actual elevation, below the top of a shaft.

LODE. The well-defined occurrence of valuable mineral bearing material.

LONG TOM. A trough for washing gold-bearing earth. It is longer than a rocker.

MARIPOSA SLATE. California term applied to slate formations found in the Sierra Nevada foothills. Frequently seen outcropping through the surface like tombstones in a vertical or slanting position.

MERCURY. A heavy, silver-white metallic element that is liquid at ordinary temperatures.

MILL. Reducing plant where ore is concentrated and/or metals recovered.

MINER'S INCH. The quantity of water that will escape from an aperture 1-inch square through a 2-inch plank, with a steady flow of water standing 6 inches above the top of the escape aperture, the quantity so discharged amounting to 2,274 cubic feet in 24 hours.

MONITOR. A high-pressure nozzle mounted in a swivel on a skid frame.

MOTHER LODE. As used in California the term applied to a mile-wide belt of gold producing country 120 miles long (162 miles by Highway 49) in the western foothills of the Sierra Nevada Mountains roughly from Mariposa on the south to Georgetown on the north. These deposits are not continuous, although popularly conceived to be one main quartz vein. Neither are they confined to quartz veins, for important production has been obtained from mineralized country rock.

MUCKING. The operation of loading broken rock by hand or machine usually in shafts or tunnels.

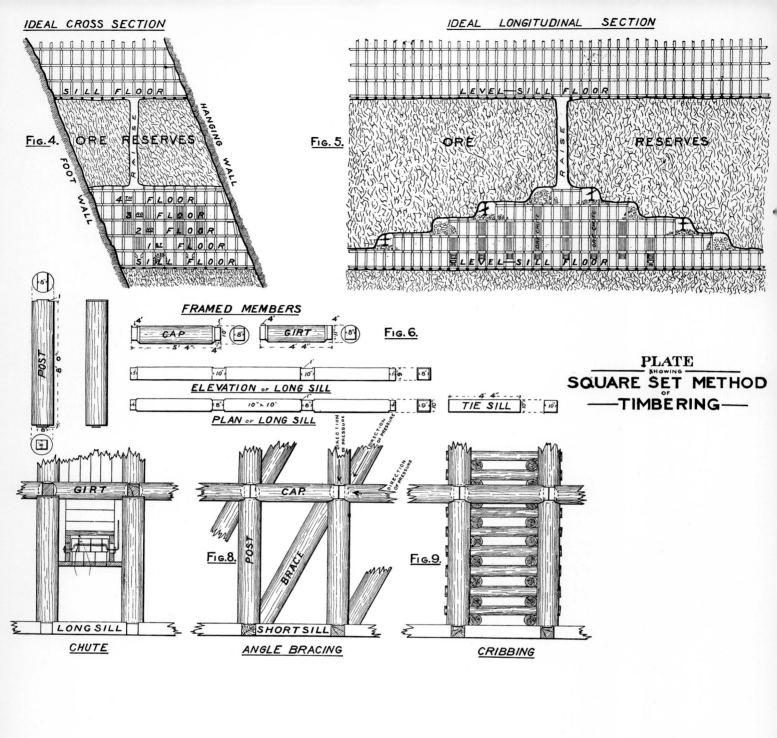

IDEAL CROSS SECTION

FIG. 4.

SILL FLOOR

ORE RESERVES

HANGING WALL

FOOT WALL

RAISE

4TH FLOOR
3RD FLOOR
2ND FLOOR
1ST FLOOR
SILL FLOOR

IDEAL LONGITUDINAL SECTION

FIG. 5.

LEVEL SILL FLOOR

ORE   RESERVES

RAISE

LEVEL SILL FLOOR

POST

8'0"

FRAMED MEMBERS

CAP

GIRT

FIG. 6.

ELEVATION OF LONG SILL

PLAN OF LONG SILL

TIE SILL

PLATE
SHOWING
SQUARE SET METHOD
OF
TIMBERING

GIRT

LONG SILL

CHUTE

CAP

POST

BRACE

SHORT SILL

FIG. 8.

ANGLE BRACING

FIG. 9.

CRIBBING

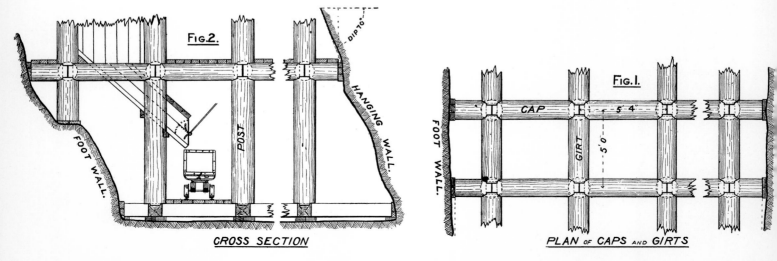

FIG. 2.

DIP 70

HANGING WALL

FOOT WALL

POST

CROSS SECTION

FIG. I.

FOOT WALL

CAP

GIRT

5' 4"

5' 0"

PLAN OF CAPS AND GIRTS

MULLER STONE. A stone used for grinding or crushing.

OIL FLOATATION. A process in which oil is used in ore concentration by floatation.

ORE. A mineral of sufficient value as to quality and quantity which may be mined with profit.

ORE BODY. A solid and fairly continuous mass of ore, which may include low-grade ore and waste as well as pay ore.

ORE SHOOT. A large and usually rich aggregation of mineral in a vein.

OUTCROP. The part of a rock formation that appears at the surface of the ground.

OVERBURDEN. Material of any nature, consolidated or unconsolidated, that overlies a deposit of useful materials or ores.

PAN. A shallow, circular, concave steel dish for washing sand, clay, etc., from gold or tin.

PELTON WATER WHEEL. Water wheel invented at Camptonville, California in 1878 by Lester Allen Pelton. Although similar to wheels made by Knight, Dodd and other inventors, the Pelton wheel had a partition in the center of the bucket causing the stream of water to be deflected into the two halves. This remarkably simple addition resulted in greatly increased efficiency and made the Pelton wheel in great demand over steam as a prime mover.

PHILOSOPHER'S STONE. An imaginary stone, or solid substance or preparation, believed by alchemists to have the power of transmuting the base metals into gold or silver.

PICTURE ROCK. Rich ore.

PLACER. A place where gold is obtained by washing.

PLACER MINING. The extraction of heavy mineral from a placer deposit by concentration in running water.

PORPHYRY. Colloquially, the word is used to mean almost any igneous rock, occurring in sheets or dikes, particularly one that is spotted, soft or light color.

PULP. A mixture of ground ore and water capable of flowing through suitably graded channels as a fluid.

QUARTZ. A crystallized silicon dioxide, SiO_2. Any hard, gold or silver ore, as distinguished from gravel or earth. Hence quartz mining as distinguished from hydraulic mining.

QUARTZ MINE. A mine in which the deposits of ore are found in veins or fissures in the rocks forming the earth's crust. Usually applied to lode gold mines.

RAISE. A vertical or inclined opening driven upward from a level to connect with the level above, or to explore the ground for a limited distance above one level. After two levels are connected, the connection may be a winze or a raise, depending upon which level is taken as the point of reference.

RAKE. The direction of an ore shoot within a vein.

RIFFLE. The lining of the bottom of a sluice, made of blocks or slats of wood, or stones, arranged in such a manner that clinks are left between them.

ROCKER. A portable sluicebox used by prospectors.

SCHIST. A crystalline rock that can be readily split or cleaved because of having a foliated or parallel structure.

SHAFT. A vertical or inclined excavation or opening from the surface.

SHALE. A laminated sediment, in which the constituent particles are predominantly of the clay grade.

SHIFT BOSS. A foreman who is in direct charge of men in a specific portion of the mine.

SHOOT. The payable section of a lode; an enriched portion of a continuous ore body.

SINGLE JACKING. A method of manual drilling with one man wielding the hammer and turning the steel.

SKIP. A large hoisting bucket which slides between guides in a shaft, the bail usually connecting at or near the bottom of the bucket so that it may be automatically dumped at the surface. An open iron vehicle or car on four wheels, running on rails and used specially on inclines or in inclined shafts.

SLICKENS. A word sometimes used to designate the debris (tailings) discharged from hydraulic mines or stamp mills.

SLIME. Ore reduced to a very fine powder and held in suspension in water so as to form a kind of thin ore mud; generally used in the plural.

SLUICE BOX. A wooden trough in which alluvial beds are washed for the recovery of gold.

SPONGE. Metal in a porous form. Herein applied to gold amalgam.

SQUARE SET. A set of timbers composed of cap, girt, and post. These members meet so as to form a solid 90° angle. They are so framed at the intersection as to form a compression joint, and join with three other similar sets. This system of timbering can be adapted to large or irregular ore bodies.

STAMP MILL. An apparatus in which rock is crushed by descending pestles or stamps operated by water, steam or electric power. Also, the building containing the machinery.

STATION. The excavation adjoining the shaft at each of the different levels, where men and material are removed or delivered.

STOPE. An underground excavation from which the ore has been or is being extracted.

STRIKE. The course or bearing of the outcrop of an inclined bed or structure on a level surface; it is perpendicular to the direction of the dip. To find a vein of ore; a valuable discovery.

SULFIDE. A compound of sulfur with more than one element.

SULFURET. In miners' phrase, the undecomposed metallic ores, usually sulfides. Chiefly applied to auriferous pyrites. Concentrate and sulfide are preferable.

TAILINGS. The gangue and other refuse material resulting from the washing, concentration, or treatment of ground ore. Those portions of washed ore that are regarded as too poor to be treated further.

TRAM. To haul or push cars about in a mine.

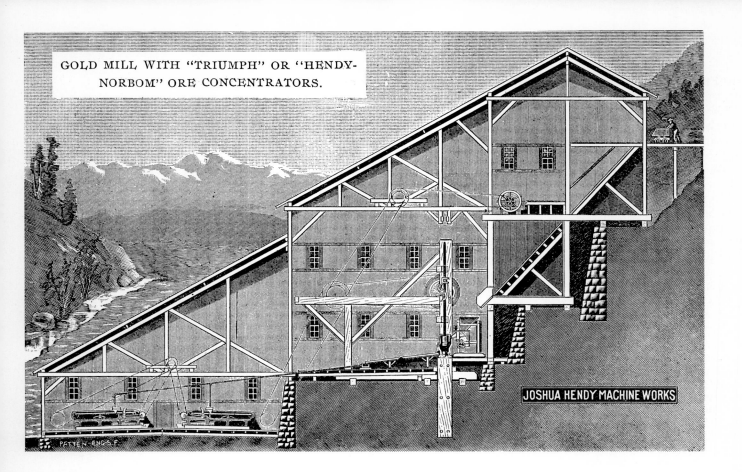

GOLD MILL WITH "TRIUMPH" OR "HENDY-NORBOM" ORE CONCENTRATORS.

JOSHUA HENDY MACHINE WORKS

RISDON HAMMERED

RISDON HAMMERED

AFTER 190 DAYS WEAR

BEFORE

AFTER

STAMP MILL. Ore was dumped into the mill over a grizzly or screen. The fine material would go through while the coarse lumps had to be put through a crusher set over the bin. It was fed mechanically to the stamps and the resulting pulp was passed over the amalgamation plates and thence to the concentrators. As the years went by many additional and more sophisticated methods were used for the recovery of the gold but to the end of gold mining, stamps played a major part in the crushing of the ores.

The actual crushing took place between the shoes which were attached to the stamps above, and the dies which sat on the bottom of the mortar. The hard quartz soon wore these surfaces away as shown by the example on the left. A set of these wearing parts could weigh as much as 500 pounds and many a California foundry was kept busy casting them.

250

TRAP (TRAPROCK). Any of various dark-colored, fine-grained, igneous rocks, including especially basalt, amygdaloid, etc.

TRIBUTORS. Miners who work ground under an agreement to pay a percentage of their production to the owners.

TUNNEL. A horizontal or nearly horizontal underground passage. Any level or drift in a mine open at one end. Often used as a synonym for adit, drift.

VEIN. A zone or belt of mineralized rock lying within boundaries clearly separating it from neighboring rock.

WHIM. A large capstan or vertical drum turned by horsepower for raising ore from a mine.

WINZE. A subsidiary shaft which starts underground. It is usually a connection between two levels.

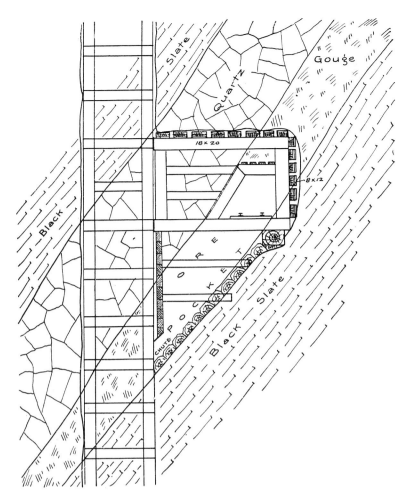

STATION. Sometimes these were merely an enlarged end of a drift or crosscut where a car was wheeled up to the shaft and dumped directly into the skip. In the example shown here, there is an ore pocket under it so the cars of ore can be dumped regardless of the availability of the skip. When a mine was worked from several levels, this pocket was necessary. In very large operations, two pockets were used, one for ore and one for waste. (all glossary pictures, Morgan North)

THE "DAVIS" SAFETY BRAKE HORSE-POWER HOISTING WHIM

(IN POSITION FOR OPERATION)

251

BIBLIOGRAPHY

BOOKS

AMADOR COUNTY HISTORY. Amador County Federation of Women's Clubs, 1927.

Bean, Edwin F., BEAN'S HISTORY AND DIRECTORY OF NEVADA COUNTY, The Daily Gazette, 1867.

Best, Gerald M. NEVADA COUNTY NARROW GAUGE. Howell-North Books, Berkeley, California, 1965.

Bohakel, Charles A. A HISTORY OF THE EMPIRE MINE. Nevada County Historical Society, 1968.

CALIFORNIA, A GUIDE TO THE GOLDEN STATE. Federal Writers Project, 1939.

CATALOG OF THE PELTON WATER WHEEL COMPANY. San Francisco, California.

Challinor, John. DICTIONARY OF GEOLOGY. Oxford University Press, 1962.

Clark, S. J. HISTORY OF SOLANO AND NAPA COUNTIES. 1926.

Coleman, Charles M. P.G. AND E. OF CALIFORNIA: THE CENTENNIAL STORY OF PACIFIC GAS AND ELECTRIC COMPANY 1852-1952. McGraw-Hill, New York, 1952.

Crane, Walter R. GOLD AND SILVER. John Wiley & Sons, New York, 1908.

Davis, H. P. GOLD RUSH DAYS IN NEVADA CITY. Berliner & McGinnis, Nevada City, California, 1948.

DICTIONARY OF AMERICAN BIOGRAPHY. Charles Scribner's Sons, New York.

DICTIONARY OF GEOLOGICAL TERMS. American Geological Institute. Doubleday & Co., Inc., New York City, 1957.

ENCYCLOPEDIA AMERICANA. Encyclopedia Americana Inc., New York.

ENCYCLOPEDIA BRITANNICA. William Benton, Publisher, Chicago.

Eissler, M. THE METALLURGY OF GOLD. D. Van Nostrand Company, New York, 1896.

Garbarini, Evelyn and Emmett H. THE KENNEDY WHEELS. Amador Progress News, Jackson, California.

Glasscock, G. B. A GOLDEN HIGHWAY. The Bobbs-Merrill Company, Indianapolis.

GLOSSARY OF GEOLOGY AND RELATED SCIENCES. The American Geological Institute, Washington, D.C., 1957.

GOLD RUSH COUNTRY: GUIDE TO CALIFORNIA'S MOTHER LODE AND NORTHERN MINES. Lane Book Company, Menlo Park, California, 1964.

Hittel, John S. COMMERCE AND INDUSTRIES OF THE PACIFIC COAST OF NORTH AMERICA. A. L. Bancroft & Co., Publishers, 1882.

Holdredge, Helen. MAMMY PLEASANT. Nourse Publishing Company, San Carlos, California.

Holmes, R. E. THE SOUTHERN MINES. Grabhorn Press, 1930.

Jackson, Joseph Henry. ANYBODY'S GOLD. D. Appleton-Century Co., New York, 1941.

Kelley, Robert L. GOLD VS GRAIN. The Arthur H. Clark Company, 1959.

Kinyon, Edmund. THE NORTHERN MINES. The Union Publishing Company, Grass Valley-Nevada City, California, 1949.

Lardner, W. B. and M. J. Brock. HISTORY OF PLACER AND NEVADA COUNTIES. Historic Record Co., Los Angeles, California, 1924.

Mason, J. D. HISTORY OF AMADOR COUNTY. 1881.

Morley, Jim and Doris Foley. GOLD CITIES: A HISTORY AND GUIDE TO GRASS VALLEY AND NEVADA CITY. Howell-North Books, Berkeley, California, 1965.

Nadeau, Remi A. GHOST TOWNS AND MINING CAMPS OF CALIFORNIA. The Ward Ritchie Press, Los Angeles, California, 1965.

Poingdestre, J. E. GRASS VALLEY AND VICINITY. Pacific Press, Oakland, California.

Rickard, T. A. THE BUNKER HILL ENTERPRISE. Reprinted from the Mining and Scientific Press, San Francisco, California, 1921.

Shaw, Frederic, Clement Fisher, Jr., and George H. Harlan. OIL LAMPS AND IRON PONIES. A chronicle of the narrow gauges. Bay Books, Ltd., San Francisco, California, 1949.

Sparkes, Boyden and Samuel Taylor Moore. THE WITCH OF WALL STREET — HETTY GREEN. Doubleday, Doran & Company, Inc., Garden City, New York, 1935.

State of California, Division of Mines. THE MOTHER LODE COUNTRY. Geologic Guidebook along Highway 49, Bulletin 141, California State Printing Office, 1948.

TUOLUMNE COUNTY CALIFORNIA. Union Democrat, Sonora, California, 1909.

Union Iron Works, Catalog No. 2, HOISTING AND PUMPING MACHINERY. San Francisco, California, 1873.

Williams, Archibald. THE ROMANCE OF MINING. J. B. Lippincott, Philadelphia, 1905.

Wilson, Eugene. HYDRAULIC AND PLACER MINING. John Wiley & Sons, New York, 1918.

REPORTS, ETC.

ANNUAL MINING REVIEW AND STOCK LEDGER. San Francisco, California, 1876.

CALIFORNIA MINES AND MINERALS. California Miners Association, San Francisco, California, 1899.

Fay, Albert H. A GLOSSARY OF THE MINING AND MINERAL INDUSTRY. U.S. Government Printing Office, Washington, D.C., 1920.

Fowler, Frederick Hall. HYDRO-ELECTRIC SYSTEMS OF CALIFORNIA. U.S. Government Printing Office, Washington, D.C., 1923.

GOLD QUARTZ VEINS OF GRASS VALLEY, THE. Professional Paper No. 194, United States Geological Survey, 1940.

GOLD QUARTZ VEINS OF NEVADA CITY AND GRASS VALLEY DISTRICTS, THE. 17th Annual Report, United States Geological Survey, 1896.

Homestake Mining Company, Annual Reports.

McBride, John. MONEY MAKES THE MARE GO. United States Government Printing Office, Washington, D.C., 1947.

McLaughlin, Donald H., Chairman of the Board, Homestake Mining Company. GOLD AND MONETARY ORDER, 1968.

MINERAL RESOURCES OF THE UNITED STATES. Department of the Interior, U.S. Government Printing Office, Washington, D.C.

Natomas Company, Annual Reports.

PRODUCTION POTENTIAL OF KNOWN GOLD DEPOSITS IN THE UNITED STATES. Bureau of Mines Information Circular 8331, United States Department of the Interior, 1967.

REGISTER OF MINES OF NEVADA COUNTY, THE. State Mining Bureau, circa 1899. Yuba Industries, Inc., Annual Reports.

MAGAZINES AND PERIODICALS

American Metal Market. August 30, 1968, June 23, 1969.

Century Magazine, The. January, 1883.

Commercial and Financial Chronicle, The. March 9, 1967.

Engineering and Mining Journal. McGraw-Hill.

Journal of Electricity, Power and Gas. San Francisco, California, January, 1900.

Metals Week. McGraw-Hill.

Mining and Scientific Press.

Pacific Coast Mining Review. San Francisco, California, 1878-1879.

Western Construction.

NEWSPAPERS

Amador Ledger

Grass Valley Union

San Francisco Call Bulletin

San Francisco Chronicle

San Francisco Examiner

Daily Union Democrat, Sonora

. . . and the files and publications of

Amador County Historical Society, and

Nevada County Historical Society.

INDEX

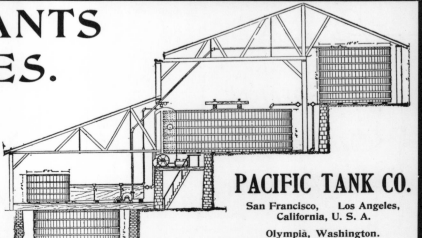

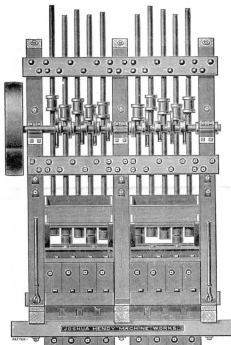